CALENDARS
OF AMERICAN LITERARY
MANUSCRIPTS

THE LITERARY MANUSCRIPTS

OF UPTON SINCLAIR

The Literary Manuscripts of Upton Sinclair is the second volume in a series of CALENDARS OF AMERICAN LITERARY MANUSCRIPTS. The series is sponsored by an agency bearing the same name, and is under the control of its Editorial Board.

THE LITERARY MANUSCRIPTS OF

UPTON SINCLAIR

BY RONALD GOTTESMAN

AND CHARLES L. P. SILET

OHIO STATE UNIVERSITY PRESS

For Lann and Grant
and for Sharon

CONTENTS

ILLUSTRATIONS

(Following page 232)

FOREWORD

No longer is there a need to justify the systematic presentation of information about American literary manuscripts. Now there is a flourishing criticism based on close and sophisticated reading of their texts; and this criticism has increased the importance of those allied scholarly arts that not only support it, but also make distinguished contributions to knowledge and understanding in their own right. The success of the *National Union Catalog of Manuscript Collections* (Washington, D.C., 1959——) and *American Literary Manuscripts* (Austin, 1960) has demonstrated amply the manifold values of establishing the breadth of this nation's manuscript resources. Calendars of American Literary Manuscripts (CALM) is a complementary organization that has the aim of contributing detailed knowledge about its depth.

This angle of attack is worth a few more words in explanation. The scholar's situation most often demands that out of all the papers of any author he must locate one manuscript or family of manuscripts. Even the most comprehensive listing of bulk collections can only suggest to him likely starting points for the arduous search to find what he really needs. Since the manuscripts of most American writers are dispersed widely, that quest usually will involve much correspondence and intensive research at the very least. Of course he never can be satisfied that he has found all there is, because of the simple and frightening fact that no one knows just what has survived any American author. To this day, nearly everyone who embarks on a study requiring manuscripts must perform this task afresh, from the beginning—even if, as frequently is true, it has been performed by countless others before him. These circumstances make one think of Hercules, certainly, but also of Sisyphus and Tantalus: redundant expenditures of time, money, and frustration are the contemporary methods for torment. No profession, this one least of all, can afford to waste its resources so foolishly.

The obvious solution to the problem is a series of books that for American literary manuscript materials are the equivalent of author bibliographies for printed matter. Calendars of American Literary Manuscripts is a pioneering attempt at providing that. Organized in 1964 and announced at the 1965 annual meeting of the Modern Language Association of America, CALM published its first volume in 1966. By continuing to foster the publication of information resulting from specialized research into the available manuscript resources of individual writers, and by a willingness to aid, advise, and coordinate such research, we hope to enlarge the body of information and to refine techniques in the area. Those are our major aims. We hope for subsidiary benefits as well—for added impetus to the sound study of American literature, increased sophistication in the use of the manuscripts in which it was first recorded, and the emergence of the incalculably large body of submerged material. We mean the term "manuscripts" in its largest sense, of course: subsumed under it are all pre- and post-publication inscriptions whether directly prepared by an author or sponsored by him.

Given the richness of our national literature in its quantity as well as in its quality, we are well aware that our efforts can at best be only a contribution to the necessary end. There is much to do, little time in which to do it, and almost no financial support for this kind of work. But one must begin. By definition, therefore, no volume in the series ought to be considered definitive. We both expect and desire supplementary information about material within the scope of volumes in CALM. Such addenda will be published in *Proof: The Yearbook of American Bibliographical and Textural Studies*. (Columbia: University of South Carolina Press, 1971——). Contributions of that kind may be addressed directly to *Proof*. They are important, and they will be welcomed.

JOSEPH KATZ

University of South Carolina
Columbia, South Carolina

PREFACE

Upton Sinclair began his career as a serious writer when he was scarcely out of his teens and continued it with relentless energy for nearly seventy years until his death in 1968. In the course of those years, few aspects of twentieth-century life escaped his notice, and he tried his hand at virtually every form of writing—expository and imaginative, popular and specialized. He wrote jokes, proposals, manifestos, polemical pamphlets, newspaper columns, scientific treatises and histories as well as autobiographies, biographies, reviews, critical essays, poems, plays, movie scenarios, and novels. These works, moreover, have been widely translated into some sixty languages in a quantity that places Sinclair among the most popular writers of all time. For decades he was a unique figure in world letters, so it is no wonder that scholars in increasing numbers are trying to take his measure and gauge his influence.

These are not easy tasks, not only because of the bulk and range of Sinclair's published writings, but also because of the amount of his work that survives in manuscript.[1] Even as a young man Sinclair was sensitive to the claims of posterity—he spoke of "founding a library" of his own works in the preface to *Springtime and Harvest* (1901)—and, with the devoted assistance of his wife of nearly fifty years, Mary Craig, he carefully preserved, in addition to copies of his printed works, his enormous correspondence, masses of various states of his publications in pre-publication forms, and an extraordinary number of unpublished manuscripts as well. Happily, the overwhelming proportion of these papers are

[1] To satisfy the need for a record of Mr. Sinclair's *published* writings, Ronald Gottesman's *Upton Sinclair: An Annotated Checklist* will be published by the Kent State University Press in 1972.

collected in one place—the Sinclair Archive of the Lilly Library at Indiana University. The account of the contents of this extraordinary archive and how it came to the Lilly Library has been told in some detail elsewhere.[2] Suffice it to say here that the Sinclair Archive includes approximately 500,000 manuscript leaves, of which nearly half represent literary manuscripts of most of the major published books and articles after 1915, and of a good many substantial unpublished works for the same period.[3] In many instances several stages of composition, from field notes to corrected proof, are available.

Obviously, from these documents much can be learned about Sinclair's writing habits, his techniques as a creator of contemporary historical fiction, his procedures as a journalist and as a muckraker, and his adventures as a publisher of his own books. Previously unexplored aspects of his career, moreover, can now be examined through inspection, for example, of the movie scenarios he prepared in the early 1930s and of the unpublished sequels to *Love's Pilgrimage* (1911) and *King Coal* (1917). Together with the rich supply of related letters, manuscripts of such books as *The Goose-Step* (1923) and *Boston* (1929) yield important insights into historical and cultural currents from which they were shaped. The serious biographer of Sinclair or of his many friends will also find an unparalleled—even intimidating—range of evidence among the preserved documents. In short, the man, his works, and his time can all be made more confidently accessible through study of Upton Sinclair's manuscripts in the Lilly Library and in other collections. It is to make the amazing range and extent of these manuscripts available that we have prepared this volume for Calendars of American Literary Manuscripts (CALM).

The number and complexity of the Sinclair manuscripts has dictated modifications of the excellent format used by Mr.

[2] See Introduction to *A Catalogue of Books, Manuscripts, and Other Materials from the Upton Sinclair Archives* (Bloomington, Ind.: Lilly Library, 1963), pp. 4-10; see also Ronald Gottesman, "Upton Sinclair and the Sinclair Archives," *Manuscripts* 17 (1965), 11-20.

[3] Sinclair's enormous correspondence is treated here following the calendar of his literary manuscripts, in Part B.

Kenneth Lohf in his *The Literary Manuscripts of Hart Crane*, the first volume in CALM. It has proved impractical, for example, to provide a truly comprehensive description of the physical nature of each manuscript; for instance, paper size and color have not been noted for every separate leaf of manuscript. Instead, we have attempted to give the user a knowledge of the content and condition of clearly discrete manuscript items sufficiently comprehensive to provide firm grounds on which to decide whether it would be profitable to examine the original more closely. This is consistent with the purposes of CALM.

We have often noted "boxing" and "folder groupings"; these reflect the Lilly Library's processing and not necessarily Mr. Sinclair's. Though the Sinclair manuscripts in the Lilly Library are temporarily divided into two major categories—book and article length—we have not listed them separately. Rather, we have listed all manuscripts alphabetically by published title (or by working title when unpublished).

The following descriptive information is provided for each manuscript:

> *Citation*: Published title (in brackets if item unpublished and untitled); type of manuscript, i.e., typewritten, autograph, etc.; notation concerning the handwriting or typing medium and color; and library location symbol.
>
> *Title*: Transcription of the title as it appears on the manuscript, indicating capitalization, line endings, underscoring (through use of italics), and corrections by use of brackets.
>
> *Key Words*: Transcription of the first five words on the first page of the text and the last five on the last page of the text.
>
> *Collation*: Number of sheets; type of paper and color; size of paper in centimeters (height preceding width); numbering of sheets; listing of verso sheets (numbered by place in series rather than in accord with recto numbering) when inscribed (or notation "none" when all are blank); notes pertaining to the physical condition of the manuscript.

Contents: Remarks pertinent to the comprehensiveness of the contents; description of the amount of revision; identification of the class of the manuscript, i.e., draft, worksheet, notes, typescript; any additional information potentially helpful to the reader in identifying the manuscript.

Dates: Specific or approximate date of composition and of publication when applicable.

Several major refinements require a word of explanation. When more than one version of a manuscript exists, we have listed them in order from earliest to latest state (but with less than complete confidence in our reconstructions). We have often transcribed chapter titles; this, of course, does not alter the primary listing under the full published title but merely is a substitute for the entry under *Title*. For manuscripts that are clearly in a final stage of composition, we have ignored the title in transcribing the first five words. For groupings of notes or miscellaneous manuscript sheets, however, the transcriptions are of the first five words on the first sheet and the last five words on the last sheet.

The Sinclair manuscripts often are made up of a wide variety of paper types and sizes. In such cases we do not describe each sheet but merely note "miscellaneous sheets" and provide the sizes of the largest and smallest. A similar shortcut has been taken with the numbering of the manuscript leaves. Only those manuscripts that appear to be consecutively and continuously numbered are given full treatment. Otherwise, we have noted "not numbered," "randomly numbered," or, when the sheets have been consecutively numbered by chapters or play acts, we have listed them as "consecutively numbered by chapters (or acts) but not continuously"; even when the manuscript is continuously numbered but contains so many variant numberings as to be overly long, we have not listed all the variations but rather have used the notation "continuously numbered with variations." We have not noted renumbering or misnumbering.

A date of composition is offered when there is an unusual discrepancy between it and the date of publication, and if specific information was available in letters or some other biographical or autobiographical source. Two dates for publication separated by a comma is a sign that the work was first published serially; hyphenated dates indicate publication during those years. Where there is a question mark, we were in genuine doubt about the information provided. We are painfully aware of the number of such question marks and can only beg our readers both to be indulgent and to send us information necessary to eliminate some of these queries in the future.

We are happy to confess that we did not labor on this volume in lonely misery; nor were we without sustenance. Indeed, it is almost embarrassing to reflect on the great number of individual and institutional contributors to the work that went into this compilation.

Two grants-in-aid were indispensable, and we wish to thank warmly the Faculty Research Committee of Indiana University and the Research Council of Rutgers University for funds for photocopying, typing, and other incidental expenses. When those funds had been exhausted, George Levine had the interest and ingenuity to discover additional resources needed for the last stages of the work. To him we are especially grateful.

For doing most of the typing and photocopying carefully and cheerfully we are indebted to Judy Bernheim, Barbara Denton, and Helen D'Espies. They also saved us from many errors.

Among the many who provided advice and encouragement at various times we would like to single out E. H. Cady, Philip B. Daghlian, C. Fred Main, and Joseph Katz. For sustaining interest and the loan of materials we are grateful to David and Jean Sinclair. We are especially grateful to our friends at the Lilly Library who did so much to expedite our labors and to make them a pleasant memory: William

Cagle, Elfrieda Lang, David Randall, Doris Reed, Kathryn Troxel, Geneva Warner, and Connie Work. Elfrieda Lang, Curator of Manuscripts, and her predecessor, Doris Reed, oversaw a large part of the initial sorting and reordering—by no means merely mechanical tasks—of the enormous mass of literary manuscripts that this calendar records. Without their informed and painstaking efforts—and that of their colleagues—our own tasks would have been multiplied many times.

But they are no more responsible for the defects of the present work than are the following, who assisted in a variety of ways: Felicia Geffen, American Academy of Arts and Letters; George W. Wakefield, Brooklyn Public Library; Richard Cary, Colby College Library; Kenneth A. Lohf, Columbia University; Kathleen Jacklin, John M. Olin Research Library, Cornell University; Donna Ferguson, Houghton Library, Harvard University; Elizabeth B. Tritle, Haverford College; John D. Kilbourne, Historical Society of Pennsylvania; Herbert C. Schulz, Henry E. Huntington Library and Art Gallery; Lois M. Jones, Los Angeles Public Library; John R. McKenna, Middlebury College; Amy Nyholm, The Newberry Library; Robert W. Hill, New York Public Library; Tyrus G. Harmsen, Occidental College Library; Myra Champion, Pack Memorial Public Library, Asheville, North Carolina; William L. Raminez, San Francisco Public Library; Patricia Palmer, Stanford University Library; Ralph Bushee, State Historical Society of Wisconsin; Lucille V. Miller, St. John's Seminary Library; Howard H. Williams, Swarthmore College Library; Brooke Whitney, University of California at Los Angeles; J. Richard Phillips, University of Chicago Library; Nancy C. Prewitt, University of Missouri Library; Neda M. Westlake, The Charles Patterson Van Pelt Library, University of Pennsylvania; Catherine D. Hayes, University of Rochester Library; Lloyd A. Arvidson, University of Southern California Library; Elizabeth Ryall, University of Virginia Library; Sylvia Pederson, the Harrmann Library, Wagner College; Hannah D. French, Wellesley College Library; Donald Gallup, Yale

University; and Shmuel Lapin, Yvo Institute for Jewish Research.

We are grateful also to the staffs at the Perkins Library, Duke University; the Plainfield (New Jersey) Public Library; the University of California at Berkeley Library; and the University of Texas Library.

We have saved for last the acknowledgment of our largest debt: Sharon Silet was involved continuously and directly in all phases of the preparation of the manuscript. Valerie Gottesman typed, proofread, and helped with the numbering and the index. Both made it possible for their husbands to do the rest of the tasks involved in preparing this calendar.

R. G.
C. L. P. S.

ABBREVIATIONS

Notational Abbreviations

a. ms.	Autograph manuscript
ca.	Approximately
c.o.	Crossed out
comp.	Composed
g. proof	Galley proof
MCS	Mary Craig Sinclair (Mrs. Upton Sinclair)
mimeo	Mimeographed
misc.	Miscellaneous
p. proof	Page proof
photo.	Photocopy
print.	Printed
pub.	Published
t. ms.	Typewritten manuscript
w.i.	Written in

Library Symbols

InU	Lilly Library, Indiana University
MoU	University of Missouri Library
ViU	Alderman Library, University of Virginia

A.

THE LITERARY MANUSCRIPTS
OF UPTON SINCLAIR

1. Citation: ABOUT PENSION PLANS; t. ms.; carbon; InU.

   Title: PENSION PLANS [w.i. pencil]

   Key Words: Everybody out here in California . . . the people have to learn.

   Collation: 3; blue watermarked; 27.9 x 21.6; [1] 2–3; none; good.

   Contents: Complete; infrequently revised in blue pencil.

   Dates: Pub. *Progressive*, 27 August 1938.

2. Citation: THE ABRAMS DISCOVERY: A REPLY TO DR. DE KRUIF IN HEARST'S INTERNA-TIONAL MAGAZINE.; t. ms.; carbon; InU.

   Title: The Abrams Discovery: A Reply to Dr. De Kruif in | "Hearst's International Magazine."

   Key Words: (Note: The enclosed reply to . . . gave it to the world.

   Collation: 11; 27.7 x 21.5; [1] 1–10; none; poor.

   Contents: Complete; infrequently revised in pencil, not all in Sinclair's hand; ms. with prefatory note titled: Albert Abrams.

   Dates: Comp. ca. March 1923. Pub. ?

   See also: IN DEFENSE OF ALBERT ABRAMS and REACTIONS OF ABRAMS.

3a. Citation: ADDRESS BY UPTON SINCLAIR; t. ms.; ribbon, carbon; InU.

Title: ADDRESS BY UPTON SINCLAIR | OVER KFI | August 2nd, 1934.

Key Words: Fellow Citizens of California: For . . . it. It's up to you.

Collation: 20; white; 27.9 x 21.6; [1] 2–6, [1] 2–6, [1] 2–4, [1] 2–4; 7, 9; good.

Contents: Complete; moderately revised in pencil; GUS INGLIS stamped in blue on upper right corner of page one; two revisions, final copy and carbon.

Dates: Pub. ?

3b. Citation: ADDRESS BY UPTON SINCLAIR; t. ms.; ribbon, carbon; InU.

Title: ADDRESS BY UPTON SINCLAIR | OVER K F I | August 2nd, 1934 – 9:00 P.M.

Key Words: Fellow Citizens of California: For . . . it. It's Up To You!

Collation: 11; white, blue watermarked; 28 x 21.7, 28 x 21.6; [1] 2–4, [1] 2–5, 5a, 6; none; good.

Contents: Complete; infrequently revised in pencil; note upper right corner page one: Return to GUS INGLIS.

Dates: Pub. ?

3c. Citation: ADDRESS BY UPTON SINCLAIR; t. ms.; ribbon, carbon; InU.

Title: ADDRESS BY UPTON SINCLAIR | OVER K F I | August 2nd, 1934.

Key Words: Fellow Citizens of California: For . . . up and the machines stop.

Collation: 12; white watermarked, blue watermarked; 28 x 21.6; [1] 2–4, [1] 2–4, [1] 2–3, 2; none; good.

Contents: Complete; unrevised.

Dates: Pub. ?

4. Citation: ADDRESS OF UPTON SINCLAIR BEFORE THE STUDENT CONFERENCE AGAINST WAR; t. ms.; ribbon, carbon; InU.

Title: Address of Upton Sinclair before the | Student Conference Against War. | University of California | at Los Angeles, Jan. 22, 1933.

Key Words: Friends and comrades: I see . . . in peace and good order.

Collation: 26; white watermarked; 28 x 21.6; [1] 2–8; [1] 2–9, [1] 2–9; none; good.

Contents: Complete; infrequently revised in pencil, revised copy and carbon plus carbon of revised version.

Dates: Pub. ?

5. Citation: ADDRESS BY UPTON SINCLAIR OVER KHJ; t. ms; ribbon; InU.

Title: Address by | Upton Sinclair | over K-H-J on | Monday Oct. 8th, | 7:30 P.M.

Key Words: Friends of the Air: Speaking . . . as to change their meaning.

Collation: 3; white; 28 x 21.6; [1] 2–3; none; good.

Contents: Complete; infrequently revised in pencil; notation at top of page one: Talk by Upton Sinclair Oct 22 to S. F. Center of the League of Women Voters in Japanese tea room St. Francis.

Dates: Pub. ?

6. Citation: ADDRESS BY UPTON SINCLAIR AT
    WESTERN WRITERS CONGRESS; t. ms.; carbon;
    InU.

    Title: Address by Upton Sinclair at Western Writers
    Congress | San Francisco, California, | November 14,
    1936 | THE WRITER IN A CHANGING WORLD

    Key Words: My Friends: This is the . . . the world
    into our camp.

    Collation: 12; white watermarked; 28 x 21.6; [1] 2–6,
    [1] 2–6; none; good.

    Contents: Complete; infrequently revised in pencil.

    Dates: Pub. *EPIC News*, 7 December 1936.

7. Citation: ADDRESS OF UPTON SINCLAIR
    [OVER] KNX; t. ms.; carbon; InU.

    Title: *ADDRESS OF UPTON SINCLAIR | KNX |
    SHRINE AUDITORIUM, AUGUST 27, 1934.*

    Key Words: Workers in the EPIC cause . . . it is up
    to you.

    Collation: 8; white, green; 15.7 x 21.7 to 28 x 21.7,
    28 x 21.6; 1–3, [1], 4–7; none; good.

    Contents: Complete; infrequently revised in pencil.

    Dates: Pub. ?

8. Citation: ADDRESS OF UPTON SINCLAIR RADIO
    STATION KFRC; t. ms.; ribbon; InU.

    Title: *ADDRESS OF UPTON SINCLAIR | RADIO
    STATION K F R C* | September 24th, 1934.

    Key Words: Fellow Democrats; and friends of . . .
    before the 27th, next Thursday.

    Collation: 7; white; 28 x 21.5; 1–7; none; good.

Contents: Complete; infrequently revised in pencil; top right of page one notation: Reading Copy.

Dates: Pub. ?

9. Citation: ADDRESS OF UPTON SINCLAIR AT SHRINE AUDITORIUM; t. ms.; ribbon, carbon; InU.

Title: Address of Upton Sinclair | At Shrine Auditorium | Over KHJ and Columbia System | And 8 Coast Stations | September 17, 1934.

Key Words: Last Saturday morning I read . . . from sea to shining sea."

Collation: 18; white, blue watermarked; 7 x 21.6 to 28 x 21.6; [1] 2–4, 1–3, 5–8, [1] 2–7; good.

Contents: Complete: infrequently revised in ink, pencil.

Dates: Pub. ?

10. Citation: ADDRESS OF UPTON SINCLAIR AT THE WESTERN WRITERS CONGRESS; t. ms.; carbon; InU.

Title: ADDRESS OF UPTON SINCLAIR AT THE WESTERN WRITERS CONGRESS | San Francisco, California, November 13, 1936

Key Words: My Friends: It is a . . . Western Writers. I thank you.

Collation: 8; white watermarked; 27.9 x 21.6; [1] 2–8; none; good.

Contents: Complete; moderately revised in pencil.

Dates: Pub. EPIC News, 7 December 1936.

11. Citation: ADVENTURE WITH A NEWSPAPER PROPRIETOR; t. ms.; carbon; InU.

Title: ADVENTURE WITH A NEWSPAPER PROPRIETOR

Key Words: Toward the end of the . . . banks, lying idle and useless.

Collation: 60; white watermarked; 28 x 21.6; [1], 2–7, [1], 2–23, [1], 2–7, [1], 2–23; none; good.

Contents: Complete, infrequently revised in pencil.

Dates: Comp. ca. 1939. Pub. ?

12. Citation: ADVERTISING SUICIDE; t. ms.; ribbon, carbon; InU.

Title: ADVERTISING SUICIDE

Key Words: In my home city of . . . in the midst of plenty.

Collation: 8; white watermarked, misc. sheets; 27.8 x 21.6, 21.4 x 21.6; [1], 2–4. [1], 2–4; 1; good.

Contents: Complete; moderately revised in pencil; original and one carbon.

Dates: Comp. ca. 1940. Pub. ?

13. Citation: ADVICE TO JUNE GRADUATES; t. ms.; carbon; InU.

Title: ADVICE TO JUNE GRADUATES

Key Words: My advice to young people . . . human race is to continue.

Collation: 1; white; 28 x 21.7; unnumbered; none; good.

Contents: Complete; unrevised.

Dates: Comp. ca. 1945. Pub. ?

14a. Citation: AFFECTIONATELY EVE; t. ms.; ribbon; InU.

Title: [none]

Key Words: If I used the real . . . ever, ever, ever dear Eve.

Collation: 299; green; 28.2 x 21.5; consecutively numbered but not continuously; 48, 56, 136, 151, 156, 211, 212, 219, 242, 288; good.

Contents: Complete; frequently revised in pencil.

Dates: Pub. ca. 28 August 1961.

14b. Citation: AFFECTIONATELY EVE; t. ms.; ribbon; InU.

Title: SNAKE IN THE GRASS | the diary of | Eve Forrester | (Affectionately, Eve) [(w.i. blue ink)]

Key Words: If I used the real . . . of Lorine's governess, and just

Collation: 276; white watermarked, white; 28 x 21.6, 27.8 x 21.6; continuously numbered with variations; 1; fair; smudged, tattered, punched for two-ring binder.

Contents: Incomplete; infrequently revised in blue, black ink, pencil; printer's notations in red ink; stamp on title page indicates it was an agent's copy:

Bertha Klausner
Artists' and Literary Agent
130 E. 40th St., New York 16, N.Y.

Dear Janey | by "Anonymous" | (alternate title | The Loving Criminal) written on back of title page; ms. in manila envelope: ms "Dear Janey" | later Affectionately Eve.

Dates: Pub. ca. 28 August 1961.

15. Citation: AFTER THE WAR: A FORECAST; t. ms.; carbon; InU.

Title: After the War: A Forecast

Key Words: It has been said that . . . the case of the Boers.

Collation: 13; white watermarked; 28 x 21.6; [1] 2–8, 8a, 9–12; none; good.

Contents: Complete; infrequently revised in black, red ink.

Dates: Pub. *American Socialist*, 30 October 1915.

16. Citation: AFTER THE WAR IS OVER; t. ms.; ribbon, carbon; InU.

Title: AFTER THE WAR IS OVER

Key Words: Young Grand Duke Carlos Pauli . . . I wonder what Hollywood is like!

Collation: 25; white watermarked, blue watermarked; 28 x 21.6; [1] 2–21, 21–24; none, good.

Contents: Complete: moderately revised in pencil by MCS.

Dates: Comp. ca. 1945? Pub.   ?

17a. Citation: ALBERT EINSTEIN: TWO REMINIS-CENCES; t. ms.; ribbon, carbon; InU.

Title: THE EINSTEIN I KNEW

Key Words: Albert Einstein came to America . . . is my friend Upton Sinclair."

Collation: 11; white watermarket; 28 x 21.6; [1] 2–11; none; good.

Contents: Complete; infrequently revised in blue ink.

Dates: Pub. *Saturday Review of Literature*, 14 April 1956.

17b. Citation: ALBERT EINSTEIN: TWO REMINIS-CENSES; t. ms.; ribbon, carbon; InU.

Title: [ALBERT (c.o. pencil)] THE [w.i. pencil)]
EINSTEIN [: RECOLLECTIONS (c.o. pencil)] I
KNEW [(w.i. pencil)]

Key Words: Albert Einstein came to America . . . is
my friend Upton Sinclair."

Collation: 22; white, white watermarked; 20.7 x 21.6 to
28 x 21.6; consecutively numbered by group but not
continuously; none; good.

Contents: Complete; infrequently revised in blue ink;
original and one carbon.

Dates: Pub. *Saturday Review of Literature*, 14 April
1956.

18. Citation: THE ALTAMIRA CAVE PAINTINGS; t.
ms.; carbon; InU.

Title: THE ALTAMIRA CAVE PAINTINGS | Out-
line for a movie or T V story

Key Words: This story is history, pre-history . . . the
paintings in the cave.

Collation: 1; white; 28 x 21.6; [1]; none; good.

Contents: Complete; infrequently revised in blue ink.

Dates: Comp. ca. 1930s. Pub. ?

19. Citation: THE AMATEUR HIGHWAYMAN; t. ms.;
black, purple carbon; InU.

Title: THE AMATEUR HIGHWAYMAN | A Sketch

Key Words: Scene; A college campus, with . . . the
uncle gets the widow.

Collation: 4; white watermarked; 28.1 x 21.8; unnumbered; none; good.

Contents: Complete; infrequently revised in black ink;
original and two carbons.

Dates: Comp. ca. 1930s? Pub. ?

20. Citation: THE AMATEUR ROBBERS; t. ms.; carbon; InU.

Title: *The Amateur Robbers*

Key Words: Story suggested by a visit . . . would have an educational touch

Collation: 2; white; 20.1 x 20.3; [1–2]; none; good.

Contents: Complete; unrevised; Gulfport, Miss. appears at top left of first leaf.

Dates: Comp. ca. 1915? Pub. ?

21. Citation: AMERICA DANCES; t. ms.; ribbon, carbon; InU.

Title: AMERICA DANCES | Outline of a Musical Comedy

Key Words: Joe Prescott is a promotor . . . bride— get onto her stride;

Collation: 22; white watermarked, green; 27.8 x 21.6, 28 x 21.6; [1] 2–12, [1] 2–10; none; good.

Contents: Complete; moderately revised in pencil; original and carbon; first twelve pages rust and water stained; note at top of page one: 1957 Note: This was written at the time of the Ham & Eggs craze in Calif.

Dates: Comp. ca. August, 1938. Pub. ?

22. Citation: AMERICAN AUTHORS SELF-AP-PRAISED; t. ms.; carbon; InU.

Title: AMERICAN AUTHORS SELF-APPRAISED

Key Words: The editor of this volume . . . where-withal shall it be salted?

Collation: 8; white watermarked, white; 27.9 x 21.6, 28 x 21.7; [1] 3, 5, [1] 2–5; 1, 2; good.

Contents: Complete; moderately revised in pencil; two carbons appear to be from a later version, pp. 2, 4, of first carbon are on versoes of pp. 1, 3.

Dates: Comp. ca. 1946. Pub. ?

23. Citation: AMERICAN CITY; t. ms.; carbon; InU.

Title: *American City* | a novel

Key Words: There stood an old barn . . . industry, and incidentally of civilization.

Collation: 138; white; 28 x 21.6; [1] 2–17, 17a, 18–58, [1] 2–8, [1], [1] 2–17, 17a, 18–58, [1] 2–67; none; poor.

Contents: Complete; infrequently revised in pencil, faded ink; copy 2 lacks final three leaves, last of which is blank; each copy fastened together with two brass studs in left margin; in addition, there are extra copies of pages [1], 59–64. Apparently an early version of *King Coal*.

Dates: Comp. ca. 1914. Pub. 1917.

24. Citation: THE AMERICAN MAGAZINE; t. ms.; ribbon; InU.

Title: THE AMERICAN MAGAZINE

Key Words: I am interested in observing . . . to their elbows! UPTON SINCLAIR.

Collation: 1; white watermarked; 28 x 21.6; [1]; none.

Contents: Complete; infrequently revised in faded ink.

Dates: Comp. ca. 1910? Pub. ?

25. Citation: AMERICAN FABLES; t. ms., a. ms.; ribbon, carbon, pencil; David and Jean Sinclair

Title: AMERICAN FABLES

Key Words: Henry was the Boy's name . . . OF DOOM SHALL REMAIN. AMEN!"

Collation: 400; white watermarked, white; 27.8 x 21.5, 21.5 x 21.5; [1–2], 17–54, [54a], 55–189, 190–1, 192, 193a–193b, 194–215, 216–17, 218–263, 263a, 264–267, 267a, 268–284, 285–99, 300–425; none; good

Contents: Of thirty fables, thirteen are not by Sinclair; moderately revised by Sinclair and MCS; agent Bertha Klausner's stamp on contents page.

Dates: Pub. 1923–48. Unpublished material composed 1952.

See: BILL PORTER, CO-OP, DEPRESSION IS-LAND, FLIVVER KING, A GIANT'S STRENGTH, HELL!, OUR LADY, THE SPOKESMAN'S SECRE-TARY, WALLY FOR QUEEN

26a. Citation: AMERICAN NIGHTS ENTERTAIN-MENT; photo; black; InU.

Title: [none]

Key Words: The signs that were ordered . . . Blank Verse by U.S. 1923

Collation: 88; brown; 27.9 x 21.5; 337–425; none; poor, punched for three-ring binder.

Contents: Incomplete; unrevised.

Dates: Comp. ca. 1940s? Unpublished.

26b. Citation: AMERICAN NIGHTS ENTERTAIN-MENT; photo; black; InU.

Title: AMERICAN [FABLES (c.o.)] Nights Enter-tain | ments [(w.i. blue ink)]

Key Words: [unreadable] . . . Verse by U.S. 1923

Collation: 427; brown; 27.9 x 21.5; [2] 17–189, [190–191], 192–193, 193a, 193b, 194–215, [216–217], 218–263, 263a, 264–267, 267a, 268–284, [285–299], 300–425; none; poor, punched for three-ring binder.

Contents: Incomplete; unrevised.

Dates: Comp. ca. 1940s? Unpublished.

26c. Citation: AMERICAN NIGHTS ENTERTAIN-MENTS; photo.; black; InU.

Title: AMERICAN [FABLES (c.o.)] Nights Entertainments [(w.i. green ink)]

Key Words: I. The Flivver King (Henry . . . report you to my lady."

Collation: 149; brown; 27.9 x 21.4; [2] 17–163; none; poor, punched for three-ring binder.

Contents: Incomplete (?); unrevised in 3 folders.

Dates: Comp. ca. 1940s? Unpublished.

26d. Citation: AMERICAN NIGHTS' ENTERTAIN-MENTS; t. ms., a. ms.; ribbon, carbon, pencil; InU.

Title: [none]

Key Words: the problem. We know that . . . following night there were told—

Collation: 277; white, misc. sheets; 27.9 x 21.6, 9.3 x 21.6 to 27.9 x 21.6; randomly numbered; 1, 22, 36, 42; good.

Contents: Incomplete; frequently revised in pencil; draft at various stages of completion of the stories in "American Nights"; ms. is in a manila folder labeled: Parts of American Nights Entertainments (unpublished.).

Dates: Comp. ca. 1940s? Unpublished.

26e. Citation: AMERICAN NIGHTS' ENTERTAIN-MENTS; t. ms., a. ms.; ribbon, carbon, pencil, black, blue ink; InU.

Title: [none]

Key Words: This story I am going . . . blood in all of them.

Collation: 238; white, misc. sheets; 28 x 21.7, 6.1 x 21.6 to 28 x 21.7; randomly numbered; 12, 235, 36, 237; good.

Contents: Incomplete; frequently revised in pencil; ms. is largely carbon copies of what appears to be complete tales from the "American Nights"; ms. is in a manila folder labeled: Parts of American Nights Entertainments.

Dates: Comp. ca. 1940s? Unpublished.

26f. Citation: AMERICAN NIGHTS' ENTERTAIN-MENTS; t. ms., a. ms.; ribbon, carbon, pencil; InU.

Title: THE AMERICAN NIGHTS' ENTERTAIN-MENTS | or | A THOUSAND NIGHTS AND A NIGHT

Key Words: IN THE NAME OF GOD . . . planting and sprouting comes again.

Collation: 289; white watermarked, misc. sheets; 27.9 x 21.6, 9 x 13 to 14 x 21.7; continuously numbered with variations; 7, 8, 9, 12, 13; good.

Contents: Incomplete(?); infrequently revised in pencil; notes appear to be directions for a typist; these notes plus the table of contents and its carbons comprise the first thirteen pages.

Dates: Comp. ca. 1940s? Unpublished.

27a. Citation: AMERICAN OUTPOST; t. ms.; carbon; InU.

Title: SPEAKING THROUGH A SMILE | A Book of Reminiscences

Key Words: For many years requests have . . . mine which they can read!

Collation: 2; white; 28 x 21.6; [1], 2; none; good.

Contents: Complete; infrequently revised in pencil.

Dates: Comp. 1928–31. Pub. 14 April 1932.

27b. Citation: AMERICAN OUTPOST; t. ms.; ribbon, carbon; InU.

Title: [none]

Key Words: Nowhere in the thirty pages . . . this sad story in detail.

Collation: 19; 28 x 21.7; white; 75a, 1–6, 75a, 75b, 75c, 75d, 75e, 75f, 75a, 75b, 75c, 75d, 75e, 75f; none; good.

Contents: Incomplete; infrequently revised in pencil; "For American Outpost" has been penciled in the upper lefthand corner of the first page; misc. sheets of the book.

Dates: Comp. 1928–31. Pub. 14 April 1932.

27c. Citation: AMERICAN OUTPOST; t. ms., a. ms.; ribbon, carbon, pencil; InU.

Title: [none]

Key Words: I was becoming less and . . . a young writer's future depends.

Collation: 27; misc sheets; 15.5 x 11.5 to 28 x 21.6; randomly numbered; 14, 23, 25; fair.

Contents: Incomplete; frequently revised in pencil; appears to be a collection of inserts and rewritten material for *American Outpost*; ms. has been tagged and labeled; fragment 23 is written on the verso of a telegram which is to Sinclair from John Farrar; it reads: "STRONGLY ADVISE OMISSION ALL DOCUMENTS FROM AUTOBIOGRAPHY MERRY CHRISTMAS"

Dates: Comp. 1928–31. Pub. 14 April 1932.

27d. Citation: AMERICAN OUTPOST; t. ms., a. ms.; ribbon, carbon, pencil; InU.

Title: [none]

Key Words: When "The Metropolis" was published . . . sue his wife for divorce.

Collation: 70; misc. sheets; 7.6 x 12.7 to 28 x 21.7; randomly numbered; 2, 30, 39, 45; good.

Contents: Incomplete; frequently revised in pencil; ms. appears to be a collection of revisions and inserts for the main ms; ms. has been tagged and labeled; in a folder labeled: American Outpost | Scattered sheets.

Dates: Comp. 1928–31. Pub. 14 April 1932.

27e. Citation: AMERICAN OUTPOST; t. ms.; carbon; InU.

Title: SPEAKING THROUGH A SMILE | A BOOK OF REMINISCENCES

Key Words: For many years requests have . . . we no more are here?

Collation: 211; white; 28 x 21.7; randomly numbered; none; good.

Contents: Incomplete; infrequently revised in pencil; folder labeled: "American Outpost" | Extra copies of | rewritten pages.

Dates: Comp. 1928–31. Pub. 14 April 1932.

27f. Citation: AMERICAN OUTPOST; t. ms.; carbon; InU.

Title: CHAPTER I | *CHILDHOOD*

Key Words: My first recollection of life . . . days were waiting on tiptoe!

Collation: 94; white; 28.1 x 21.8; [1]–7, 7a, 8–31, 31a, 32–60, 62–93; none; fair.

Contents: Complete three chapters; infrequently revised in pencil; folder bears the label: *American Outpost* | chap. I–III.

Dates: Comp. 1928–31. Pub. 14 April 1932.

27g. Citation: AMERICAN OUTPOST; t. ms.; ribbon, pencil; InU.

Title: SPEAKING [(w.i. pencil)] THROUGH A SMILE | A Book of Reminiscences [(w.i. pencil)]

Key Words: For many years requests have . . . of those dreadful books! (over)

Collation: 288; white, misc. sheets; 28.2 x 21.6, 14 x 21.4 to 28 x 21.6; consecutively numbered by chapters but not continuously; 10, 52, 64, 74, 97, 99, 149, 192, 193, 198, 207, 215, 234, 249, 261, 288; fair.

Contents: Complete; frequently revised in pencil; ms. is in a manila folder labeled: American Outpost—A Draft —Earliest Draft.

Dates: Comp. 1928–31. Pub. 14 April 1932.

27h. Citation: AMERICAN OUTPOST; t. ms.; ribbon, carbon; InU.

Title: SPEAKING THROUGH A SMILE | A BOOK OF REMINISCENCES

Key Words: For many years requests have . . . we no more are here?

Collation: 256; white; 28 x 21.7; continuously numbered with variations; none; fair, discolored.

Contents: Complete; infrequently revised in pencil; ms. is in a manila folder labeled: American Outpost—A draft—Carbon of Later Draft; in the upper right hand corner of the first leaf is stamped:

PLEASE RETURN MS
TO HENRY GALLUP PAINE
2 E. 23rd St., New York, N.Y.
This has been crossed out and Upton Sinclair Long Beach written in.

Dates: Comp. 1928–31. Pub. 14 April 1932.

27i. Citation: AMERICAN OUTPOST; t. ms.; ribbon; InU.

Title: SPEAKING THROUGH A SMILE | A BOOK OF REMINISCENCES

Key Words: For many years requests have . . . we no more are here?

Collation: 257; white; 27.8 x 21.7; continuously numbered with variations; none; fair but a little faded.

Contents: Complete; moderately revised in pencil; ms. is in a gray box labeled: SPEAKING THROUGH A SMILE | Pub. as American Outpost | Original of later draft; written in right corner: PLEASE RETURN MS. TO HENRY GALLUP PAINE, 2 E. 23rd St., New York, N. Y.

Dates: Comp. 1928–31. Pub. 14 April 1932.

27j. Citation: AMERICAN OUTPOST; t. ms., a. ms.; ribbon, pencil; InU.

Title: SPEAKING THROUGH A SMILE | A BOOK OF REMINISCENCES

Key Words: For many years requests have . . . we no more are here?

Collation: 264; white, green; 28 x 21.7; continuously numbered with variations; 60, 63, 216; fair and faded.

Contents: Complete; frequently revised in pencil; a carbon of the following original; ms. is in a manila folder labeled: American Outpost | a complete draft | Carbon of Later Draft.

Dates: Comp. 1928–31. Pub. 14 April 1932.

27k. Citation: AMERICAN OUTPOST; t. ms.; carbon; InU.

Title: American Outpost | A BOOK OF REMINIS-CENCES

Key Words: For many years requests have . . . we no more are here?

Collation: 237; white, brown; 28 x 21.7, 29.7 x 23; [3], 1–118, [2], 119–147, 147a, 147b, 148–230; none; good.

Contents: Complete in two folders; infrequently revised in pencil; both folders are bound by two brass studs; on the covers the title SPEAKING THROUGH A SMILE has been crossed out and American Outpost inked in; also an additional note: Carbon of Printer's Copy appears on both folders. Folder 1: contains chaps. I–IV, Folder 2: chaps. V–VIII.

Dates: Comp. 1928–31. Pub. 14 April 1932.

28. Citation: AMERICAN PLUTOCRACY; t. ms.; carbon; InU.

Title: AMERICAN PLUTOCRACY.

Key Words: As a novelist I like . . . basic struggle in your mind.

Collation: 16; white watermarked; 28 x 21.6; [1] 2–8, [1] 2–8; none; good.

Contents: Complete; infrequently revised in pencil, not in Sinclair's hand.

Dates: Comp. ca. 1938? Pub. ?

29. Citation: THE AMERICAN RICH; t. ms.; carbon; InU.

Title: THE AMERICAN RICH

Key Words: A year or two ago . . . to our million-aires to say!

Collation: 14; white watermarked, blue; 28 x 21.6, 27.9
x 21.6; [1] 2–7, [1] 2–7; none; good.

Contents: Complete; infrequently revised in pencil, not
in Sinclair's hand; dated in black ink: "Jan. 5–39."

Dates: Pub. *Progressive Weekly,* 19 February 1939.

30.   Citation: AMERICAN SUNRISE OVER JAPAN; t.
ms.; carbon; InU.

Title: AMERICAN SUNRISE OVER JAPAN

Key Words: This little book has been . . . back to his
"U.S.N." allegiance.

Collation: 3; white; 27.9 x 21.5; [1] 2–3; none; good.

Contents: Complete; infrequently revised in pencil, blue
ink.

Dates: Comp. ca. 1961. Pub. ?

31.   Citation: THE AMERICAN SUN ROSE OVER
JAPAN; t. ms.; carbon; InU.

Title: The American Sun Rose Over Japan

Key Words: This is a proposal for . . . the Sekiguchi
manuscript on request.

Collation: 3; white; 27.9 x 21.6; [1] 2–3; none; good.

Contents: Complete; infrequently revised in blue ink.

Dates: Comp. ca. 1960. Pub. ?

32a. ANOTHER PAMELA; t. ms., a. ms.; ribbon, pencil;
InU.

Title: PAMELA LIVES: | Or [(w.i. pencil)] [And
Virtue Is (c.o.)] Still Rewarded | A Story [(w.i. pencil)]
[Novel (c.o.)]

Key Words: Pries has studied it word . . . to be read as such.

Collation: 300; white, green; 15 x 21.5 to 28 x 21.6, 28 x 22; consecutively numbered by chapter but not continuously; 18, 24, 35, 110, 136, 240, 241, 269, 291, 295; good.

Contents: Complete; frequently revised in pencil; manila folder is labeled: Another Pamela Earlier Draft.

Dates: Pub. ca. 6 May 1950.

32b. Citation: ANOTHER PAMELA; t. ms.; ribbon, carbon; InU.

Title: PAMELA TWO: [(w.i. pencil)] [Lives (c.o.)] | Or | Virtue Still Rewarded | A Story

Key Words: Two hundred and ten years . . . Your devoted Little Sister | Pamela.

Collation: 328; white, white watermarked; 27.9 x 21.5; continuously numbered with variations; none; fair.

Contents: Complete; infrequently revised in pencil; the manila folder labeled: Another | Pamela | another Copy of Printer's Copy; but it appears to have been an agent's copy; label on the front cover: FRANZ J. HORCH Authors' and Publishers' Representative.

Dates: Pub. ca. 6 May 1950.

32c. Citation: ANOTHER PAMELA; t. ms., a. ms.; ribbon, carbon, pencil; InU.

Title: ANOTHER PAMELA | or, Virtue Still Rewarded [design] A Story | BY Upton Sinclair [design] | New York | The Viking Press | 1950

Key Words: Two hundred and ten years . . . to be read as such.

Collation: 336; printer's white layout paper, white; 30 x 22.8, 27.9 x 21.5; continuously numbered with variations; none; varies from very poor to good.

Contents: Complete; infrequently revised in regular, blue pencil; printer's copy including the layouts for the title page, dedication, and copyright; printer's notations in red pencil; manila folder is labeled: "Another | Pamela | Printer's Copy."

Dates: Pub. ca. 6 May 1950.

33. Citation: ANSWERING CORRESPONDENTS; t. ms.; carbon; InU.

Title: ANSWERING CORRESPONDENTS

Key Words: I like very much the . . . in the paper next week.

Collation: 10; white, watermarked; 28 x 21.6; [1] 2–5, [1] 2–5; none; good.

Contents: Complete; infrequently revised in pencil by MCS.

Dates: Comp. ca. 1938? Pub. ?

34. Citation: ART AND IMMEDIACY; t. ms.; carbon; InU.

Title: ART AND IMMEDIACY

Key Words: William Shakespeare, poet, was walking . . . die before the world changes.

Collation: 10; white watermarked; 28 x 21.7; [1] 2–5, [1] 2–5; none; good.

Contents: Complete; infrequently revised in pencil, not in Sinclair's hand; on first sheet is written: "copy sent to Petrov "Literaturnaya Gazeta" | 9/29/38," and Malcolm Cowley— | League Am Writers."

Dates: Pub. in *International Literature* (Moscow), VIII (1938).

35. Citation: ARTIFICIAL SELECTION; t. ms.; carbon; InU.

Title: ARTIFICIAL SELECTION

Key Words: My friend Mencken reads this . . . and insists that he won't.

Collation: 12; white; 27.9 x 21.6; 1–5, [1] 2–7; none; good.

Contents: Complete; unrevised.

Dates: Comp. ca. 1930s. Pub. ?

36. Citation: THE ASSOCIATED PRESS AND THE CATHOLICS; t. ms.; carbon; InU.

Title: THE ASSOCIATED PRESS AND THE CATHOLICS

Key Words: I have received from the . . . a score of different reasons!

Collation: 3; brown; 27.8 x 21.6; [1] 2–3; none; good.

Contents: Complete; unrevised; note in pencil on page one: Mailed 4-10-22.

Dates: Pub. *Appeal to Reason*, 29 April 1922.

37. Citation: AS I SEE IT: REDS BRING REACTION; t. ms.; ribbon; InU.

Title: THE REDS BRING REACTION

Key Words: Away back in the days . . . public, and keep them there.

Collation: 3; yellow; 28.1 x 21.5; [1] 2–3; none; good.

Contents: Complete; infrequently revised in blue ink.

Dates: Pub. *New America*, 1 December 1960.

38. Citation: AS WE SEE IT; photo; black; InU.

Title: *AS WE SEE IT* | AFL-CIO Public Service Program

Key Words: Flannery: Upton Sinclair, As We . . . for As We See It.

Collation: 3; brown; 35 x 21.6; [1] 2–3; none; good.

Contents: Complete; infrequently revised in ink, pencil; As We See It | AFL-CIO Public Service Program, Subject: Upton Sinclair on his Books broadcast by American Broadcasting Network, Sunday, Jan. 11, 1959.

Dates: Pub. as mimeograph transcript.

39. Citation: AS WE SEE IT: UPTON SINCLAIR'S STORY—#1; t. ms., mimeo; ribbon, black mimeo; InU.

Title: *AS WE SEE IT* | AFL-CIO Public Service Program | *SUBJECT*: UPTON SINCLAIR'S STORY— #1

Key Words: Flannery: As We See It . . . series As We See It.

Collation: 8; white watermarked; 15.5 x 10 to 33.8 x 21.3; [1], [1] 2–3, [1], [1] 2–3; none; good.

Contents: Complete; infrequently revised in blue pencil; contains two notes from Harry Flannery to Hunter Kimbrough and to Sinclair; transcription of AFL-CIO Public Service Program, ABC, Sunday, May 22, 1960; Part I only.

Dates: 22 May 1960. Recorded: Tape available for 1–4 in series, Lilly Library.

40. Citation: ATOMIC ENERGY FOR PEACE; t. ms.;
     carbon; InU.

     Title: ATOMIC ENERGY FOR PEACE

     Key Words: I am living amoid [*sic*] the . . . his mind
     to the situation.

     Collation: 7; white; 27.8 x 21.7 to 28 x 21.7; [1] 2–3,
     [1] 2–3, [1]; none; good.

     Contents: Complete; infrequently revised in blue ink,
     signed in pencil; folder labeled: "af — | to | at —."

     Dates: Comp. ca. 1952? Pub. ?

41. Citation: THE AUTOBIOGRAPHY OF UPTON
     SINCLAIR; t. ms.; ribbon, carbon; InU.

     Title: [none]

     Key Words: [?] was a set of . . . spread a little enlight-
     enment through

     Collation: 18; white, white watermarked; 27.8 x 21.4 to
     28 x 21.7; randomly numbered; none; good.

     Contents: Incomplete; moderately revised in pencil, blue,
     black, red ink; notes for The Autobiography; folder
     labeled: Sinclair MSS | miscellaneous pages.

     Dates: Pub. ca. 3 December 1962.

     See: AMERICAN OUTPOST

42. Citation: THE AUTOBIOGRAPHY OF UPTON
     SINCLAIR; t. ms., print, xerox; ribbon, print, xerox;
     InU.

     Title: The Autobiography | of | Upton Sinclair

     Key Words: MY FIRST recollection of life . . . peace
     —and of social justice.

Collation: 531; white, white watermarked; 28 x 21.5
to 28 x 21.7; 10, 1–3, 3a, 3b, 4–36, 1–181, 181a, 181b,
181c, 181d, 181e, 181f, 181g, 182–476; 407; fair, several sheets badly damaged.

Contents: Complete; moderately revised in blue, red,
black ink, pencil, not all in Sinclair's hand; ms. also
bears printer's notations that are sometimes indistin-
guishable from the corrections; ms. is housed in two
boxes labeled: PRINTER'S COPY. He has mounted
pages from *American Outpost* on sheets and updated
them, adding additional material where pertinent.

Dates: Pub. ca. 3 December 1962.

See: AMERICAN OUTPOST

43a. Citation: BETWEEN TWO WORLDS; t. ms., a. ms.;
ribbon, carbon, pencil; InU.

Title: [none]

Key Words: The gossips told a funny . . . husband
& wife!" mused Irma.

Collation: 43; green, misc. sheets; 28 x 21.6, 15.3 x
21.3 to 28 x 21.7; randomly numbered; 23; good.

Contents: Incomplete; moderately revised in pencil; ms.
labeled: "Misc p. | Are these | all | *Between* | *two*
worlds? | check; apparently pages to be inserted into
another ms."

Dates: Pub. March 1941.

43b. Citation: BETWEEN TWO WORLDS; t. ms., a. ms.;
ribbon, carbon, pencil; InU.

Title: [none]

Key Words: [dedication page] To my friends in England . . . until the tide rises again.

Collation: 16; green, misc. sheets; 27.9 x 21.6, 21.7 x 20.3 to 28 x 21.6, 27.9 x 21.5; randomly numbered; 1; good.

Contents: Incomplete; moderately revised in pencil; these are pages for insertion into the ms; there is an accompanying instruction sheet; the folder is labeled: Misc pages | Between Two Worlds | Identified.

Dates: Pub. March 1941.

43c. Citation: BETWEEN TWO WORLDS; t. ms., a. ms.; ribbon, pencil; InU.

Title: [DRAGON'S TEETH (c.o.)] Between Two Worlds [(w.i. pencil)] | A NOVEL

Key Words: When one has been away . . . but tomorrow I'll be sober!"

Collation: 1400; green, misc. sheets; 28.1 x 21.6, 27.9 x 21.6; numbered consecutively by chapter but not continuously; 5, 20, 34, 40, 41, 43, 47, 57, 59, 60, 61, 87, 97, 105, 111, 132, 134, 149, 184, 187, 188, 197, 198, 199, 203, 221, 230, 231, 268, 278, 290, 294, 305, 306, 323, 331, 333, 352, 355, 360, 366, 369, 379, 394, 402, 406, 438, 439, 447, 448, 452, 459, 462, 470, 483, 549, 550, 566, 567, 574, 575, 586, 614, 627, 661, 662, 670, 689, 703, 706, 711, 712, 715, 739, 744, 761, 767, 770, 777, 787, 793, 800, 809, 813, 828, 859, 860, 881, 916, 928, 934, 938, 950, 955, 957, 974, 982, 998, 1009, 1015, 1020, 1040, 1041, 1047, 1049; good.

Contents: Complete; frequently revised in pencil; box is labeled: BETWEEN TWO WORLDS | Original: Green copy | Chapters 1 to 14; box II labeled: BETWEEN TWO WORLDS | Original: Green copy | Chapters 15 to 39; boxes are in library boxes labeled: BETWEEN TWO WORLDS | EARLIEST DRAFT | I [and] | II.

Dates: Pub. March 1941.

43d. Citation: BETWEEN TWO WORLDS; t. ms.; ribbon; InU.

Title: BETWEEN TWO WORLDS | A NOVEL

Key Words: When one has been away . . . I'm serious about that, too!

Collation: 793; white watermarked; 27.9 x 21.6; continuously numbered with variations; none; good.

Contents: Complete copy of chapters I–XVII; infrequently revised in pencil; folder I labeled: Printer's copy (carbon); folder II contains the remaining portion of the ms; three loose sheets in the library box read: Between Two Worlds | printer's copy [in Sinclair's hand], Chapter 1–27 inclusive, and: MFg. | File with other | material on | Sinclair: *Between Two | Worlds*. Dates: Pub. March 1941.

43e. Citation: BETWEEN TWO WORLDS; t. ms.; ribbon; InU.

Title: [none]

Key Words: When one has been away . . . but tomorrow I'll be sober!

Collation: 1164; white watermarked; 12.5 x 21.6 to 28 x 21.6; continuously numbered with variations; none; ms. is in uneven condition, some pages are badly soiled, all are full of ink prints; spindled.

Contents: Complete; infrequently revised in pencil with printer's notations in red, blue, green, brown pencil; box I labeled: Printer's copy (original) Chaps. 1–20; box II labeled: Printer's copy (original) Chaps. 21–40 and completes the ms.

Dates: Pub. March 1941.

44. Citation: BEWARE CAMPAIGN DISHONESTIES;
t. ms.; carbon; InU.

Title: BEWARE CAMPAIGN DISHONESTIES

Key Words: Exactly ten years ago, this . . . able to
register and vote.

Collation: 3; white; 28 x 21.6; [1] 2–3; none; good.

Contents: Complete; infrequently revised in pencil.

Dates: Pub. *Editor's Bulletin for the Roosevelt-Truman
Ticket,* 1 November 1944.

45a. Citation: BILL PORTER; a. ms., t. ms.; ribbon, pencil; InU.

Title: Caliph of Bagdad

Key Words: Will has got a job . . . ragged soapy stroll
into immortality.

Collation: 86; white watermarked; 28 x 21.5; [1] 13–97;
none; good.

Contents: Complete, infrequently revised in pencil; in
manila folder, in pencil on insert: (Bill Porter); early
version?

Dates: Pub. 1 September 1925.

45b. Citation: BILL PORTER; t. ms.; ribbon; InU.

Title: BILL PORTER A Drama of the Prison Life of
O. Henry.

Key Words: The central figure of this . . . S2 3 4 as
marked

Collation: 96; green; 27.9 x 21.6; numbered consecutively by acts but not continuously; 4, 41, 42, 44, 59,
63, 89; good.

Contents: Complete; frequently revised in pencil, ink; final version.

Dates: Pub. 1 September 1925.

46. Citation: BLANK CHECK POLITICS: t. ms.; ribbon, carbon; InU.

Title: BLANK CHECK POLITICS

Key Words: Somebody sends me a pamphlet . . . and you took that advice.

Collation: 12; white watermarked; 28 x 21.6; 1, 1a, 2–5 [6], [1] 2–5; none; good.

Contents: Complete; moderately revised in pencil by Sinclair and MCS.

Dates: Pub. *EPIC News,* 2 May 1938.

47. Citation: BLASPHEMY IN GERMANY; t. ms.; ribbon, carbon; InU.

Title: BLASPHEMY IN GERMANY

Key Words: A Correspondent sends me a . . . before this article reaches the reader.

Collation: 2; brown; 27.8 x 21.6; [1–2]; none; good.

Contents: Complete; infrequently revised in ink, clipping from Florida *"Times-Union"* pasted on first leaf; two copies of article concerning German book "The Disagreeable Message."

Dates: Comp. ca. 1924? Pub. ?

48. Citation: THE BLIND ALLEY; t. ms.; ribbon, carbon; InU.

Title: THE BLIND ALLEY | A Story

Key Words: "Get out of this business . . . business— it's a blind alley."

Collation: 65; white; 27.9 x 21.7, 28.2 x 21.6; [1] 2–12, 13–14, 15–21, [1] 2–12, 13–14, 15–21, 1–25; 43; good.

Contents: Complete; moderately revised in pencil, not all in Sinclair's hand; early draft and complete ribbon copy; all are copies of the same material; the later two are typed copy of a revised early draft.

Dates: Comp. ca. 1920s? Pub. ?

49. Citation: THE BLUE-SHIRTS OF LOS ANGELES; t. ms.; carbon; InU.

Title: THE BLUE-SHIRTS OF LOS ANGELES

Key Words: This is a story about . . . much nearer than anybody realizes.

Collation: 14; white; 28 x 21.6; [1] 2–7, [1] 2–7; none; good.

Contents: Complete; two copies infrequently revised in pencil.

Dates: Comp. 1932–33? Pub. ?

50a. Citation: THE BOOK OF LIFE: MIND AND BODY [See THE MEANING OF GRAFT, A NUMBER OF THINGS, and THE QUESTION OF VIOLENCE]; t. ms.; carbon; InU.

Title: [none]

Key Words: In the Marquesas Islands in . . . of the so-called civilized world.

Collation: 83; brown; 27.8 x 21.5 to 28 x 21.6; consecutively numbered by chapter but not continuously, some randomly numbered; 1; good.

Contents: Incomplete; unrevised; folder labeled: Book of the Body | Page 113 thru end of Book | Carbon copies; ms. has been tagged and labeled; extra sheet enclosed in the box reads: Book of the Mind | No mss found | Book of the Body (2 folders) | 1) Carbons of p. 113 — end of book | 2) Misc. originals and carbons.

The Book of Life: Mind and Body was originally published in *Appeal to Reason*, 8 December 1920–16 April 1921 and separately as a single volume in 1921. *The Book of Life: Love and Society* volume two, was originally published in part in *Appeal to Reason* irregularly from 16 April 1921 to 25 February 1922. Volume II was first published separately in mid-May 1922; at the same time, both volumes were printed as a composite volume.

Dates: Pub. 1920–21.

50b. Citation: THE BOOK OF LIFE: MIND AND BODY [See THE MEANING OF GRAFT, A NUMBER OF THINGS, and THE QUESTION OF VIOLENCE]; t. ms.; ribbon, carbon; InU.

Title: [none]

Key Words: The manufacture of our vaccines . . . root channels of the teeth?

Collation: 34; brown; 28 x 21.8; randomly numbered; 1; a little worn in places.

Contents: Incomplete; infrequently revised in pencil; folder labeled: "Miscellaneous Original and/or carbons of pages from | Book of Life: Mind & Body | Book of the Body | Identified in Book; ms. has been tagged and labeled."

Dates: Pub. 1920–21.

50c. Citation: THE BOOK OF LIFE: LOVE AND SOCIETY [See THE MEANING OF GRAFT, A NUMBER OF THINGS, and THE QUESTION OF VIOLENCE]; t. ms., a. ms.; ribbon, carbon, pencil; InU.

Title: [none]

Key Words: In the moving picture world . . . con-
venient, because it saves all

Collation: 70; brown; 28 x 21.7; randomly numbered;
1, 9; good.

Contents: Incomplete; infrequently revised in pencil;
folder labeled: "Miscellaneous Original | and/or carbons
of pages from | 'Book of Life'/Book of Love' | Original
with | holographic corrections. Identified in book | Earli-
est Draft; extra enclosed sheet reads: Book of Love Draft
partly consisting of printed clippings | (complete) Book
follows this draft | 2 earlier drafts (both incomplete
and | both containing original and carbons | of some
pages and more than one | draft of some pages)."

Dates: Pub. 1921–22.

50d. Citation: THE BOOK OF LIFE: LOVE AND SO-
CIETY [See THE MEANING OF GRAFT, A NUM-
BER OF THINGS, and THE QUESTION OF VIO-
LENCE]; t. ms., a. ms.; ribbon, pencil, print; InU.

Title: THE BOOK OF LIFE | Volume Two: | Love
and Society

Key Words: Discusses the sex-custome now existing
. . . day we hope to write.

Collation: 121; brown; 27.9 x 21.7; [1], 1–59, 59a, 59b,
60–68, 68, 69–91, 91a, 92–98, [1]–17; 14, 31, 48, 63,
88, 90, 102, 104, 114, 118; fair, tattered in places.

Contents: Complete; frequently revised in pencil; folder
labeled: Book of love | chap. XXVIII– | XLVII. p. 100 |
Book of Love Complete | (Chapters XXVIII thru XXXII
| printed, remainder original typed pages. | all have
holograph corrections.) | Latest draft; ms. appears to be
a complete draft of Vol. 2 of *The Book of Life*; the first
26 pages of the text Sinclair makes extensive use of
previously printed material apparently from the newspapers.

Dates: Pub. 1921–22.

50e. Citation: THE BOOK OF LIFE: LOVE AND SO-
CIETY [See THE MEANING OF GRAFT, A NUM-
BER OF THINGS, and THE QUESTION OF VIO-
LENCE]; t. ms., a. ms.; ribbon, carbon, pencil; InU.

Title: PART THREE | THE BOOK OF LOVE. |
The Evolution of Marriage. | (Discusses the sex rela-
tionship, what it means, how it | comes to be, and the
changes it has undergone in the | progress of human
society.)

Key Words: We have now to investigate . . . The
Money arrangements of maria

Collation: 96; brown; 27.8 x 21.7; randomly numbered;
29; good.

Contents: Incomplete; infrequently revised in pencil;
folder labeled: "Book of Love" | various original & car-
bon pages | Middle Draft.

Dates: Pub. 1921–22.

51. Citation: A BOOK ON SOCIALISM; t. ms.; carbon;
InU.

Title: A BOOK ON SOCIALISM

Key Words: Every now and then a . . . and tell others
about it.

Collation: 1; brown; 27.8 x 21.5; unnumbered; none;
good.

Contents: Complete; infrequently revised in pencil;
someone has written in pencil: Mailed to U.S. 4/14/22;
folder labeled: "Appeal to Reason."

Dates: Pub. Probably in *Appeal to Reason* about May
1922.

52. Citation: BOOK URCHINS; t. ms., a. ms.; ribbon, carbon; InU.

Title: BOOK URCHINS | A Study of Literary Tropisms

Key Words: Seventeen years ago I visited . . . most optimistic seed-catalog has predicted.

Collation: 37; white; 28 x 21.6; 1–6, 1–4, [1] 2–9, [1] 2–5, [6] 7–9, [1] 2–9; none; good.

Contents: Complete; infrequently revised in pencil; partial early draft and carbon, three carbons of complete late draft, two identical, one contains variations, all three are unrevised.

Dates: Pub. *Forum*, November 1927.

53. Citation: BOOKS OF UPTON SINCLAIR IN RUSSIA; t. ms.; ribbon, carbon; InU.

Title: *Books of* | UPTON SINCLAIR | *In Russia* | PROCEEDINGS OF LITERARY GROUPS AND WORKERS' CLUBS OF THE METAL WORKERS OF Leningrad.

Key Words: The books of Upton Sinclair . . . primary. Aged about 30. (over)

Collation: 20; white; 28 x 21.7 to 35 x 22; randomly numbered; 1–3, 16; good.

Contents: Complete; moderately revised in pencil, ink; setting copy of this pamphlet; carbon apparently not prepared by Sinclair.

Dates: Pub. 1931.

54. Citation: BOOKS OF UPTON SINCLAIR IN TRANSLATIONS AND FOREIGN EDITIONS; t. ms., a. ms., g. proof, print; carbon, pencil, print; InU.

Title: Books of | UPTON SINCLAIR | *In Translations and Foreign Editions* | A BIBLIOGRAPHY OF 525 TITLES | IN 34 COUNTRIES | *August, 1930*

Key Words: ENGLAND | T. Werner Laurie Ltd. . . . I will have them soon

Collation: 226; misc. sheets; 19.5 x 12.8 to 58.4 x 17.6; unnumbered; none; fair.

Contents: Incomplete; moderately revised in pencil; includes tearsheets and marked copy of the 1930 list and represents drafts, notes, paste-ups, and revised proof for 1938 edition of this pamphlet.

Dates: Pub. 1930, 1938.

55. Citation: BOOST OUR SPECIAL EDITIONS; t. ms.; ribbon, carbon; InU.

Title: BOOST OUR SPECIAL EDITIONS

Key Words: The most important way we . . . getting word to the voters.

Collation: 1; white watermarked; 28 x 21.6; unnumbered; none; good.

Contents: Complete; unrevised.

Dates: Pub. *Upton Sinclair's EPIC News*, 16 July 1934.

56. Citation: THE BORROWED BABY; t. ms.; ribbon, carbon; InU.

Title: THE BORROWED BABY

Key Words: I was waiting for Harriett . . . Centre with my 'little Jonathan'!"

Collation: 121; white watermarked; 26.3 x 20.4; [1] 2–19, [1] 1–25, [1] 1–21, 1–27, 1–27; none; good.

Contents: Incomplete; infrequently revised in ink; complete and partial drafts; first three copies marked "6,000 words," the fourth and fifth, "6,500 words"; all marked: Gulfport, Miss.; on original this is deleted and replaced by Coronado, Cal.

Dates: Comp. ca. 1915. Pub. ?

57a. Citation: BOSTON; t. ms.; ribbon, carbon; InU.

Title: [none]

Key Words: . . . opinionated, unjudicial manner, in ignorance . . . house of prost. fear police.

Collation: 360; green, misc. sheets; 27.8 x 21.8, 17.8 x 21.6 to 28 x 21.7; numbered consecutively but not continuously; none; fair.

Contents: Incomplete; infrequently revised in blue, regular pencil; ms. consists of a set of notes that exists in original, carbons, and cut into strips and rearranged; it is in various stages of completion; box labeled: BOSTON/NOTES.

Dates: Pub. 11 November 1928.

57b. Citation: BOSTON; t. ms., a. ms.; ribbon, carbon, pencil; InU.

Title: [none]

Key Words: "Murphy" out — O'Brien in II . . . eliminate quote marks on ad-men's.

Collation: 19; white; 14.1 x 21.7 to 28 x 21.7; [15], 2–3, 1–2; none; good.

Contents: Incomplete; infrequently revised in pencil; folder labeled: Boston | Corrections; it contains a cover letter explaining the corrections.

Dates: Pub. 11 November 1928.

57c. Citation: BOSTON; t. ms., a. ms.; ribbon, carbon, pencil, black, blue ink; InU.

Title: [none]

Key Words: Dear Upton Sinclair: Here's the . . . It touched me very much.

Collation: 25; misc. sheets; 12 x 16 to 33 x 20.3; numbered consecutively by item but not continuously; 20, 21, 25; fair.

Contents: Incomplete; infrequently revised in pencil; folder labeled: Sacco-Vanzetti; contains further notes in the case including two holograph letters; much of the material not by Sinclair.

Dates: Pub. 11 November 1928.

57d. Citation: BOSTON; t. ms.; ribbon, carbon; InU.

Title: [none]

Key Words: Guards for trial at Dedham . . . leading up to strike. Aftermath.

Collation: 51; brown, misc. sheets; 28 x 21.5 to 33 x 21.6; numbered consecutively by item but not continuously; none; good.

Contents: Incomplete; infrequently revised in black ink, not in Sinclair's hand; folder labeled: Sacco-Vanzetti; it contains Sinclair's notes in the case, personalities, and events, a chronological listing of events, and a copy of one of Vanzetti's messages.

Dates: Pub. 11 November 1928.

57e. Citation: BOSTON; t. ms., a. ms.; ribbon, carbon, pencil; InU.

Title: [none]

Key Words: REASONING IN MY DEFENSE—B. Vanzetti . . . find on Earth no parallels!

Collation: 119; misc. sheets; 21.1 x 16.9 to 33 x 21.5; numbered consecutively by item but not continuously; 9, 116; fair.

Contents: Incomplete; infrequently revised in black ink, not in Sinclair's hand; folder contains briefs, notes, and incidental information on the Sacco-Vanzetti trial; included are: REASONING IN MY DEFENSE—B. Vanzetti with inserts and corrections in black ink in Vanzetti's hand; a brief of the State's case against Vanzetti, a letter from T. Niland, a poem "ATONEMENT" by W. L. Rosenberg, and a series of notes on various personalities, places, and events surrounding the trial, sample labels and groupings, Galleani Plymouth Trial, DEDHAM trial, Plymouth Cordage Company, and Sacco's HAT; folder labeled: Sacco-Vanzetti.

Dates: Pub. 11 November 1928.

57f. Citation: BOSTON; t. ms., a. ms.; ribbon, black, blue carbon, pencil, ink; InU.

Title: [none]

Key Words: Police Strike Notes. | Newspapers and . . . filed with Palmer's report. | end.

Collation: 174; misc. sheets; 10.5 x 21.6 to 30.2 x 20.4; numbered consecutively by item but not continuously; 85; fair.

Contents: Incomplete; infrequently revised in pencil, not all in Sinclair's hand; folder labeled: Sacco-Vanzetti; contains a collection of letters, legal briefs, and extended Sinclair notes on aspects of the Sacco-Vanzetti case.

Dates: Pub. 11 November 1928.

57g. Citation: BOSTON; t. ms.; ribbon, carbon; InU.

Title: CHAPTER NINE | The Web of Fate

Key Words: Plymouth Court-house stands at the . . . break his word to us!"

Collation: 429; white; 28 x 21.8; renumbered consecutively by chapter but not continuously; none; good.

Contents: Incomplete; infrequently revised in pencil, not all in Sinclair's hand; box labeled: EARLIER DRAFTS – CARBON.

Dates: Pub. 11 November 1928.

57h. Citation: BOSTON; t. ms.; ribbon, carbon; InU.

Title: [none]

Key Words: While presidents of great colleges . . . "Remember Justice Crucified. August 22—remember."

Collation: 657; white; 28 x 21.7; numbered consecutively by chapters but not continuously; 537; fair.

Contents: Incomplete; infrequently revised in pencil, blue ink; ms. partially at least a printer's copy as the printer's notations would indicate; there are also a number of carbon duplicates; ms. has been tagged and labeled: ORIGINAL – 2 DRAFTS.

Dates: Pub. 11 November 1928.

57i. Citation: BOSTON; t. ms., a. ms.; ribbon, carbon, pencil; InU.

Title: CORRECTIONS BY JNB ON SINCLAIR NOVEL MS.

Key Words: *Boston* | galley 181 IV p.2 . . . them had friends in America."

Collation: 82; green, misc. sheets; 21.6 x 14, 8.7 x 11.4 to 28.1 x 21.7; consecutively numbered by chapter but not continuously; 3; good.

Contents: Incomplete: infrequently revised in pencil; folder labeled: Boston; contents seem to be a line-by-line set of corrections, original and carbons.

Dates: Pub. 11 November 1928.

57j. Citation: BOSTON; t. ms., a. ms.; ribbon, carbon, pencil; InU.

Title: PREFACE TO BOSTON

Key Words: Of course I am pleased . . . admonitory hand, and that Jesus

Collation: 24; green watermarked, white; 28 x 21.6, 27.9 x 21.4; randomly numbered; none; fair.

Contents: Incomplete; infrequently revised in pencil; ms. consists of fragmentary notes for *Boston*; folder labeled: Boston | Misc.

Dates: Pub. 11 November 1928.

57k. Citation: BOSTON; t. ms., a. ms.; ribbon, carbon, pencil; InU.

Title: *SEWARD COLLINS | CORRECTIONS FOR "BOSTON"*

Key Words: Chapter 8, page 78A, line . . . not worth a moments attention!

Collation: 72; misc. sheets; 16 x 11.4 to 28.1 x 21.7; randomly numbered; 2, 3, 4, 19, 21, 22, 23, 24, 30, 43, 45, 48, 65, 70; fair.

Contents: Incomplete; frequently revised in pencil; folder labeled: Various miscellaneous | Earlier pages of Mss; it contains corrections for *Boston*. First published in *Bookman*, edited by Collins.

Dates: Pub. 11 November 1928.

58. Citation: A BOY AND THE LAW; t. ms.; carbon; InU.

Title: A BOY AND THE LAW

Key Words: Many boys don't know what . . . and why we have them.

Collation: 5; white watermarked; 27.9 x 21.6; [1] 2–5; 3; good.

Contents: Complete; moderately revised in blue ink.

Dates: Comp. ? Pub. ?

59. Citation: BOY MEETS GIRL; t. ms.; ribbon; InU.

Title: BOY MEETS GIRL | Outline of a Motion Picture Story

Key Words: Cyril Vanderwalker is the only . . . alone embrace shyly and hesitatingly.

Collation: 19; green; 28 x 21.6; [1] 2–19; none; good.

Contents: Complete; frequently revised in pencil.

Dates: Comp. ca. 1930s? Pub. ?

60. Citation: A BOY WHO MIGHT HAVE BEEN YOU; t. ms.; ribbon; InU.

Title: A Boy Who Might Have BEEN You

Key Words: A boy stood upon a . . . dark past couldn't do - - - think!

Collation: 4; white watermarked; 27.9 x 21.6; [1] 2, [1] 2; none; good.

Contents: Complete; moderately revised in blue ink; two drafts.

Dates: Comp. ? Pub. ?

61a. Citation: THE BRASS CHECK; t. ms., a. ms.; black, blue ribbon, carbon, pencil, brown ink; InU.

Title: [none]

Key Words: Upton Sinclair presented to the . . . the midst of them forever.' "

Collation: 384; brown, white; 12.8 x 7.5 to 28 x 21.7; continuously numbered with variations; 23, 25, 26, 27, 28, 29, 33, 40, 54, 56, 57, 71, 72, 74, 78, 82, 85, 86, 87, 89, 90, 92, 93, 99, 128, 134, 137, 140, 149, 154, 155,

156, 160, 183, 201, 247, 254, 271, 281, 289, 292, 312, 327, 340, 354, 356, 359, 360; fair.

Contents: Incomplete; frequently revised in pencil, faded ink; ms. is an early draft; it has been tagged and labeled.

Dates: Pub. 1919–20.

Note: Published first as a series of articles in the *Appeal to Reason*, then as a book of slightly different content.

See also: THE STORY OF ADELAIDE BRANCH.

61b. Citation: THE BRASS CHECK; t. ms., a. ms., print; ribbon, black, purple carbon, pencil, print; InU.

Title: [none]

Key Words: In this book I have . . . of these ancient Hebrew prophesies:

Collation: 345; brown, white; 5.5 x 21.7 to 28 x 21.7; randomly numbered or numbered consecutively by item but not continuously; 21, 22, 26, 28, 36, 38, 41, 50, 51, 52, 76, 82, 85, 90, 92, 96, 98, 99, 103, 107, 109, 116, 145, 179, 180, 182, 184, 198, 207, 210, 225, 226, 237, 242, 248, 268, 270, 291, 308, 338, 342, 343; poor.

Contents: Incomplete; frequently revised in pencil.

Dates: Pub. 1919–20.

See also: THE STORY OF ADELAIDE BRANCH.

61c. Citation: THE BRASS CHECK; t. ms.; ribbon, carbon; InU.

Title: [none]

Key Words: I refused again and again . . . are starving all the time."

Collation: 56; brown, white; 11 x 21.7 to 28 x 21.7; randomly numbered or numbered consecutively by item but not continuously; 2, 8, 10, 15, 47, 48; fair.

Contents: Incomplete; frequently revised in pencil, faded ink; folder labeled: *not located* | but are in book and | consists of misc ms pieces and belong In manu I (?)

Dates: Pub. 1919–20.

See also: THE STORY OF ADELAIDE BRANCH.

61d. Citation: THE BRASS CHECK; t. ms.; ribbon; InU.

Title: [none]

Key Words: . . . the week was over he . . . the midst of them forever."

Collation: 36; brown, white; 7.5 x 21.7 to 28 x 21.7; randomly numbered; none; fair.

Contents: Incomplete; frequently revised in pencil; folder labeled: These are repeats | of manu II; they appear to be misc. sheets of the ms.

Dates: Pub. 1919–20.

See also: THE STORY OF ADELAIDE BRANCH.

61e. Citation: THE BRASS CHECK; t. ms., a. ms.; carbon, pencil; InU.

Title: [none]

Key Words: My Dear Sinclair – In this . . . party when the final decision

Collation: 3; white watermarked, white; 13.8 x 21.5, 12 x 21.5 to 27.7 x 21.5; [2], 353c; 1; fair.

Contents: Complete; infrequently revised in pencil; ms. folder labeled: Material on Triggs | used in book; the first page is a ALS from Triggs to Sinclair on the verso of Sinclair's TLS to him.

Dates: Pub. 1919–20.

See also: THE STORY OF ADELAIDE BRANCH.

61f. Citation: THE BRASS CHECK; t. ms.; ribbon, black, purple, blue carbons; InU.

Title: [none]

Key Words: My dear Mr. Sinclair | Everybody's . . . Russia. | Respectfully yours, | Judson King."

Collation: 21; brown, misc. sheets; 27.3 x 21.5 to 33 x 21.3; [4], [1]–16, [1]; 1; fair.

Contents: Incomplete; infrequently revised in pencil; folder labeled: Material which | chapt. entitled "Heartwife" | was based upon . .; it contains copies of three letters and an article copied from the New York Call of August 9, 1914.

Dates: Pub. 1919–20.

See also: THE STORY OF ADELAIDE BRANCH.

61g. Citation: THE BRASS CHECK; t. ms., a. ms.; ribbon, carbon, pencil; InU.

Title: [none]

Key Words: One of the most dramatic . . . I answered: "Toby, that's you!"

Collation: 14; brown, white; 11 x 20.6 to 30.7 x 22.7; 6–8, 5, Ross-4, Ross-5, [2], Ross-6, [1], 7–8, 10, [1]; none; fair.

Contents: Incomplete; frequently revised in pencil, faded ink; folder labeled: haven't located | and not sure they were | used—seem to belong | in M.I.; ms. appears to be additional misc. material.

Dates: Pub. 1919–20.

See also: THE STORY OF ADELAIDE BRANCH.

61h. Citation: THE BRASS CHECK; t. ms., a. ms.; ribbon, carbon, pencil; InU.

Title: [none]

Key Words: In Boston the "News-Writer's Union" . . . the re-election of Woodrow Wilson!

Collation: 6; brown, misc. sheets; 12 x 21.7 to 30.7 x 21.7; [2], 132, 59, [2]; 4, 5; fair.

Contents: Incomplete; frequently revised in pencil; folder labeled: Couldn't locate | (most was used in book); apparently material used in *The Brass Check*.

Dates: Pub. 1919–20.

See also: THE STORY OF ADELAIDE BRANCH.

61i. Citation: THE BRASS CHECK; a. ms.; pencil; InU.

Title: The Brass Check

Key Words: It was our desire to . . . on my ninetieth & hundredth.

Collation: 4; white; 13.1 x 12.7 to 20.3 x 12.7; 148a, [1], 244a, [1]; 4; fair.

Contents: Incomplete; infrequently revised in pencil; appear to be notes to *The Brass Check*; pages are loose inside front cover of second edition of book.

Dates: Pub. 1919–20.

See also: THE STORY OF ADELAIDE BRANCH.

61j. Citation: THE BRASS CHECK; t. ms.; ribbon; InU.

Title: *The Brass Check A Study of American Journalism*

Key Words: Whatever evil you mention to . . . the company of civilized men.

Collation: 6; brown, white; 27.9 x 21.5, 27.7 x 21.5; 1, 1a, 2–5; 5; fair.

Contents: Complete; frequently revised in pencil; this is apparently a copy of the introduction to *The Brass Check*; there is a note appended to it which reads:

NOT | SAME | AS BOOK | INTRO!; not in Sinclair's hand.

Dates: Pub. 1919–20.

See also: THE STORY OF ADELAIDE BRANCH.

61k. Citation: THE BRASS CHECK; t. ms.; ribbon; InU.

Title: Chapter XIX | *Greed and Lust*

Key Words: I have explained my understanding . . . are engaged in "nationalizing women"!

Collation: 10; brown; 28 x 21.7; 125a, [1], 3–10; 7; fair.

Contents: Complete; frequently revised in pencil; folder labeled: An extra chapter in Man I? | "Greed and Lust."

Dates: Pub. 1919–20.

See also: THE STORY OF ADELAIDE BRANCH.

62a. Citation: THE BRASS CHECK WEEKLY; t. ms.; carbon; InU.

Title: THE BRASS CHECK WEEKLY

Key Words: Several times in these columns . . . "Oregonian" has published the letter.

Collation: 24; brown; 28 x 21.6; [1] 2, [1], [1] 2–3, [1] 2–3, [1–22], [1] 2–4, [1] 2–4, [1] 2–5; 5; good.

Contents: Incomplete; infrequently revised in pencil by MCS; complete and partial drafts of articles published in the *Appeal to Reason*.

Dates: Pub. ca. 1922?

62b. Citation: THE BRASS CHECK WEEKLY; t. ms.; black carbon; InU.

Title: THE BRASS CHECK WEEKLY

Key Words: Just a few little items . . . is the Boston "Evening Transcript!

Collation: 3; brown; 27.9 x 21.5; [1] 2–3; none; good.

Contents: Complete; unrevised, someone has written in pencil on page 1: Mailed 4/18/22 folder is labeled: "Appeal to Reason."

Dates: Pub. *Appeal to Reason*, 6 May 1922.

63. Citation: THE BRIDE OF DREAMS [A REVIEW] BY FREDERIK VAN EEDEN; t. ms.; purple carbon; InU.

Title: THE BRIDE OF DREAMS | By | Frederick [*sic*] van Eeden. | Reviewed by Upton Sinclair.

Key Words: The writings of Frederick van Eeden . . . as the Bride of Dreams.

Collation: 6; white; 28.3 x 21.5; [1], [1] 2–5; none; poor.

Contents: Complete; unrevised.

Dates: Pub. ?

64. Citation: A BRIEF STATEMENT TO FRIENDS OF LIBERAL THOUGHT; t. ms.; carbon; InU.

Title: A BRIEF STATEMENT TO FRIENDS OF LIBERAL THOUGHT

Key Words: For the last twenty years . . . of mankind in the future.

Collation: 4; white; 27.8 x 21.7; [1] 2–4; none; fair.

Contents: Complete; unrevised.

Dates: Comp. ca. 1916–17. Pub. ?

65. Citation: THE BROTHERHOOD OF THE RAILS; t. ms.; carbon; InU.

Title: *The Brotherhood of the Rails* | A Moving Picture in Ten Episodes.

Key Words: The purpose of the story . . . Johns and the three Toms.

Collation: 5; white; 28 x 21.6; 1–5; none; good.

Contents: Complete; unrevised.

Dates: Comp. ca. 1927–28. Unpublished.

66. Citation: BROTHER LOGAN; t. ms.; carbon; InU.

Title: BROTHER LOGAN | by Gertrude Erik

Key Words: It was Old Home Week . . . man that uses a tooth-brush?

Collation: 20; green; 27.9 x 21.3; [1–20]; none; good.

Contents: Complete; frequently revised in pencil. The style and the nature of the revision suggest that Sinclair was the author.

Dates: Comp. ca. 1915–20. Pub. ?

67. Citation: BUILD EPIC PRESS t. ms.; carbon; InU.

Title: BUILD EPIC PRESS

Key Words: You will notice that a . . . magazine calling for a poll.

Collation: 1; white watermarked; 28 x 21.6; [1]; none; good.

Contents: Incomplete; unrevised.

Dates: Pub. *EPIC News*, 23 March 1936.

68. Citation: BUILDING THE EPIC MOVEMENT; t. ms.; ribbon; InU.

Title: BUILDING THE EPIC MOVEMENT

Key Words: I am telling you about . . . vote for the EPIC Plan.

Collation: 5; white; 28 x 21.7; 1–5; none; good.

Contents: Complete; infrequently revised in pencil.

Dates: Comp. ca. September 1934. Pub. ?

69. Citation: A BUSINESS REPUBLIC; t. ms.; carbon; InU.

Title: A BUSINESS REPUBLIC | An Outline of the People's Corporation | King C. Gillette

Key Words: This book offers a solution . . . birth, a reconception of life.

Collation: 116; white, white watermarked; 28.3 x 21.8, 28 x 21.6; [2], 1–44, 45–46–47, 48–69, 69a, 69b, 69c, 69d, 69e, 69f, 70–110; none; good.

Contents: Complete; moderately revised in pencil, faded ink, not all in Sinclair's hand; the ms. is bound with brass studs in a manila cover. Written by Gillette, rewritten and revised by Sinclair.

Dates: Comp. ca. 1923? Pub. 1924.

70. Citation: THE BUZZARDS GATHER! t. ms.; ribbon; InU.

Title: THE BUZZARDS GATHER!

Key Words: This is a story which . . . Gay – pay – oo intelligence department U.S.A. 967X41.

Collation: 7; green watermarked; 28 x 21.5; 1–7; 6; good.

Contents: Complete; frequently revised in pencil by author and MCS.

Dates: Comp. ca. 1936. Pub. ?

71. Citation: BY UPTON SINCLAIR; t. ms.; ribbon, carbon; InU.

Title: By Upton Sinclair | (Recording for the Voice of America)

Key Words: My old friend Norman Thomas . . . will be grateful to us.

Collation: 26; white watermarked; 27.6 x 21.3 to 28 x 21.7; [1] 2–8, [1] 2–9, [1] 2–9; none; good.

Contents: Complete; infrequently revised in blue ink, pencil; in upper right corner of page one: November 1950.

Dates: Recorded ca. November 1950. Tape in Lilly Library.

72. Citation: THE CAMPAIGN TO END POVERTY IN CIVILIZATION; t. ms.; ribbon, carbon; InU.

Title: "The Campaign to End Povery in Civilization."

Key Words: Friends of the Air In . . . over this same station, KNX

Collation: 10; white watermarked; 27.9 x 21.6; [1] 2–5, [1] 2–5; none; good.

Contents: Complete; infrequently revised in pencil; headnote on page one: KNX April 17 1934 8:15 p.m.; original and one carbon.

Dates: Comp. ca. April 1934. Pub.?

73. Citation: CAN CALIFORNIA END POVERTY?; t. ms., a. ms.; ribbon, carbon, pencil; InU.

Title: CAN CALIFORNIA END POVERTY

Key Words: As a rule, the politics . . . and marching on a crusade.

Collation: 39; white, misc. sheets; 28 x 21.6, 20 x 12.6; numbered consecutively by item but not continuously; 3, 4, 5, 6, 7, 8, 9, 10, 11, 12, 13, 14, 15; good.

Contents: Complete; infrequently revised in pencil, not all in Sinclair's hand; autograph original, ribbon copy and two carbons.

Dates: Comp. ca. June 1934. Pub. ?

74. Citation: CAN DEMOCRACY WORK?; t. ms.; carbon; InU.

Title: CAN DEMOCRACY WORK?

Key Words: Our Forefathers hand down to . . . is brief and yet endless."

Collation: 3; green; 28 x 21.6; [1] 2-3; none; good.

Contents: Complete; unrevised.

Date: Comp. ca. April 1934. Pub. ?

75. Citation: CAN WE CHANGE THE WORLD?; t. ms.; ribbon, carbon; InU.

Title: [HOW (c.o. pencil)] CAN WE CHANGE THE WORLD?

Key Words: You and I were not . . . instead of our personal gain.

Collation: 25; green, misc. sheets; 28.3 x 21.6, 27.8 x 21.5 to 27.9 x 21.6; 1-12, [1] 2-12, 12; 4; good.

Contents: Complete; infrequently revised in pencil, not all in Sinclair's hand; carbon copy of what appears to be a later final copy, carbon incorporates revisions beyond the present draft.

Dates: Comp. ca. 1937. Pub. ?

76. Citation: CAN WE CIVILIZE MACHINES?; t. ms.; ribbon, carbon; InU.

Title: CAN WE CIVILIZE MACHINES?

Key Words: A year and a half . . . and return humanity to barbarism!

Collation: 8; white letterhead, white; 27.8 x 21.5, 28 x
21.6; [1] 2–4, [1] 2–4; 2, 3; good.

Contents: Complete; moderately revised in pencil; carbon is of a typed copy of the draft incorporating revisions.

Dates: Pub. *EPIC News*, 20 April 1936.

77. Citation: CARADRION; t. ms.; carbon; InU.

Title: CARADRION | by Upton Sinclair | A one-reel
moving picture idyll.

Key Words: The following story is told . . . of him
that went away.

Collation: 14; brown, white watermarked; 28 x 21.6,
26.8 x 20.4; numbered continuously by grouping but not
consecutively; none; good.

Contents: Complete; unrevised; two carbon copies of
the film proposal and a carbon of Sinclair's poem
"Caradrion" from his novel: *Love's Pilgrimage*.

Dates: Comp. 1930s? Pub. ?

78. Citation: CARRYING OUT THE EPIC PLAN;
t. ms.; ribbon; InU.

Title: CARRYING OUT THE EPIC PLAN

Key Words: Last fall the EPIC plan . . . count follows the illiction [*sic*] returns."

Collation: 5; white watermarked; 28 x 21.8; [1] 2–5;
none; good.

Contents: Complete; unrevised.

Dates: Comp. ca. July 1934. Pub. ?

79. Citation: THE CASE OF THE HIDDEN WOMAN;
t. ms.; blue ribbon, blue carbon; InU.

Title: *The Case of the Hidden Woman*

Key words: It has been a long . . . to human happiness and progress.

Collation: 6; white; 28 x 21.7; [1] 2–3, [1] 2–3; none; good.

Contents: Complete; infrequently revised in ink, pencil, not all in Sinclair's hand.

Dates: Comp. ca. 1914. Pub. ?

80. Citation: THE CASE OF QUINN VERSUS SINCLAIR; a. ms.; pencil; InU.

Title: The Case of | QUINN VERSUS SINCLAIR

Key Words: University of Pennsylvania Professor forbids . . . Professor Quinn (insert as marked).

Collation: 4; blue watermarked; 23.8 x 21.5 to 28 x 21.6; 1–4; none; good.

Contents: Incomplete; frequently revised in pencil; draft of a reply to Professor Arthur H. Quinn, University of Pennsylvania; copies to be sent to the members of the committee recommending Sinclair for the Nobel Prize.

Dates: Comp. ca. January 1932. Pub. ?

81. Citation: THE CASE OF WALTER LIGGETT;
t. ms.; carbon; InU.

Title: THE CASE OF WALTER LIGGETT

Key Words: This is a painful story . . . but his secretary writes me:

Collation: 3; blue watermarked; 28 x 21.6; [1] 2–3; none; good.

Contents: Incomplete; unrevised.

Dates: Comp. ca. 1935. Pub. ?

82. Citation: CAVALCADE OF BOOKS; t. ms.; ribbon, carbon; InU.

Title: CAVALCADE OF BOOKS – NOVEMBER 22, 1959

Key Words: Dr. Frederick Shroger: I feel . . . The Guilt" by Upton Sinclair.

Collation: 6; white watermarked; 28 x 21.6; [1] 2–3, [1] 2–3; none; good.

Contents: Complete; unrevised.

Dates: Comp. ca. November 1959. Pub. ?

83. Citation: C.B.S. COLUMBIA SQUARE, HOLLY-WOOD; t. ms., a. ms.; carbon, pencil; InU.

Title: C.B.S. COLUMBIA SQUARE, HOLLY-WOOD

Key Words: (Note 1 for p.5 . . . but to Upton Sinclair's novels."

Collation: 26; misc. sheets; 20.3 x 12.2 to 27.9 x 21.6; consecutively numbered but not continuously; 3, 4; fair.

Contents: Complete; moderately revised in pencil, blue ink; contains notes and two drafts, one earlier than the other, of the speech.

Dates: Comp ? Pub. ?

84. Citation: CELESTIAL SPECULATION; t. ms.; ribbon, carbon; InU.

Title: CELESTIAL SPECULATION

Key Words: Dear mother earth, I'm packing . . . it far in empty space?

Collation: 2; white; 27.9 x 21.6; unnumbered; none; good.

Contents: Complete; unrevised.

Dates: Pub. *Saturday Evening Post*, 2 January 1954.

85a. Citation: CERVANTES; t. ms.; carbon; InU.

Title: CERVANTES; Outline For Motion Picture

Key Words: The life story of Miguel . . . trumpets rides forth to immortality.

Collation: 25; blue, white watermarked; 27.7 x 21.4, 27.9 x 21.5; [1] 2–12, [1] 2–13; 8; poor, stained.

Contents: Complete; revised in black, blue pencil; two carbons, one the revised version of the other.

Dates: Comp. ca. 1930s. Pub. ?

85b. Citation: CERVANTES; t. ms.; carbon; InU.

Title: CERVANTES | Outline for Motion Picture

Key Words: The life story of Miguel . . . trumpet, rides forth to immortality.

Collation: 13; blue; 27.9 x 21.5; [1] 2–13; none; good.

Contents: Complete; unrevised.

Dates: Comp. ca. 1930. Pub. ?

86. Citation: THE CHANGES OF PEACE; t. ms.; ribbon, carbon; InU.

Title: THE CHANGES OF PEACE

Key Words: I hear people discussing the . . . by beating the war drums?

Collation: 6; white; 27.9 x 21.6; [1] 2–3, [1] 2–3; none; good.

Contents: Complete; unrevised; one carbon bears Sinclair's signature on pages one and three in blue ink with a notation "for Spadea Syndicate | 1954" at the end and "Copy 8/14/53" penciled on the ribbon page one.

Dates: Comp. 1953–54. Pub. ?

87a. Citation: A CHANGED AMERICA; t. ms.; ribbon, carbon; InU.

Title: A CHANGED AMERICA

Key Words: The editor of "Preuves" Paris . . . will be grateful to us.

Collation: 24; white, white watermarked; 27.8 x 21.5, 27.9 x 21.6; [1] 2–8, [1] 2–8, [1] 2–8; none; good.

Contents: Complete; infrequently revised in blue ink, pencil; two carbons and a ribbon copy; one of the carbons and the ribbon are revised versions of the first carbon; the second carbon is not that of the ribbon copy even though it appears to be of the revised version.

Dates: Comp. ca. February 1952. Pub. ?

87b. Citation: A CHANGED AMERICA; t. ms.; ribbon, carbon; InU.

Title: A CHANGED AMERICA

Key Words: The editor of "Preuves" (Paris) . . . will be grateful to us.

Collation: 78; white, white watermarked; 27.8 x 21.5 to 28 x 21.6, 27.9 x 21.7 to 28.1 x 21.7; numbered continuously by copies but not consecutively; 1; good.

Contents: Complete; infrequently revised in regular, orange pencil, blue ink; contains a number of ribbon and carbon copies; most of the copies are signed by Sinclair at the top of page one.

Dates: Comp. ca. February 1952. Pub. ?

88. Citation: CHANGES I HAVE SEEN; t. ms.; carbon; InU.

Title: CHANGES I HAVE SEEN

Key Words: I am writing on the . . . END OF POVERTY IN CALIFORNIA.

Collation: 4; blue watermarked; 28 x 21.7; [1] 2–4; none; good.

Contents: Complete; infrequently revised in pencil; editorial.

Dates: Comp. 8 November 1934. Pub. ?

89. Citation: CHEER UP FRIENDS; t. ms.; carbon; InU.

Title: CHEER UP FRIENDS!

Key Words: When I was a boy . . . of humanity happy and noble.

Collation: 4; blue; 28 x 21.6, 14.5 x 21.6; [1] 2–4, 3; good.

Contents: Complete; moderately revised in pencil; page 4 on the verso of sheet 3.

Dates: Pub. *Writer's Digest,* September 1938.

90a. Citation: CICERO; t. ms.; blue, black ribbon; InU.

Title: CICERO | A Tragedy of Ancient Rome

Key Words: 2 cc dbl space consuls . . . work just as hard! *Curtain.*

Collation: 74; white watermarked, white; 27.9 x 21.6, 27.8 x 21.4; numbered consecutively by acts but not continuously; 63; good.

Contents: Complete; infrequently revised in blue, green, regular pencil, blue ink; in an envelope labeled: Original ms. of Cicero by US.

Dates: Comp. 1959–60. Produced 9 February 1961.

90b. Citation: CICERO; t. ms., a. ms., print; blue, green, black ribbon, carbon, pencil, print; InU.

Title: CICERO | A Tragedy of Ancient Rome

Key Words: 2 cc dbl space consuls exec . . . work just as hard! *Curtain.*

Collation: 267; misc. sheets; 6.5 x 4.6 to 28 x 21.7; either randomly numbered or numbered consecutively by act but not continuously; 2, 3, 4, 5, 7, 8, 20, 21, 23, 24, 25, 26, 27, 115, 131, 153, 154, 218, 232, 235, 236, 240, 267; fair.

Contents: Complete; frequently revised in pencil and blue ink; notes, correction and the play "Cicero"; a collection of revisions, playbill, synopsis and other papers concerning the play.

Dates: Comp. 1959–60. Produced 9 February 1961.

91. Citation: CINDERELLA FROM BALTIMORE; t. ms.; ribbon; InU.

Title: CINDERELLA FROM BALTIMORE

Key Words: To the Editor: Hardened cynics . . . and my dear Edward Windsor!

Collation: 11; green; 28 x 21.6; [1] 2–11; 4, 10; good, spindled.

Contents: Complete; moderately revised in pencil; a series of three articles with separate release dates, December 17, 18, 19, on the Windsor abdication.

Dates: Comp. ca. December 1936. Pub. 1936 (as leaflet).

See: WALLY FOR QUEEN

92. Citation: CIVIL LIBERTIES, REAL AND PHONY; t. ms.; carbon; InU.

Title: CIVIL LIBERTIES UNLIMITED

Key Words: Just thirty years ago, in . . . real. Watch out for them!

Collation: 3; white watermarked; 28.1 x 21.7; [1] 2–3; none; good.

Contents: Complete; infrequently revised in blue ink.

Dates: Pub. *Meriden* (Conn.) *Journal*, 12 June 1954.

93. Citation: CLASSES IN AMERICA; t. ms.; carbon; InU.

Title: CLASSES IN AMERICA

Key Words: I have received a long . . . ancient Roman and Greek plutocracies.

Collation: 10; white watermarked; 28 x 21.7; [1] 2–5, [1] 2–5; none; good.

Contents: Complete; infrequently revised in pencil.

Dates: Comp. ca. 1940. Pub. ?

94. Citation: CLOSING ANNOUNCEMENT; t. ms.; ribbon, carbon; InU.

Title: Sinclair - KNX | Closing Announcement | August 20th. | By Richard S. Otto

Key Words: Friends, you have just heard . . . message for you. Mr. Otto:

Collation: 9; white; 27.8 x 21.4; [3] 2–7; none; good.

Contents: Complete; infrequently revised in pencil; pages 1, 2, are two copies of message by Richard Otto that was meant to follow the Sinclair address on pages 3–7; note on upper right corner page 3: Return to GUS INGLIS; upper left corner page three: Monday, August 20.

Dates: Comp. 20 August 1934. Pub. ?

95. Citation: THE COAL STRIKE: t. ms.; carbon; InU.

Title: THE COAL STRIKE

Key Words: The latest civil war in . . . in the Saturday Evening Post.

Collation: 5; brown; 27.8 x 21.5; [1] 2–5; none, good.

Contents: Complete; unrevised, pencil note: "Mr. Sinclair took this with him" appears on page 1, not in Sinclair's hand; article appeared in the *Appeal to Reason*; folder labeled: "Appeal to Reason."

Dates: Pub. ca. May–June 1914?

96a. Citation: THE COAL WAR; t. ms., a. ms.; carbon; InU.

Title: [none]

Key Words: Monday, and they were dancing . . . nor, if the company officials

Collation: 303; misc. sheets; 27.7 x 21.5 to 27.8 x 21.7; numbered consecutively in groups but not continuously; fair, punched for a two-ring binder.

Contents: Incomplete; moderately revised in blue, black ink, pencil, black markings, not in Sinclair's hand; this series of notes is loose in box, there are verso markings, but due to the changing nature of their order no numbers have been recorded. Sequel to *King Coal*.

Dates: Comp. 1916–17. Unpublished.

96b. Citation: THE COAL WAR; t. ms., a ms.; ribbon, carbon; InU.

Title: [none]

Key Words: Springtime came late in these . . . men from losing their jobs!

Collation: 180; white watermarked; 27.9 x 21.5 to 28 x 21.7; numbered consecutively within each group but not continuously; 147, 174; fair.

Contents: Incomplete; infrequently revised in blue ink, pencil; ms. is a series of carbons of the same material.

Dates: Comp. 1916–17. Unpublished.

96c. Citation: THE COAL WAR; t. ms.; ribbon; InU.

Title: *The Coal War* | A SEQUEL TO KING COAL

Key Words: It was the last afternoon . . . college had barely escaped a . . .

Collation: 44; white watermarked; 28.1 x 21.7; [3], 1–41; none; fair, punched for a two-ring binder.

Contents: Incomplete; infrequently revised in black ink; ms. bears a title page, a table of contents and the title for Book One; appears to be incomplete; enclosed in a brown manila cover but the brass studs are missing.

Dates: Comp. 1916–17. Unpublished.

96d. Citation: THE COAL WAR; t. ms.; ribbon, carbon; InU.

Title: *THE COAL WAR* | *A SEQUEL TO KING COAL*

Key Words: It was the last afternoon . . . future of brotherhood and co-operation.

Collation: 126; white watermarked; 28.1 x 21.6; [3] 1–82, 42–82; none; good, spindled.

Contents: Complete; infrequently revised in ink; the first of four parts, each in a separate folder.

Dates: Comp. 1916–17. Unpublished.

96e. Citation: THE COAL WAR; t. ms.; carbon; InU.

Title: *THE COAL WAR* | *BOOK TWO*

Key Words: The office of the Western . . . Shouting the battle cry of union!"

Collation: 96; white watermarked; 28 x 21.7; 1, 1–95; none; fair.

Contents: Complete; infrequently revised in black ink; ms. is bound in a brown folder with two brass studs; appears to be a complete copy of Book Two.

Dates: Comp. 1916–17. Unpublished.

96f. Citation: THE COAL WAR; t. ms.; ribbon; InU.

Title: THE COAL WAR | BOOK TWO

Key Words: The office of the Western . . . Shouting the battle-cry of union!"

Collation: 96; white watermarked; 28 x 21.6; [1] 1–95; none; good, spindled.

Contents: Complete; moderately revised in ink; second of four parts.

Dates: Comp. 1916–17. Unpublished.

96g. Citation: THE COAL WAR; t. ms.; black, purple carbon; InU.

Title: *The Coal War* | *Book Three* [Law and Order (w.i. ink)]

Key Words: The next two weeks were . . . the subject of the coalstrike.

Collation: 123; white watermarked; 28 x 21.7; [1], 1–110, 110a, 110b, 111–116, 116a, 117–119; none; fair.

Contents: Complete; infrequently revised in black ink, not all in Sinclair's hand; ms. has been bound in a brown folder by two brass studs; appears to be a complete copy of Book Three.

Dates: Comp. 1916–17. Unpublished.

96h. Citation: THE COAL WAR; t. ms.; ribbon; InU.

Title: THE COAL WAR | BOOK THREE | Law and Order

Key Words: The next two weeks were . . . the subject of the class-war!

Collation: 123; white watermarked; 28.1 x 21.7; [1] 1–110, 110a, 110b, 111–116, 116a, 117–119; none; good, spindled.

Contents: Complete; infrequently revised in ink; the third of four parts.

Dates: Comp. 1916–17. Unpublished.

96i. Citation: THE COAL WAR; t. ms.; black, purple carbon; InU.

Title: [none]

Key Words: 1. In the month of . . . straight upon a [r]ocky shore!

Collation: 223; white watermarked, white; 16.6 x 21.7 to 28.2 x 21.7; 1–10, 12–81, 81, 82–104, 106–224; 222; fair.

Contents: Complete; infrequently revised in blue, black ink, pencil; copy has been bound with two brass studs. Book Four of The Coal War.

Dates: Comp. 1916–17. Unpublished.

96j. Citation: COAL WAR; t. ms.; ribbon; InU.

Title: BOOK FOUR | CIVIL WAR

Key Words: Springtime came late in these . . . Spartacus and Eunus against Rome.

Collation: 157; white, white watermarked; 27.9 x 21.4, 28 x 21.7; [1] 1–62, 62a–f, 63–124, 124a–e, 125–135, 1–10; none; good, spindled.

Contents: Complete; infrequently revised in ink; fourth of four parts.

Dates: Comp. 1916–17. Unpublished.

97a. Citation: A COINCIDENTAL CORRESPONDENCE; t. ms.; blue carbon; InU.

Title: A COINCIDENTAL CORRESPONDENCE

Key Words: (Anna Mary Dudley to Priscilla . . . have begun! Always tenderly, Priscilla.

Collation: 17; white; 26.7 x 20.6; [1] 2–17; none, fair.

Contents: Complete; infrequently revised in faded ink; apparently another carbon of the ms. below; has most but not all of the corrections in that ms.

Dates: Comp. ca. 1914? Pub. ?

97b. Citation: A COINCIDENTAL CORRESPON-DENCE; t. ms.; carbon; InU.

Title: A COINCIDENTAL CORRESPONDENCE

Key Words: (Anna Mary Dudley to Priscilla . . . have begun! Always tenderly, Priscilla.

Collation: 17; white; 26.6 x 20.5; [1] 2–17; none; fair, torn.

Contents: Complete; infrequently revised in faded ink.

Dates: Comp. ca. 1914? Pub. ?

98. Citation: COLUMN FOR VICTOR REISEL; t. ms.; ribbon, carbon; InU.

Title: COLUMN FOR VICTOR REISEL

Key Words: This is a chance to . . . idealists of your own country.

Collation: 31; misc. sheets; 25.4 x 20.4 to 28 x 21.7; [1] 2–4, [3], [1] 2–3, [1] 2–3, [1] 2–3, [1] 2–5, [1] 2–4, [1] 2–6; none; good.

Contents: Complete; infrequently revised in pencil; an article in various stages of composition.

Dates: Pub. *Arizona Republican*, 17 July 1952.

99. Citation: COME IN OUT OF THE WET, BODDY; t. ms.; carbon; InU.

Title: COME IN OUT OF THE WET, BODDY.

Key Words: My dear Manchester Boddy, You . . . of their own destinies. Sincerely

Collation: 6; white watermarked, blue watermarked; 28 x 21.6; [1] 2–3; [1] 2–3; none; good.

Contents: Complete; moderately revised in pencil, not in Sinclair's hand.

Dates: Comp. 17 June 1934. Pub. ?

100. Citation: COMMENT ON HENRY MILLER; t. ms.; carbon; InU.

Title: COMMENT ON HENRY MILLER

Key Words: I have been invited to . . . people who read his books.

Collation: 1; brown; 28.1 x 21.6; unnumbered; none; good.

Contents: Complete; unrevised.

Dates: Comp. ca. 1958. Pub. ?

101. Citation: COMMUNISM IN CHINA; t. ms.; carbon; InU.

Title: COMMUNISM IN CHINA

Key Words: I will start this article . . . move into heaven over night.

Collation: 5; brown; 28 x 21.6; [1] 2–5; none; good.

Contents: Complete; unrevised; someone has written on page 1 in pencil: Mailed 4/18/22; folder labeled: "Appeal to Reason."

Dates: Pub. *Appeal to Reason*, 24 June 1922.

102. Citation: COMMUNISTS AND EPIC; t. ms.; carbon; InU.

Title: COMMUNISTS AND EPIC

Key Words: I have received a letter . . . American program by American methods.

Collation: 4; blue watermarked; 28 x 21.7; [1] 2–4; none; good.

Contents: Complete; infrequently revised in pencil, not in Sinclair's hand.

Dates: Pub. *Upton Sinclair's National EPIC News,* 12 August 1935.

103. Citation: COMRADE KAUTSKY AND THE DROMEDARY; t. ms.; ribbon, carbon; InU.

Title: COMRADE KAUTSKY AND THE DROME-DARY

Key Words: Twenty-four years ago the winter . . . miseries of our collapsing profit-system.

Collation: 35; white; 28.1 x 21.8; [1] 2–14, [1] 2–10, [1] 2–11; none; good.

Contents: Complete; moderately revised in pencil, second a typed copy incorporating the revisions of the first; a carbon of a later draft not all in Sinclair's hand.

Dates: Pub. *International Press Conference,* 13 August 1931; also as pamphlet.

104. Citation: CONCERNING ANARCHISTS; t. ms.; carbon; InU.

Title: CONCERNING ANARCHISTS

Key Words: I have learned by long . . . about it, ask the Anarchists!

Collation: 1; brown; 27.9 x 21.5; unnumbered; none; good.

Contents: Complete; unrevised; someone has written on page 1 in pencil: Mailed 4-18-22; folder labeled: "Appeal to Reason."

Dates: Pub. *Appeal to Reason,* 6 May 1922.

105. Citation: CONCERNING BETWEEN TWO
WORLDS; t. ms., a. ms.; ribbon, carbon, pencil; InU.

Title: CONCERNING ["(c.o.)] "BETWEEN TWO
WORLDS."

Key Words: Viking Press announced for publication
. . . a course of great events.

Collation: 13; green, white; 21.4 x 13.9 to 28 x 21.8,
27.9 x 21.6; [1], 1–4, 1–4, [1]–4; 4; good.

Contents: Complete; infrequently revised in pencil; ms.
for a short article or advertising piece, plus carbon;
folder labeled: "*Between Two Worlds* | MISC."

Dates: Pub. *Publisher's Circular and Bookseller's Record*, 17 May 1941.

106. Citation: CONCERNING CONSCIENTIOUS OB-
JECTORS; t. ms.; carbon; InU.

Title: CONCERNING CONSCIENTIOUS OB-
JECTORS

Key Words: We live in a world . . . Company, 811
Rees Street, Chicago.

Collation: 8; brown; 27.8 x 21.2; 1–8; none; good.

Contents: Complete; unrevised

Dates: Comp. ca. 1918. Pub. ?

107. Citation: CONCERNING EMMA GOLDMAN; t.
ms.; carbon; InU.

Title: CONCERNING EMMA GOLDMAN

Key Words: Emma Goldman has at last . . . foolish
quarrel with history.

Collation: 5; brown; 27.8 x 21.5; [1] 2–5; none; good.

Contents: Complete; unrevised; someone has written on
page 1 in pencil: Mailed to U.S. 4-14-22; folder labeled:
"Appeal to Reason."

Dates: Pub. *Appeal to Reason,* 6 May 1922.

108. Citation: CONCERNING THE GOLDFISH BOWL;
t. ms., a. ms.; carbon, red pencil; InU.

Title: CONCERNING THE GOLDFISH BOWL

Key Words: Is there a blue carbon . . . the essentials
of their affairs.

Collation: 4; white, white watermarked; 7.5 x 9.8, 28 x
21.6; [1] 2, [1] 2; none; good.

Contents: Complete; unrevised.

Dates: Comp. ca. August 1934. Pub. ?

109a. Citation: CONCERNING LANNY BUDD; t. ms.;
ribbon; InU.

Title: CONCERNING LANNY BUDD

Key Words: Some of my friends have . . . this book
goes to press.

Collation: 102; white; 28 x 21.6; randomly numbered;
none; good.

Contents: Complete [?]; infrequently revised in pencil;
Sinclair's note on envelope that contains ms. reads: "This
material consists of expansions of episodes in American
Outpost which I propose to include in new book. You
may find some of it worth using. Page numbers are those
of Am. Outpost."

Dates: Pub. *Book Find News,* August 1946.

See: AMERICAN OUTPOST.

109b. Citation: CONCERNING LANNY BUDD; t. ms.;
carbon; InU.

Title: CONCERNING LANNY BUDD | by | Upton
Sinclair | In which the author discusses the growth of
his hero.

Key Words: Some of my friends have . . . drawn into World War III.

Collation: 2; white; 28 x 21.7; 1–2; none; good.

Contents: Complete; infrequently revised in pencil.

Dates: Pub. *Book Find News*, August 1946.

See: AMERICAN OUTPOST.

110. Citation: CONCERNING OUR LEAGUE PRESI-DENT; t. ms.; carbon; InU.

Title: CONCERNING OUR LEAGUE PRESIDENT

Key Words: I am informed that attacks . . . of ending poverty in California.

Collation: 6; blue watermarked, white; 27.8 x 21.6, 28 x 21.6; [1] 2–3, [1] 2–3; none; fair.

Contents: Complete; unrevised.

Dates: Comp. ca. 1935. Pub. ?

111. Citation: CONCERNING THE PULITZER PRIZE; t. ms., a. ms.; ribbon, carbon, pencil; InU.

Title: CONCERNING THE PULITZER PRIZE

Key Words: In the Minneapolis "Star" for . . . 66 Fifth Avenue, New York.

Collation: 17; white; 27.9 x 21.6 to 28.2 x 21.6; 1–4, [1] 2–4, [1], 1a, 2–4, [1] 2–4; none; good.

Contents: Complete; moderately revised in pencil, black ink, not all in Sinclair's hand; various stages of article.

Dates: Pub. *Author's League Bulletin*, May 1929. (Also as circular letter and leaflet.)

112. Citation: CONCERNING REGISTRATION; t. ms.; carbon; InU.

Title: CONCERNING REGISTRATION
Key Words: It is of the utmost . . . of California. Therefore, the first
Collation: 3; white watermarked, blue; 27.9 x 21.6, 28.1 x 21.6; unnumbered; 3; good.
Contents: Complete; unrevised.
Dates: Pub. *Upton Sinclair's EPIC News*, 4 June 1934.

113. Citation: CONCERNING SOCIALIST CANDI-DATES: t. ms.; carbon; InU.
Title: CONCERNING SOCIALIST CANDIDATES
Key Words: I have noted in the . . . liberal planks in the platform.
Collation: 4; white; 27.9 x 21.7; [1] 2, [1] 2; none; good.
Contents: Complete; unrevised.
Dates: Pub. *New York Call*, 20 November 1951.

114. Citation: CONCERNING THREE BOOKS: t. ms.; carbon; InU.
Title: CONCERNING "THREE BOOKS"
Key Words: It is always an uncomfortable . . . has set for your feet.
Collation: 3; white; 27.9 x 21.6; [1] 2–3; none; good.
Contents: Complete; infrequently revised in blue ink.
Dates: Comp. ca. 1948. Pub. ?

115a. Citation: THE CONVICT; t. ms.; black, blue carbon; InU.
Title: THE CONVICT: A Story by Upton Sinclair.
Key Words: "No, Mr. Atherton," said Adele, . . . dogs! Bring up the dogs!"

Collation: 74; white, white watermarked; 26.8 x 20.6 to 29 x 20.3; randomly numbered; none; good.

Contents: Complete; infrequently revised in pencil.

Dates: Pub. (as play) *Labour Leader* (Manchester), 7 November 1912–2 January 1913.

115b. Citation: THE CONVICT; t. ms., a. ms.; black, blue carbon, pencil; InU.

Title: THE CONVICT: A DRAMA IN THREE ACTS

Key Words: Scene shows a forest of . . . The dogs! The dogs! CURTAIN.

Collation: 118; white, misc. sheets; 26.8 x 20.5, 11.3 x 10.6 to 28 x 21.6 [3], [1] 2–25, [26], 27–37, [3], [1] 2–25, [26], 27–37, [1], [1] 2–16, 17–36; none; good.

Contents: Complete; infrequently revised in black ink.

Dates: Pub. *Labour Leader* (Manchester), 7 November 1912–2 January 1913.

116a. Citation: CO-OP; t. ms., a. ms.; ribbon, carbon, pencil; InU.

Title: [none]

Key Words: *"Contents* | Book One: 1932 | Chapter . . . gangs sprig of sage brush.

Collation: 58; misc. sheets; 10.3 x 21.2 to 27.9 x 24.6; [8], [1]–12, [1]–12, 1–13, 1–13; none; good.

Contents: Incomplete; infrequently revised in regular, blue pencil; misc. collection of notes and carbons containing: a table of contents, advertising blurbs, and working notes for the book.

Dates: Pub. 1936–37 (serially), 1936 (as book).

116b.Citation: CO-OP; t. ms., a. ms., print; ribbon, carbon, pencil, print; InU.

Title; CO-OP | A Novel of Living Together

Key Words: *Copy for back of cover* . . . gangs sprig of sage brush.

Collation: 170; misc. sheets; 5 x 8.8 to 28 x 21.6; [3], 1–2, 1–2, 1–3, [6], 1–50, [59], [5], 1–3, [9], 19, [1]–12, 1–13, 2, 3, 15, 18, 36, 37, 38, 39, 40, 41, 42, 43, 44, 46, 47, 48, 49, 50, 51, 52, 53, 54, 55, 56, 57, 58, 59, 60, 61, 62, 63, 137, 139, 142; fair.

Contents: Incomplete; frequently revised in pencil; folder labeled: Notes for *Co-op*; ms. is misc. collection of notes, advertising material, and Werner Laurie correction sheets.

Dates: Pub. 1936–37 (serially), 1936 (as book).

116c.Citation: CO-OP; a. ms.; pencil; InU.

Title: [none]

Key Words: They strolled on and Leslie . . . ones that know the way!"

Collation: 2; white, brown; 28.1 x 21.2, 21.5 x 13.9; 171a, 526a; none; good.

Contents: Incomplete; infrequently revised in pencil; folder labeled: Coop? | Scattered sheets; they appear to be addenda.

Dates: Pub. 1936–37 (serially), 1936 (as book).

116d.Citation: CO-OP; t. ms., a. ms.; ribbon, pencil; InU.

Title: CO-OP | A Novel

Key Words: A booklet published in 1935 . . . hanging breathless on thy fate!

Collation: 589; blue watermarked, white; 27.9 x 21.6, 26.5 x 20.2; numbered consecutively by chapters but not continuously; 5, 11, 29, 54, 112, 119, 135, 144, 168, 174, 180, 181, 185, 186, 206, 207, 220, 231, 236, 242, 246, 258, 260, 262, 263, 284, 285, 286, 300, 301, 328, 331, 334, 335, 340, 348, 390, 407, 414, 422, 431, 433, 466, 469, 493, 532, 558, 560, 563, 564, 579, 583; good.

Contents: Complete; frequently revised in pencil; ms. housed in four folders labeled: chapt. 1–5, 6–9, 10–14, 15–17; all folders in box labeled: late, complete draft.

Dates: Pub. 1936–37 (serially), 1936 (as book).

116e. Citation: CO-OP; t. ms.; ribbon; InU.

Title: CO-OP | A Novel | [by Upton Sinclair (c.o.)] | A FEW WORDS TO THE READER

Key Words: A booklet published in 1935 . . . on thy fate! | The End.

Collation: 591; white watermarked, misc. sheets; 28 x 21.6, 27.9 x 21.5 to 28 x 21.6; continuously numbered with variations; none; good, tattered, smudged, punched for two-ring binder.

Contents: Complete; infrequently revised in pencil, red pen, not in Sinclair's hand; ms. bears printer's corrections in red, purple pencil.

Dates: Pub. 1936–37 (serially), 1936 (as book).

116f. Citation: CO-OP; t. ms.; carbon; InU.

Title: CO-OP: A DRAMA | In Three Acts and Thirteen Scenes

Key Words: Note: This is a dramatization . . . bleed the poor In Californiy-ay!

Collation: 246; brown cardboard, white watermarked; 18.6 x 16.2, 28 x 21.6; continuously numbered with variations; none; good.

Contents: Complete; infrequently revised in pencil; two copies of ms. in separate folders; two spindle marks along left margin.

Dates: Pub. 1936–37 (serially), 1936 (as book).

116g.Citation: CO-OP; t. ms.; ribbon; InU.

Title: CO-OP

Key Words: A set in 1: Pipe . . . Californiy-ay! | (cheers and applause) | CURTAIN

Collation: 124; white watermarked; 28 x 21.6; [4], [1] 2, 2b, 2c, 2d, 3–7, 7a, 8–26, 27a, 27–83, 83a, 84–104, 104a, 105–112 [1]; none; good.

Contents: Complete; infrequently revised in pencil; bound in a brown wrapper with three brass studs; printed on the front wrapper: Library, Bureau of Research and Publication, Federal Theatre Project, W.P.A.

Dates: Pub. 1936–37 (serially), 1936 (as book).

117. Citation: THE CORN-FIELD LADY; t. ms.; carbon; InU.

Title: THE CORN-FIELD LADY

Key Words: The following suggestions are for . . . the negroes' delight in this.

Collation: 10; brown; 28 x 21.7; [1] 2–5, [1] 2–5; none; good.

Contents: Complete; infrequently revised in faded ink; both groupings are identical carbons; they bear the same revisions.

Dates: Comp. ca. 1930s? Pub. ?

118a.Citation: COUNT ROMAN OSTOJA; t. ms.; carbon; InU.

Title: COUNT ROMAN OSTOJA; An Introduction

Key Words: Count Ostoja is a Polish . . . address is Hotel Regent, Hollywood.

Collation: 3; white watermarked; 28 x 21.5; 1–3; 3; good.

Contents: Complete; infrequently revised in blue ink; by Sinclair and MCS.

Dates: Comp. 1929–30? Pub. ?

118b. Citation: COUNT ROMAN OSTOJA; t. ms.; carbon; InU.

Title: COUNT ROMAN OSTOJA: An Introduction

Key Words: Count Ostoja is a Polish . . . address is Hotel Regent, Hollywood.

Collation: 3; white; 28.1 x 21.7; 1–3; none; good.

Contents: Complete; unrevised; by Sinclair and MCS.

Date: Comp. ca. 1929–30? Pub. ?

118c. Citation: COUNT ROMAN OSTOJA; t. ms.; ribbon; InU.

Title: COUNT ROMAN OSTOJA; An Introduction

Key Words: Count Ostoja is a Polish . . . address is Hotel Regent, Hollywood.

Collation: 3; white; 28.1 x 21.6; 1–3; none; good.

Contents: Complete; unrevised; by Sinclair and MCS.

Dates: Comp. ca. 1929–30? Pub. ?

118d. Citation: COUNT ROMAN OSTOJA; t. ms.; ribbon, carbon; InU.

Title: COUNT ROMAN OSTOJA: An Introduction

Key Words: Count Ostoja is a Polish . . . address is Hotel Regent, Hollywood.

Collation: 6; white; 27.7 x 21.3 to 27.8 x 21.5; 1–3,
1–3; none; good.

Contents: Complete; unrevised; by Sinclair and MCS.

Dates: Comp. ca. 1929–30? Pub. ?

119. Citation: CREDIT CONTROL AGAIN; t. ms.; carbon; InU.

Title: CREDIT CONTROL AGAIN

Key Words: I have had another long . . . have succeeded with my name!

Collation: 5; brown; 27.8 x 21.5; [1] 2–5; none; good.

Contents: Complete; unrevised; folder labeled; Appeal
to Reason; note in pencil on page one: Mailed 4-10-22.

Dates: Pub. *Appeal to Reason*, ca. June–July 1922.

120. Citation: CREDIT REFORM; t. ms.; carbon; InU.

Title: CREDIT REFORM

Key Words: I am in receipt of . . . of England dated
March 13th.

Collation: 1; brown; 27.9 x 21.6; unnumbered; none;
good.

Contents: Complete; unrevised; someone has written in
pencil: Mailed to U.S. 4/14/22, and Letter of Mr.
Kitson of England dated March 13th; folder labeled:
"Appeal to Reason."

Dates: Pub. *Appeal to Reason*, 8 July 1922.

121a. Citation: THE CRY FOR JUSTICE; t. ms.; ribbon,
carbon; InU.

Title: [none]

Key Words: *A Consecration* by John Masefield . . .
meat, they can eat hay.

Collation: 185; white watermarked; 27.9 x 21.5 to 28 x 21.6; unnumbered; none; good.

Contents: Incomplete; infrequently revised in pencil, black ink, not all in Sinclair's hand; folder labeled: Cry for Justice | used in book | I; a collection in most cases of multiple copies of material used in Sinclair's anthology *Cry for Justice*; this box of material is the last of four in the Lilly collection labeled: for *The Cry for Justice*; previous three contain material not used in the anthology.

Dates: Pub. ca. 26 September 1915.

121b. Citation: THE CRY FOR JUSTICE; t. ms.; ribbon, carbon; InU.

Title: PREFACE

Key Words: When the idea of this . . . I have still on hand.

Collation: 10; white, white watermarked; 27.9 x 21.7; [1]–5, [1]–2, 3–4, 5–6; none; good.

Contents: Complete; moderately revised in pencil; this folder contains a copy of the preface and a carbon.

Dates: Pub. ca. 26 September 1915.

121c. Citation: THE CRY FOR JUSTICE; t. ms.; carbon; InU.

Title: [none]

Key Words: The Furred Law-cats are most . . . longing toward the other shore."

Collation: 107; white watermarked; 26.5 x 20.5 to 28 x 21.6; unnumbered; none; excellent.

Contents: Incomplete; infrequently revised in pencil, black ink, not all in Sinclair's hand; folder labeled: Cry for Justice | used in book | II; another group of multiple copies of materials for the anthology; ms. has been tagged and labeled.

Dates: Pub. ca. 26 September 1915.

121d. Citation: THE CRY FOR JUSTICE; t. ms., a. ms.; carbon, pencil; InU.

Title: *JUSTICE:* | 9 Collection of the Literature of Social Protest | from twenty languages and four thousand years

Key Words: "The Cry for Justice" is . . . in piece by Walter Crane.

Collation: 10; white watermarked, white; 21.6 x 13.9 to 28 x 21.7; [1], [1]–2, [7]; 5, 6, 7, 9; fair.

Contents: Incomplete; infrequently revised in pencil, ink; folder labeled misc; it contains various organizational material for the book, a table of contents, an open letter concerning a trustee publication of the volume, and several pages of notes on the "art" material for the book.

Dates: Pub. ca. 26 September 1915.

121e. Citation: THE CRY FOR JUSTICE; t. ms.; blue, black ribbon; carbon; InU.

Title: [none]

Key Words: At first, this Earth, a . . . what the Wild Drama means.

Collation: 21; white, white watermarked; 19.1 x 20.3 to 28 x 21.5; [6], 2, 4–5, [12]; none; good.

Contents: Incomplete; infrequently revised in pencil; folder labeled unidentified and contains material for which the author and/or title are unknown.

Dates: Pub. ca. 26 September 1915.

122a. Citation: THE CUP OF FURY; t. ms.; carbon; InU.

Title: ENEMY IN THE MOUTH

Key Words: Note by Upton Sinclair This . . . not mind in the least.

Collation: 139; white watermarked, white; 27.9 x 21.6, 27.9 x 21.6 to 28 x 21.7; [3], i–iv, 1–132; none; good.

Contents: Complete; infrequently revised in pencil, not in Sinclair's hand; enclosed in the folder is a "note" by Sinclair stating that this is the original ms.; on the title sheet is noted that it was edited by J. Ellison; Sinclair explains the situation in his letter.

Dates: Comp. ca. 1953–55. Pub. ca. 7 May 1956.

122b. Citation: THE CUP OF FURY; t. ms.; carbon; InU.

Title: ENEMY IN THE MOUTH | A Study of Alcoholics

Key Words: In 1914 the opening here . . . put an end to it.

Collation: 187; white, misc. sheets; 28 x 21.7, 12.7 x 7.7; [3], 1–4, 8–77, 77, 78–116, 116a, 117–125, [2], 126–142, 142a, 143–182; none; good.

Contents: Incomplete; unrevised; folder labeled: Very Earliest- | 1st Manu- | Copy E-; appears to be complete except for pages 5–7.

Dates: Comp. ca. 1953–55. Pub. ca. 7 May 1956.

122c. Citation: THE CUP OF FURY; t. ms., a. ms.; ribbon, pencil; InU.

Title: ENEMY IN THE MOUTH | [A Study of Alcoholics I have known (c.o.)]

Key Words: "Oh. God, that men should . . . answer (to be supplied) years.

Collation: 215; misc. sheets; 22.9 x 14.5 to 27.9 x 21.6; continuously numbered with variations; 27, 46, 60–61, 156, 160, 183, 193; good.

Contents: Complete; frequently revised in pencil; folder labeled: Copy D- *Earliest*; sheet one is an explanatory sheet inserted by someone other than Sinclair.

Dates: Comp. ca. 1953–55. Pub. ca. 7 May 1956.

122d. Citation: THE CUP OF FURY; t. ms., print; carbon, print; InU.

Title: ENEMY IN THE MOUTH

Key Words: Shakespeare makes one of his . . . The 11 suicides proved that!

Collation: 236; gray, white; 14.2 x 21.9, 20.9 x 2.5 to 28 x 21.6; [2] 2–8, [2] i–iii, [1] 2–43, [8], 44–61, [1], 63–68, [2], 71–133, [3], 137–153, [4], 158–171, [10], 182–214; 50, 57, 60, 61, 63, 64; fair, torn, punched for three-ring binder.

Contents: Incomplete; infrequently revised in blue ink, blue, black pencil; pages 91, 156, 157, 176–178, 194–202 have been entirely torn away, leaving only a narrow left margin that is blank; ms. arranged in two separate folders.

Dates: Comp. ca. 1953–55. Pub. ca. 7 May 1956.

122e. Citation: THE CUP OF FURY; t. ms., mimeo., carbon, mimeo.; InU.

Title: ENEMY IN THE MOUTH

Key Words: In 1913, the year before . . . your one for a sample:

Collation: 223; white, misc. sheets; 27.9 x 21.6, 13.9 x 21.7 to 28 x 21.6; [2] i–iii, [1] 2–214, [2], 128, 90a; 18, 20, 26, 96, 98; good.

Contents: Complete; infrequently revised in pencil, blue ink; folder labeled: Copy B | Cup of Fury | *earlier* than copy A.

Dates: Comp. ca. 1953–55. Pub. ca. 7 May 1956.

122f. Citation: THE CUP OF FURY; t. ms., mimeo.; ribbon, carbon, mimeo.; InU.

Title: ENEMY IN THE MOUTH

Key Words: In 1913, the year before . . . and stayed for long periods.

Collation: 272; white, manila envelope; 27.9 x 21.5 to 27.9 x 21.7, 31.3 x 19.8; continuously numbered with variations; none; fair, punched for three-ring binder.

Contents: Complete; frequently revised in pencil, not all in Sinclair's hand; folder labeled: Copy D— | Very similar to copy A . . . ; someone has clipped on criticisms in various places in the ms.; folder and sheet 1 describe the relations between this copy and copy A; Harry S. Evans | Author's Agent | . . . has been typed on the title page.

Dates: Comp. ca. 1953–55. Pub. ca. 7 May 1956.

122g. Citation: THE CUP OF FURY; t. ms., mimeo; ribbon, carbon, mimeo; InU.

Title: [none]

Key Words: Corrections for Enemy ms and . . . early Christians must have been."

Collation: 244; white, misc. sheets; continuously numbered with variations; 1–3; good, punched for three-ring binder.

Contents: Incomplete; frequently revised in pencil, not all in Sinclair's hand; folder labeled: *Copy A* . . . ; first three pages of the folder are a detailed page-by-page analysis of the ms. not by Sinclair; appears to be an incomplete early draft.

Dates: Comp. ca. 1953–55. Pub. ca. 7 May 1956.

122h. Citation: THE CUP OF FURY; t. ms., a. ms., mimeo; ribbon, carbon, pencil, mimeo; InU.

Title: [none]

Key Words: We get a curious glimpse . . . skein of an awful destiny.

Collation: 92; misc. sheets; 20.5 x 12.2 to 28 x 21.7; randomly numbered; 15, 18, 20; fair.

Contents: Incomplete; frequently revised in pencil; folder labeled: Contains notes—and correction | inserts— (most not used); it is a misc. collection of material.

Dates: Comp. ca. 1953–55. Pub. ca. 7 May 1956.

122i. Citation: THE CUP OF FURY; t. ms., a. ms., mimeo; ribbon, carbon, pencil, mimeo; InU.

Title: [none]

Key Words: Dear Jerry: | congratulations, first, on . . . lose? | What do you think?

Collation: 14; misc. sheets; 26.6 x 20.3 to 28.3 x 21.6; [1], 215–221, [1], 12, 2, 1–2, [1]; none; fair.

Contents: Incomplete; frequently revised in pencil, blue ink; this is a folder of: Notes and inserts mostly not used; sheets 1 and 14 are letters concerning the publishing history of the ms.

Dates: Comp. ca. 1953–55. Pub. ca. 7 May 1956.

122j. Citation: THE CUP OF FURY; t. ms., a. ms., mimeo; ribbon, carbon, pencil, mimeo; InU.

Title: [none]

Key Words: Send me the part page . . . of his wife and children.

Collation: 116; misc. sheets; 20.4 x 12.7 to 28 x 21.6; randomly numbered; 3, 13, 19, 21, 28–34, 37, 38; fair.

Contents: Incomplete; frequently revised in regular, red pencil, blue ink, not all in Sinclair's hand; folder labeled: *Cup of Fury* | Misc. pages; ms. has been tagged and labeled.

Dates: Comp. ca. 1953–55. Pub. ca. 7 May 1956.

123. Citation: THE DAUGHTER OF THE CONFEDERACY; t. ms.; carbon; InU.

Title: THE DAUGHTER OF THE CONFEDERACY; The Life Story of Winnie Davis, daughter of Jefferson Davis.

Key Words: The following scenario is the . . . bed and never rises again.

Collation: 16; brown watermarked; 28 x 21.7; [1] 2–8, [1] 2–8; none; good.

Contents: Complete; unrevised. Apparently by Sinclair; but see *The Autobiography of Upton Sinclair*, p. 166.

Dates: Comp. ca. 1915? Unpublished.

124. Citation: THE DEAD HAND; t. ms.; carbon; InU.

Title: THE DEAD HAND: An Essay in the Economic Interpretation of Culture

Key Words: This is a book of . . . through uncounted ages and eternities.

Collation: 90; white; 27.9 x 21.4; consecutively numbered by groups but not continuously; none; good, punched for two-ring binder.

Contents: Incomplete; infrequently revised in faded ink, pencil. Apparently an early stage of the "Dead Hand" series: *Profits of Religion* (1918), *The Brass Check* (1920), *The Goose-Step* (1923), *The Goslings* (1924), *Mammonart* (1925), and *Money Writes!* (1927).

Dates: Comp. ca. 1917–18. Unpublished in this form.

125. Citation: THE DEATH OF FRANKLIN D. ROOSEVELT [See O SHEPHERD, SPEAK!]; t. ms.; carbon; InU.

Title: The death of Franklin D. Roosevelt | From "O Shepherd Speak."

Key Words: He had done his praying . . . the waves might be thoughts.

Collation: 1; white; 27.9 x 21.6; [1]; none; good.

Contents: Complete; unrevised.

Dates: Comp. ca. 1948–49. Unpublished separately.

126. Citation: DEBATE OF UPTON SINCLAIR WITH HAMILTON FISH, JR.; t. ms.; carbon; InU.

Title: Debate of Upton Sinclair with Hamilton Fish, Jr., | Chautauqua, N.Y., July 20. | Release July 21. | "Is the EPIC Plan Constitutional?"

Key Words: Since I have been maintaining . . . driven so rapidly into bankruptcy.

Collation: 2; white; 27 x 18.5; [1] 2; none; good.

Contents: Complete; infrequently revised in pencil.

Dates: Pub. See *Upton Sinclair's National EPIC News,* 1 July 1935.

127. Citation: DEBS AND THE POETS; t. ms., a. ms.; ribbon, black, blue carbon, pencil, faded ink; InU.

Title: [DEBS AND THE POETS; Edited by Ruth LePrade; With an Introduction by Upton Sinclair (c.o.)] INTRODUCTION.

Key Words: The United States has an . . . "The Poet in the Desert."

Collation: 57; misc. sheets; 28 x 21.3 to 28 x 21.7; randomly numbered; 42; good.

Contents: Incomplete; frequently revised in pencil, ink, not all in Sinclair's hand.

Dates: Pub. ca. 6 November 1920.

128a. Citation: DEMOCRATIC DEFENSE; t. ms.; carbon; InU.

Title: DEMOCRATIC DEFENSE: A Practical Program for Socialism.

Key Words: The following ideas are submitted . . . have signed it, I know.")

Collation: 5; white watermarked; 28.1 x 21.7; [1] 2–5; none; good.

Contents: Complete; unrevised; full manifesto with names of those signing it appended to end.

Dates: Pub. *New Republic*, 31 March 1917.

128b. Citation: DEMOCRATIC DEFENSE; t. ms.; carbon; InU.

Title: DEMOCRATIC DEFENSE: A Practical Program for Socialism.

Key Words: The following is submitted for . . . building of the Co-operative Commonwealth.

Collation: 5; white; 27.9 x 21.5; [1] 2–5; 5; good.

Contents: Complete; frequently revised in pencil, blue ink.

Dates: Pub. *New Republic*, 31 March 1917.

128c. Citation: DEMOCRATIC DEFENSE; t. ms.; carbon; InU.

Title: DEMOCRATIC DEFENSE: A Practical Program for Socialism.

Key Words: The following is submitted for . . . building of the Co-operative Commonwealth.

Collation: 2; white; 27.9 x 21.5; [1] 2; none; fair.

Contents: Complete; infrequently revised in blue ink.

Dates: Pub. *New Republic*, 31 March 1917.

129a. Citation: DEPRESSION ISLAND; t. ms.; ribbon, carbon; InU.

Title: DEPRESSION ISLAND: A Sketch for a Motion Picture

Key Words: In a little Socialist booklet, . . . soon be there. THE END.

Collation: 141; misc. sheets; 27.8 x 21.5 to 28 x 21.8; consecutively numbered but not continuously; 124, 136, 137; good.

Contents: Incomplete; frequently revised in pencil.

Dates: Pub. ca. October 1935.

129b. Citation: DEPRESSION ISLAND; t. ms., a. ms.; ribbon, carbon, pencil; InU.

Title: INTRODUCTION TO DEPRESSION ISLAND

Key Words: Mrs. Tanchar, Upton Sinclair and . . . I will soon be there.

Collation: 233; white watermarked, misc. sheets; 13.8 x 21.6 to 28 x 21.5; [1] 2–4, [1] 2–3, [1] 2, [1] 2, [1] 2–105, [1] 2–43, 41–48, 48a, 49–59, 82–83, 2–14, [2] 2–38; none; fair, burned, punched for two-ring binder.

Contents: Complete; infrequently revised in pencil, green ink; ms. arranged in three folders labeled: Introduction to . . . , Scenario by Gordon Rigby, and Sketch for a Motion Picture Comedy.

Dates: Pub. ca. October 1935.

130. Citation: DID I STEAL EPIC?; t. ms.; carbon; InU.

Title: DID I STEAL EPIC?

Key Words: It happens in the life . . . benefit of the EPIC movement.

Collation: 20; blue watermarked; 27.8 x 21.6; [1] 2–10, [1] 2–10; none; good.

Contents: Complete; infrequently revised in pencil; pencil note on page one of both copies not in Sinclair's hand.

Dates: Comp. ca. 1934. Pub. ?

131. Citation: DISCUSSION BY UPTON SINCLAIR; t. ms.; ribbon, carbon; InU.

Title: DISCUSSION BY UPTON SINCLAIR | ON THE SUBJECT OF O'NEILL'S "STRANGE INTERLUDE," | Delivered at Symposium at Biltmore Theatre, Los Angeles, March 11, 1929.

Key Words: When I was invited to . . . Simon Biltmore Theatre, Los Angeles.

Collation: 6; white watermarked, white; 32.5 x 21.5, 28 x 21.6 to 28 x 21.7; [1] 2–5, [1]; 5; good.

Contents: Complete; infrequently revised in pencil, unidentifiable; page six is a letter to Sinclair from Bernard Simon on letterhead: Theatre Guild, 245 West 52nd Street, New York City.

Dates: Unpublished.

132. Citation: THE DISTURBANCE OF MAX EASTMAN; t. ms.; carbon; InU.

Title: The Disturbance of Max Eastman

Key Words: Max Eastman, whom I have . . . can still be "radicals" together!

Collation: 2; white; 27.9 x 21.6; [1] 2; none; good.

Contents: Complete; infrequently revised in blue ink.

Dates: Comp. ca. 1939. Pub. ?

133. Citation: DR. FAUSTUS TODAY; t. ms.; carbon; InU.

Title: Dr. Faustus Today

Key Words: In mediaeval days, when wonders . . . next few years—or weeks.

Collation: 2; white; 27.9 x 21.6; [1] 2; none; good.

Contents: Complete; infrequently revised in pencil.

Dates: Comp. ca. 1954. Unpublished.

134a. Citation: DOCTOR FIST; t. ms., a. ms.; ribbon, pencil; InU.

Title: DOCTOR FIST: A Drama in Three Acts

Key Words: Nearly four hundred years ago . . . they are reaching the door.

Collation: 131; white watermarked, white; 25.4 x 20.4, 27.9 x 21.6; [1], [1] 2, [1] 2–16, 16a, 17–66, 66a, 67–126; 2, 3, 4, 8, 15, 19, 28, 38, 49, 53, 65, 66, 68, 94, 114; good.

Contents: Complete; frequently revised in pencil; in folder labeled: Dr. Fist, original.

Dates: Comp. ca. 1954. Unpublished.

134b. Citation: DOCTOR FIST; t. ms.; ribbon; InU.

Title: DOCTOR FIST: A Drama in Three Acts

Key Words: Study of Dr. Fist. Evening . . . they are reaching the door.)

Collation: 130; white; 27.9 x 21.6; 1, 1a, 2–129; none; good.

Contents: Complete; infrequently revised in pencil, blue ink.

Dates: Comp. ca. 1954. Unpublished.

135. Citation: DOES CAPITALISM MEAN FREEDOM? t. ms.; carbon; InU.

Title: RECONSIDERING SOCIALISM

Key Words: These are the days when . . . deception as a party policy.

Collation: 11; white watermarked, blue; 27.9 x 21.6, 28 x 21.6; [1] 2–5, [1] 2–5, [1]; 4, 5; good.

Contents: Complete; moderately revised in pencil.

Dates: Pub. *New Leader*, 2 May 1955.

136. Citation: THE DOLE, AND OTHER THINGS; t. ms., a. ms.; carbon, pencil; InU.

Title: THE DOLE, AND OTHER THINGS

Key Words: After discussing my offer to . . . my tale be told. AMEN."

Collation: 7; blue, yellow; 27.9 x 21.6, 6.4 x 13.2; [1]
1a, [1], [1] 2–4; none; good.

Contents: Complete; unrevised.

Dates: Pub. *EPIC News*, 27 January 1936.

137. Citation: THE DOUBLE STANDARD; t. ms.; carbon; InU.

Title: THE DOUBLE STANDARD

Key Words: "Upton Sinclair's idea of literature . . .
which controlled colleges and universities.

Collation: 4; white; 28 x 21.6; 1–4; none; good.

Contents: Complete; infrequently revised in pencil.

Dates: Comp. ? Pub. ?

138. Citation: DOUBLE THE TOWNSEND OFFER;
t. ms.; carbon; InU.

Title: DOUBLE THE TOWNSEND OFFER

Key Words: A $400 a month pension . . . before; we
urge it now.

Collation: 8; blue watermarked; 27.8 x 21.6; [1] 2–4,
[1] 2–4; none; good.

Contents: Complete; unrevised.

Dates: Pub. *Upton Sinclair's National EPIC News*, 14
October 1935.

139. Citation: [DOWN, DOWN TO THE BOTTOM];
t. ms.; ribbon, carbon; InU.

Title: [none]

Key Words: Down, down to the bottom . . . the sea
Has gone Germania!

Collation: 4; white watermarked; 27.9 x 21.8; unnumbered; none; good.

Contents: Complete; infrequently revised in pencil, ink; revised original, ribbon, second carbon of revision.

Dates: Comp. ? Pub. ?

140a. Citation: DRAGON HARVEST; t. ms., a. ms.; ribbon, pencil, ink; InU.

Title: [none]

Key Words: The Bureau of Foreign and . . . called a taxi and was

Collation: 136; misc. sheets; 6.7 x 20.4 to 27.9 x 21.6; randomly numbered; 5–15, 17, 20, 21, 23–25, 27, 29, 33–34, 81, 86, 90–93, 95, 102, 110, 111, 113, 115, 116, 120, 121, 127; fair.

Contents: Incomplete; moderately revised in pencil, ink, not all in Sinclair's hand; folder contains misc. notes largely concerned with the foreign languages used in the novel, primarily German and French; it is mixed material, some of it by Sinclair, some by others obviously in answer to queries he had sent out.

Dates: Pub. ca. 8 June 1945.

140b. Citation: DRAGON HARVEST; t. ms., a. ms.; ribbon; InU.

Title: DRAGON HARVEST | A Novel

Key Words: The telephone rang, and it . . . from sea to shining sea!

Collation: 1156; white watermarked, misc. sheets; numbered consecutively by chapter but not continuously; 32, 79, 84, 87, 98, 102, 136, 141, 172, 193, 214, 250, 307, 310, 325, 337, 353, 372, 389, 396, 397, 399, 432, 451, 455, 469, 504, 524, 537, 539, 599, 625, 636, 666, 676, 686, 688, 697, 706, 796, 830, 844, 852, 864, 865, 897,

909, 957, 972, 976, 1047, 1051, 1052, 1117, 1129, 1136; good.

Contents: Complete; frequently revised in pencil; these three boxes are labeled: Earlier Draft I, chaps 1–10; Earlier Draft II, chaps 11–19; Earlier Draft III, chaps 20–32; the first box contains a description of the missing and unused material according to the printed copy of the book.

Dates: Pub. ca. 8 June 1945.

140c. Citation: DRAGON HARVEST; t. ms.; ribbon; InU.

Title: DRAGON HARVEST

Key Words: The telephone rang, and it . . . from sea to shining sea!

Collation: 952; white watermarked, white; 28 x 21.7, 28 x 21.6; continuously numbered with variations; 608; good, smudged, spindled.

Contents: Complete; frequently revised in regular, blue pencil, not in Sinclair's hand; the ms. is a printer's copy; it bears both blue and orange pencil notations by the printer; ms. is housed in two boxes labeled: Printer's Copy I, chaps I–IV (sect XVI middle); Printer's Copy II, chaps 14–32.

Dates: Pub. ca. 8 June 1945.

141a. Citation: DRAGON'S TEETH; t. ms.; carbon; InU.

Title: Synopsis – Dragon's Teeth

Key Words: There is a boom in . . . out the charges to Röhm.

Collation: 16; white watermarked, blue; 27.9 x 21.7, 28 x 21.6; 5–16, [4]; none; good.

Contents: Incomplete; infrequently revised in regular, blue pencil; folder contains a carbon of a plot synopsis, a memorandum on the ages of the characters, and a note for *Dragon's Teeth.*

Dates: Pub. ca. 5 January 1942.

141b. DRAGON'S TEETH; t. ms.; ribbon, carbon; InU.

Title: Vol. II – Dragon's Teeth

Key Words: There is a boom in . . . which have yet to happen.

Collation: 11; white watermarked; 27.9 x 21.5; 5–15; none; fair, punched for two-ring binder.

Contents: Complete; infrequently revised in pencil; folder contains a carbon of a corrected plot synopsis.

Dates: Pub. ca. 5 January 1942.

141c. Citation: DRAGON'S TEETH; t. ms.; ribbon; InU.

Title: Dragon's Teeth | A Novel | By US

Key Words: Lanny Budd was the only . . . is left unto you desolate.

Collation: 860; green, misc. sheets; 27.9 x 21.4, 27.7 x 21.4 to 27.9 x 21.6; numbered consecutively by chapters but not continuously; 56, 57, 59, 111, 135, 146, 149, 151, 195, 209, 219, 220, 263, 267, 312, 318, 320, 321, 334, 336, 364, 369, 415, 427, 438, 454, 464, 475, 486, 488, 491, 496, 505, 521, 522, 533, 542, 551, 554, 560, 563, 585, 586, 607, 608, 612, 627, 650, 655, 702, 704, 728, 729, 732, 746, 754, 755, 786, 788, 789, 792, 809, 811, 822, 823, 845; good.

Contents: Complete; frequently revised in pencil; early draft housed in two boxes labeled: Early Draft I [bks I–III], Early Draft II [Bks IV–VI].

Dates: Pub. ca. 5 January 1942.

141d. Citation: DRAGON'S TEETH; t. ms.; ribbon; InU.

Title: BOOK ONE The Morning Opes [*sic*] Her Golden Gates.

Key Words: Lanny Budd was the only . . . is left unto you desolate."

Collation: 872; white watermarked; 27.9 x 21.5; continuously numbered with variations; none; good, spindled.

Contents: Complete; infrequently revised in pencil; bears the blue and orange markings of the printer, additional corrections in blue pencil, not in Sinclair's hand; ms. is housed in two boxes labeled: Printer's Copy I [Bks I–III]; Printer's Copy II [Bks IV–VI].

Dates: Pub. ca. 5 January 1942.

141e. Citation: DRAGON'S TEETH; t. ms., a. ms.; ribbon, carbon, pencil; InU.

Title: [none]

Key Words: I was about to say: . . . young athlete like yourself, Hugo."

Collation: 12; green, white watermarked: 27.9 x 21.6, 27.9 x 21.6; randomly numbered; 7, 10; good.

Contents: Incomplete; frequently revised in pencil; this folder contains misc. pages for *Dragon's Teeth*.

Dates: Pub. ca. 5 January 1942.

141f. Citation: DRAGON'S TEETH; t. ms.; carbon; InU.

Title: CORRECTIONS FOR DRAGON'S TEETH

Key Words: Page 397, last line, insert . . . Karl *der diche* (the Stout).

Collation: 3; blue; 14.1 x 21.6 to 28 x 21.6; unnumbered; none; fair.

Contents: Incomplete; unrevised; correction sheets for *Dragon's Teeth.*

Dates: Pub. ca. 5 January 1942.

142. Citation: AN EFFORT AT PRACTICAL CO-OPER-ATION; t. ms.; carbon; InU.

Title: AN EFFORT AT PRACTICAL CO-OPER-ATION

Key Words: The lesson of our time . . . mutual protection and human fellowship.

Collation: 2; white watermarked; 28.1 x 21.8; [1] 2; none; good.

Contents: Complete; infrequently revised in black ink; in folder E.

Dates: Comp. ca. 1936. Pub. ?

143. Citation: EISENSTEIN COMES TO HOLLY-WOOD; t. ms., a. ms.; ribbon, carbon, pencil; InU.

Title: EISENSTEIN COMES TO HOLLYWOOD: | A Contribution to Moving Picture History.

Key Words: This is the story of . . . they will make themselves heard.

Collation: 101; misc. sheets; 27.7 x 21.6 to 28.1 x 21.7; consecutively numbered by group but not continuously; 16, 85; good.

Contents: Complete; moderately revised in pencil, not all in Sinclair's hand; an original and many carbons in various states in a folder.

Dates: Comp. ca. January-February 1931. Unpublished.

144. Citation: EISENSTEIN REPENTS; t. ms.; ribbon, carbon; InU.

Title: EISENSTEIN REPENTS

Key Words: Several years ago I had . . . up that two million rubles!

Collation: 20; white watermarked, gray; 27.9 x 21.6, 27.8 x 21.5; [1] 2–10, [1] 2–10; none; good.

Contents: Complete; unrevised.

Dates: Comp. ca. 1936. Pub. ?

145. Citation: THE ELECTION RESULTS; t. ms.; carbon; InU.

Title: THE ELECTION RESULTS

Key Words: Our enemies of the Los . . . what our elected EPICS do.

Collation: 4; white watermarked, blue watermarked; 28 x 21.6, 28 x 21.7; unnumbered; none; good.

Contents: Complete; infrequently revised in pencil; two identical carbons.

Dates: Pub. *Upton Sinclair's EPIC News,* 13 May 1935.

146. Citation: THE EMANCIPATED HUSBAND; t. ms.; black, purple carbon; InU.

Title: THE EMANCIPATED HUSBAND: *A Sketch in One Act*

Key Words: Scene: Dolly's drawing room. At . . . ginger beer. (*horrified*) John! CURTAIN.

Collation: 56; misc. sheets; 26.3 x 20.3 to 29.1 x 22.8; consecutively numbered by group but not continuously; 1; fair.

Contents: Complete; infrequently revised in pencil, blue, black ink, not all in Sinclair's hand; two copies of the play, one bound in an agent's folder: Sada Cowan, copies of a synopsis.

Dates: Comp. ca. 1910–20? Unpublished.

147. Citation: END POVERTY MOVIES; t. ms.; carbon; InU.

Title: "END POVERTY" MOVIES

Key Words: While our State Legislature has . . . up in your neighborhood theatre.

Collation: 3; blue watermarked; 27.9 x 21.6; [1] 2–3; none; good.

Contents: Complete; unrevised; in folder E.

Dates: Pub. *Upton Sinclair's EPIC News,* 21 January 1935.

148. Citation: THE ENEMY BEHAVES ACCORDING TO SCHEDULE; t. ms.; carbon; InU.

Title: THE ENEMY BEHAVES ACCORDING TO SCHEDULE

Key Words: In the book, "I, Governor . . . speeches: "IT'S UP TO YOU!"

Collation: 5; white watermarked, blue; 28 x 21.6, 28 x 21.6; [1] 2–3, [1] 2; none; good.

Contents: Complete; infrequently revised in pencil, unidentified hand.

Dates: Comp. ca. June 1934. Pub. ?

149a. Citation: THE ENEMY HAD IT TOO; t. ms., a. ms.; ribbon, carbon, pencil; InU.

Title: THE ENEMY HAD IT TOO A Play in Three Acts

Key Words: Scene: Jungle dwelling on the . . . me about this queer-looking place.

Collation: 153; white; 7.3 x 14.1 to 28 x 21.6; randomly numbered: 82, 103, 105, 114, 123, 124, 125; fair, burned.

Contents: Complete [?]; moderately revised in blue ink, black, red pencil; two copies in separate folders.

Dates: Pub. ca. 25 August 1950.

149b. Citation: THE ENEMY HAD IT TOO; t. ms.; ribbon, carbon; InU.

Title: THE ENEMY HAD IT TOO: | A Play in Three Acts

Key Words: A dwelling of the Vichada . . . the least of our losses.

Collation: 105; white, white watermarked; 28 x 21.6; 1–101, [4]; none; fair, spindled.

Contents: Complete; moderately revised in blue, red, regular pencil, not all in Sinclair's hand; appears to be a printer's copy.

Dates: Pub. ca. 25 August 1950.

150a. Citation: ENEMY IN THE MOUTH; t. ms.; ribbon; InU.

Title: "ENEMY IN THE MOUTH" | A STATE-MENT BY UPTON SINCLAIR

Key Words: For three-quarters of a century . . . I have news to report.

Collation: 3; white; 27.9 x 21.6; [1] 2–3; 2; good.

Contents: Complete; frequently revised in pencil.

Dates: Pub. New Republic, 21 March 1955.

See: CUP OF FURY

150b. Citation: ENEMY IN THE MOUTH; mimeo; InU.

Title: "ENEMY IN THE MOUTH" | A Statement by Upton Sinclair

Key Words: For three-quarters of a century . . . Darrell K. Wolfe, Book Director.

Collation: 3; white; 27.9 x 21.6; [1] 2–3; none; good.

Contents: Complete; unrevised, blue ink notation in upper left corner.

Dates: Pub. *New Republic*, 21 March 1955.

See: CUP OF FURY

151. Citation: EPIC ANSWERS: HOW TO END POVERTY IN CALIFORNIA; t. ms.; carbon; InU.

Title: EPIC ANSWERS

Key Words: The book, "I, Governor of . . . , IT IS UP TO YOU.

Collation: 38; green; 27.9 x 21.7; [1] 2–6, 6a, 6b, 7–21, 21a, 21b, 22–34; none; good.

Contents: Complete; infrequently revised in pencil, unidentified hand.

Dates: Pub. ca. February 1934.

152. Citation: EPIC DRAMA; t. ms.; carbon; InU.

Title: EPIC Drama

Key Words: My friend, Frank Scully, writes . . . a publicly owned radio station!

Collation: 8; blue watermarked; 28 x 21.6; [1] 2–4, [1] 2–4; none; good.

Contents: Complete; infrequently revised in pencil.

Dates: Comp. 2 April 1935. See "Wanted – An EPIC Drama," *Upton Sinclair's EPIC News*, 25 February 1935.

153. Citation: THE EPIC MOVEMENT; t. ms.; ribbon; InU.

Title: THE EPIC MOVEMENT

Key Words: People in California who know . . . of ending poverty in California.

Collation: 6; white; 27.7 x 21.4; [1] 2–6; none; good.

Contents: Complete; infrequently revised in pencil.

Dates: Comp. ca. August 1934. Pub. ?

154. Citation: THE EPIC PLAN; t. ms.; carbon; InU.

Title: THE EPIC PLAN: | Can Poverty be Ended? | Upton Sinclair wants to be governor of California and | try it.

Key Words: Can Americans end the depression? . . . the outside, wait and see!

Collation: 11; white; 28 x 21.7; 1–11; none; good.

Dates: Pub. *The Pacific Cooperator*, March 1934.

155. Citation: EPICS AND DEMOCRATS; t. ms.; ribbon; InU.

Title: EPICS and DEMOCRATS

Key Words: In the past two-and-one-half weeks . . . determined by truly democratic methods.

Collation: 4; white; 28 x 21.6; [1] 2–3, 3; none; good.

Contents: Complete; moderately revised in pencil.

Dates: Pub. *Upton Sinclair's EPIC News*, 3 December 1934.

156a. Citation: EPICS WILL DECIDE; t. ms.; ribbon; InU.

Title: EPICS WILL DECIDE

Key Words: Since my return from the . . . will be clear and courageous.

Collation: 4; white watermarked; 27.9 x 21.6; [1] 2–4; none; good.

Contents: Complete; infrequently revised in pencil.

Dates: Comp. ca. December 1935. Pub ?

156b. Citation: EPICS WILL DECIDE; t. ms.; carbon; InU.

Title: EPICS WILL DECIDE

Key Words: Since my return from the . . . will be clear and courageous.

Collation: 4; blue; 27.9 x 21.6; [1] 2–4; none; good.

Contents: Complete; infrequently revised in pencil; not in Sinclair's hand; incorporates some revisions as above.

Dates: Comp. ca. December 1935. Pub. ?

157. Citation: ESSAYS IN REVOLUTION; a. ms.; pencil; InU.

Title: Essays in Revolution

Key Words: The papers here gathered together . . . story which these essays unfold.

Collation: 3; brown; 33 x 21.5; [3]; none; fair.

Contents: Complete, Preface only; moderately revised in pencil.

Dates: Comp. ca. 1908. Pub. ?

158. Citation: AN EVANGELIST DROWNS; t. ms.; ribbon, carbon; InU.

Title: *An Evangelist Drowns*

Key Words: Through green-white breakers swift I . . . forgot that which is not!

Collation: 4; green, white; 27.8 x 21.3, 28 x 21.6; unnumbered; none; good.

Contents: Complete; infrequently revised in pencil, blue ink; revised original and two carbons, one bears the comments of George Sterling.

Dates: Pub. *New Republic*, 30 June 1926.

159. Citation: AN EVANGELIST PRAYS; t. ms., a. ms.; carbon, pencil; InU.

Title: An Evangelist Prays

Key Words: Oh Lord, I grovel at . . . Satan dances on the walls!

Collation: 6; green, misc. sheets; 27.7 x 21.3, 28 x 21.6; unnumbered; 1; fair.

Contents: Complete; moderately revised in pencil; autograph original, two revised carbons, two unrevised carbons.

Dates: Comp. ? Pub. ?

160. Citation: AN EX-KING'S RANSOM; t. ms.; carbon; InU.

Title: AN EX-KING'S RANSOM | A Letter to Edward, Duke of Windsor.

Key Words: The editor of "Liberty" has . . . enough opportunity to show intent

Collation: 43; white, misc. sheets; 27.8 x 21.6 to 28 x 21.7, 10.1 x 12.8 to 27.9 x 21.6; numbered consecutively but not continuously; 29, 37, 43; good.

Contents: Complete; moderately revised in pencil.

Dates: Comp. ca. December 1936. Pub. ?

161. Citation: EXPECT NO PEACE!; t. ms., a. ms.; ribbon, carbon, pencil; InU.

Title: EXPECT NO PEACE!

Key Words: Proposed book made up from . . . race for all future time.

Collation: 42; misc. sheets; 14.5 x 21.5 to 27.9 x 21.5; consecutively numbered but not continuously; 12, 18, 19; good.

Contents: Incomplete; moderately revised in pencil, not all in Sinclair's hand.

Dates: Pub. 1939.

162. Citation: EXPLAINING MY ATTITUDE TO-WARD THE PROBLEM OF SOCIAL REVOLU-TION; t. ms.; carbon; InU.

Title: Explaining my attitude toward the problem of Social/Revolution:

Key Words: I think that morally speaking . . . supporting Social Democracy. Upton Sinclair.

Collation: 1; white; 28 x 21.7; unnumbered; none; fair.

Contents: Complete; infrequently revised in pencil.

Dates: Comp. 1920s? Pub. ?

163a. Citation: EXPLAIN THIS TO ME!; t. ms.; carbon; InU.

Title: EXPLAIN THIS TO ME!: | An Account of Some Psychic Mysteries.

Key Words: For some thirty years I . . . new forces of our beings.

Collation: 68; white; 28.1 x 26.7; consecutively numbered but not continuously; none; good.

Contents: Complete; infrequently revised in pencil, ink, not all in Sinclair's hand; three carbons of the same article, but in different states.

Dates: Comp. ca. 1929–30. Pub. ?

See: MENTAL RADIO

163b.Citation: EXPLAIN THIS TO ME!; t. ms., a. ms.; carbon, pencil; InU.

Title: EXPLAIN THIS TO ME!: | An Account of Some Psychic Mysteries.

Key Words: For some thirty years I . . . it upon patients with success.

Collation: 115; misc. sheets; 27.8 x 21.5 to 28.1 x 21.7; consecutively numbered but not continuously; 115; good.

Contents: Complete; infrequently revised in pencil, not all in Sinclair's hand; second carbon copies of the article in various states of revision.

Dates: Comp. ca. 1929–30. Pub. ?

See: MENTAL RADIO

164a.Citation: FAMILY FAVORITES; t. ms.; ribbon; InU.

Title: FAMILY FAVORITES

Key Words: (All these incidents happened either . . . inspiration: "His mother was there!"

Collation: 4; white watermarked; 27.9 x 21.6; [1] 2–4; none; good, water-stained.

Contents: Complete; infrequently revised in pencil.

Dates: Comp. ca. 1920s? Pub. ?

164b.Citation: FAMILY FAVORITES; t. ms.; carbon; InU.

Title: FAMILY FAVORITES

Key Words: All these incidents happened either . . . inspiration: "His mother was there!"

Collation: 8; white; 28.1 x 21.6; [1] 2–4, [1] 2–4; none; good.

Contents: Complete; infrequently revised in pencil, not in Sinclair's hand.

Dates: Comp. ca. 1920s? Pub. ?

165. Citation: F A T; t. ms.; carbon; InU.

Title: "F A T" Addressed to Will Dyson, Cartoonist of the London "Herald."

Key Words: I met them, Will, old . . . the one selling for sixpence.

Collation: 4; brown watermarked, white watermarked; 27.9 x 21.6; unnumbered; none; good.

Contents: Complete; unrevised; two carbons of poem.

Dates: Comp. ca. 1915? Pub. ?

166. Citation: FEDERATION IN EUROPE; t. ms.; ribbon, carbon; InU.

Title: Federation in Europe

Key Words: My mail brings many letters . . . it. So let them choose!

Collation: 9; green, white; 27.9 x 21.6, 28 x 21.8; [1] 2–5, [1] 2–4; 1; good.

Contents: Complete; moderately revised in pencil.

Dates: Comp. ca. 1930s. Pub. ?

167a. Citation: FIAT JUSTITIA!; a. ms.; pencil; InU.

Title: Fiat Justitia!

Key Words: Can a "radical" be libelled? . . . none for the California Socialist.

Collation: 13; white; 13.8 x 21.6 to 27.9 x 21.6; 1, [2], 3–8, 8a, 9–10, [11], 12; good.

Contents: Complete; moderately revised in pencil.

Dates: Pub. *New Leader*, 3 August 1929.

167b. Citation: FIAT JUSTITIA!; t. ms.; ribbon; InU.

Title: Fiat Justitia!

Key Words: Can a "radical" be libeled? . . . none for the California Socialist.

Collation: 8; white, white watermarked; 28 x 21.6, 27.9 x 21.6; [1] 2–8; none; good.

Contents: Complete; infrequently revised in pencil.

Dates: Pub. *New Leader*, 3 August 1929.

168a. Citation: THE FLIVVER KING; t. ms.; ribbon; InU.

Title: FORD-AMERICA | A Story

Key Words: "Mom," said Little Abner, "there's . . . the world has gone crazy."

Collation: 258; green; 28 x 21.6; numbered consecutively by chapter but not continuously; 10, 12, 24, 28, 38, 39, 44, 45, 50, 86, 100, 121, 133, 139, 145, 148, 150, 152, 154, 160, 191, 211, 216, 217, 234, 237, 251, 252; good.

Contents: Complete; frequently revised in pencil; three folders contain a complete ms. of *The Flivver King* I–III.

Dates: Pub. ca. November 1937.

168b. Citation: THE FLIVVER KING; t. ms.; carbon; InU.

Title: [none]

Key Words: To the Printer:— | The following . . . it," replied the sister, quietly.

Collation: 8; white watermarked, white; 27.8 x 21.6, 14 x 21.5 to 27.8 x 21.5; randomly numbered; none; good.

Contents: Incomplete; infrequently revised in pencil, not in Sinclair's hand; appear to be printer's notations.

Dates: Pub. ca. November 1937.

168c. Citation: THE FLIVVER KING; t. ms., a. ms.; ribbon, pencil; InU.

Title: [none]

Key Words: Another thing that H would . . . Henry Ford against Wall Street.

Collation: 10; white watermarked, galley sheet; 27.9 x 21.6, 33 x 17; randomly numbered; 2, 3, 6, 7; good, punched for two-ring binder.

Contents: Incomplete; frequently revised in pencil; folder contains a misc. collection of sheets.

Dates: Pub. ca. November 1937.

168d. Citation: THE FLIVVER KING; t. ms., a. ms.; carbon, pencil; InU.

Title: [none]

Key Words: To the Reader: | The problem . . . version of "The Flivver King."

Collation: 10; misc. sheets; 28 x 21.6 to 45.2 x 17.6; not numbered; 3; good.

Contents: Incomplete; infrequently revised in pencil; folder labeled: Promotional Material; it contains material for a foreword, several broadside drafts, and a PROPOSAL FOR A "FLIVVER KING" FILM.

Dates: Pub. ca. November 1937.

169. Citation: FLOYD DELL, ME, AND THE WAR; t. ms.; carbon; InU.

Title: Floyd Dell, Me, and the War

Key Words: Floyd Dell has sat in . . . able to guess its identity!

Collation: 6; green; 27.9 x 21.5; unnumbered; 6; good.

Contents: Complete; infrequently revised in pencil.

Dates: Comp. ca. 1927. Pub. ?

170. Citation: FORD'S PEACE SHIP; t. ms.; ribbon; InU.

Title: FORD'S PEACE SHIP

Key Words: Has conference with Rosika Schwimmer
. . . news—has heard nothing personally.

Collation: 3; brown; 28 x 21.6; [1] 2–3; none; good.

Contents: Complete; unrevised.

Dates: Comp. ca. January 1916. Pub. ?

171. Citation: FOR THE 50TH ANNIVERSARY OF THE L[EAGUE FOR] I[NDUSTRIAL] D[EMOCRACY]; t. ms.; carbon; InU.

Title: FOR THE 50TH ANNIVERSARY OF THE L.I.D.

Key Words: I would like nothing better . . . Bless you, my grandchildren all!

Collation: 3; white; 27.9 x 21.6; [1] 2–3; none; good.

Contents: Complete; infrequently revised in blue ink.

Dates: Pub. *50 Years of Democratic Education*, 23 April 1955.

172. Citation: FOR A NEW APPEAL TO REASON; t. ms.; carbon; InU.

Title: FOR A NEW APPEAL TO REASON

Key Words: I have a proposition to . . . guns trained upon the enemy.

Collation: 34; white, white watermarked; 27.8 x 21.5, 28 x 21.6; [1] 2–19, 21, 23, 25–31, [1]–2, [1], [2], 2; 34; good.

Contents: Complete; infrequently revised in pencil.

Dates: Comp. ca. May 1920. Pub. ? See pamphlet *The National News*, ca. 1 December 1919.

173. Citation: FOR SALE TO THE HIGHEST BIDDER —YOUNG WOMAN INDUSTRIAL SLAVE: t. ms.; purple ribbon; InU.

Title: FOR SALE | To the Highest Bidder | YOUNG WOMAN INDUSTRIAL SLAVE.

Key Words: Intelligent, educated, refined; true, honest . . . the American masters of privilege!

Collation: 4; white; 27.8 x 21.5; [1] 2–4; none; good.

Contents: Complete; infrequently revised in pencil, hand unidentified.

Dates: Comp. ca. 1915–20? Pub ?

174. Citation: FOR SHADIA; t. ms.; ribbon; InU.

Title: For Shadia

Key Words: As I write this, the . . . what if George is drunk?

Collation: 2; white watermarked; 27.9 x 21.7; 1–2; none; good.

Contents: Complete; infrequently revised in pencil, blue ink.

Dates: Comp. ca. 1954–55? Pub. ?

175a. Citation: FOR THE VOICE OF AMERICA; t. ms.; carbon: InU.

Title: FOR THE VOICE OF AMERICA

Key Words: I have spent nearly all . . . it alive in your hearts.

Collation: 3; white watermarked; 27.9 x 21.6; [1] 2–3; none; good.

Dates: Recorded 23 September 1958. (Tape in Lilly Library.)

175b.Citation: FOR THE VOICE OF AMERICA; t. ms.; carbon; InU.

Title: FOR THE VOICE OF AMERICA

Key Words: I have spent nearly all . . . it alive in your hearts.

Collation: 3; white watermarked; 28 x 21.6; [1] 2–3; none; good.

Contents: Complete; infrequently revised in blue ink, unidentified hand.

Dates: Recorded 23 September 1958. (Tape in Lilly Library.)

176. Citation: FORWARD EPIC; t. ms.; carbon; InU.

Title: FORWARD EPIC

Key Words: I am very happy over . . . proposes I would back wholeheartedly.

Collation: 2; white watermarked; 28 x 21.6; [1] 2; none; good.

Contents: Complete; infrequently revised in pencil, not in Sinclair's hand.

Dates: Pub. *EPIC News*, 17 February 1936.

177. Citation: [FRANK HARRIS ASKS ME TO]; t. ms.; carbon; InU.

Title: [none]

Key Words: Frank Harris asks me to . . . he threw the Haymarket bomb.

Collation: 7; white watermarked; 28 x 21.7; [1] 2–7; none; good.

Contents: Complete; unrevised.

Dates: Comp. ca. 1920? Pub. ?

178a. Citation: FREE SPEECH: WHAT IS IT?; t. ms.; carbon; InU.

Title: FREE SPEECH: WHAT IS IT

Key Words: One day last June a . . . this article with the same.

Collation: 19; white watermarked; 28 x 21.6; [1] 2–19; none; good.

Contents: Incomplete; unrevised.

Dates: Comp. ca. 1914–15. Pub. ?

178b. Citation: FREE SPEECH: WHAT IS IT?; t. ms.; blue ribbon, carbon; InU.

Title: FREE SPEECH: WHAT IS IT?

Key Words: One day last June a . . . cause it to be withdrawn.

Collation: 40; white watermarked; 28 x 21.6; [1] 2–20, [1] 2–20; none; good.

Contents: Complete; infrequently revised in black, blue ink, not all in Sinclair's hand.

Dates: Comp. ca. 1914–15. Pub. ?

179. Citation: FREESTATE; t. ms.; ribbon; InU.

Title: FREESTATE | A Plan for European Reconstruction

Key Words: As these words are put . . . is brief and yet endless!

Collation: 12; white, white watermarked; 28 x 21.7, 28 x 21.6; [1] 2–12; none; good.

Contents: Complete; infrequently revised.

Dates: Comp. ca. 1944. Pub. ?

180a. Citation: FROM FRYING PAN INTO FIRE; t. ms.; carbon; InU.

Title: FROM FRYING PAN INTO FIRE

Key Words: For thirty years I have . . . hope for your Democratic party.

Collation: 23; white watermarked; 28 x 21.7; [1] 2–11, [1] 2–11, 11; none; good.

Contents: Complete; infrequently revised in pencil, not in Sinclair's hand; two carbon copies.

Dates: Comp. 28 December 1932. Pub. ?

180b. Citation: FROM FRYING PAN INTO FIRE; t. ms.; carbon; InU.

Title: FROM FRYING PAN INTO FIRE

Key Words: For thirty years I have . . . hope for your Democratic party.

Collation: 15; white watermarked; 28 x 21.5; [1], 1–14; none; good.

Contents: Complete; unrevised; stapled into booklet form.

Dates: Comp. 28 December 1932. Pub. ?

181. Citation: THE FUTURE OF EPIC; t. ms.; carbon; InU.

Title: THE FUTURE OF E P I C

Key Words: Everybody asks me what is . . . Keep your eyes on California!

Collation: 2; blue watermarked; 27.9 x 21.6; [1] 2; none; good.

Contents: Complete; unrevised.

Dates: Pub. *Nation*, 28 November 1934.

182. Citation: GENERAL ELECTION RADIO SPEECH NO. 5; t. ms.; carbon; InU.

Title: GENERAL ELECTION | RADIO SPEECH | NO. 5 | COLUMBIA SYSTEM MONDAY, OCT. 15, 1934. — 6:45

Key Words: Three weeks from tomorrow we . . . Thank you and good night.

Collation: 6; white watermarked; 27.9 x 21.5; [1] 2–6; none; good.

Contents: Complete; unrevised.

Dates: Pub. ?

183. Citation: GEORGE STERLING; t. ms.; carbon; InU.

Title: George Sterling

Key Words: Many strange experiences have been . . . poison. Love, beware! Sag Harbor.

Collation: 7; white; 28 x 21.6; 1–7; none; good.

Contents: Complete; infrequently revised in pencil.

Dates: Comp. ca. 1926. Pub. ?

184a. Citation: A GIANT'S STRENGTH; t. ms., a. ms.; ribbon, pencil, blue ink; InU.

Title: A GIANT'S STRENGTH | Drama in Three Acts

Key Words: This is a play about . . . & not to hate! CURTAIN

Collation: 113; white watermarked, brown; 27.8 x 21.5, 21.7 x 13.9; 1–3, [4], 5–16, [1], 17–27, [1], 28–74,

76–105, 105a, 106–111; 1, 14, 19, 21, 25, 45, 54, 82, 84; good.

Contents: Complete; moderately revised in pencil, blue ink, not all in Sinclair's hand.

Dates: Pub. 1948.

184b. Citation: A GIANT'S STRENGTH; t. ms.; ribbon, carbon; InU.

Title: A GIANT'S STRENGTH | Drama in Three Acts

Key Words: This is a play about . . . last sentence is being spoken.

Collation: 105; white watermarked, white; 27.9 x 21.6, 28 x 21.7; [1] 2–14, 14a, 15–102, 15–16; none; good.

Contents: Complete; infrequently revised in pencil, not all in Sinclair's hand; ms. labeled as a final version.

Dates: Pub. 1948.

185. Citation: GIVE ME A LITTLE PITY; t. ms.; ribbon; InU.

Title: [none]

Key Words: "Give me a little pity . . . And then let me go."

Collation: 1; white; 27.9 x 21.6; unnumbered; none; good.

Contents: Complete; infrequently revised in pencil.

Dates: Comp. ca. 1934. Pub. ?

186a. Citation: THE GNOMOBILE; t. ms., a. ms.; ribbon, carbon, pencil; InU.

Title: THE GNOMOBILE: | A Story

Key Words: A little girl was walking . . . guests at his "press conference."

Collation: 154; blue watermarked, white watermarked; 27.9 x 21.6, 28 x 21.6; consecutively numbered by chapters but not continuously; 69, 81, 88, 153; good.

Contents: Complete; frequently revised in pencil.

Dates: Pub. ca. November 1936.

186b. Citation: THE GNOMOBILE; t. ms.; ribbon, carbon; InU.

Title: THE GNOMOBILE: | A Gnice Gnew Gnarrative with Gnonsense but Gnothing | Gnaughty

Key Words: This story for children tells . . . clump of bright green laurel.

Collation: 134; white watermarked, white; 27.9 x 21.6; randomly numbered; none; good.

Contents: Complete; infrequently revised in regular, blue pencil.

Dates: Pub. ca. November 1936.

187. Citation: GOD AND BIRTH CONTROL: WHY PRIESTS DEMAND AN ENDLESS STREAM OF DUPES; t. ms.; carbon; InU.

Title: GOD AND BIRTH CONTROL

Key Words: An author of controversial books . . . into the arms of Communism.

Collation: 4; white; 27.9 x 21.6; 1–4; none; good.

Contents: Complete; infrequently revised in pencil, not all in Sinclair's hand.

Dates: Pub. *Critic and Guide*, March 1950.

188a. Citation: GOD AND MYSELF; t. ms., a. ms.; carbon, pencil; InU.

Title: GOD AND MYSELF

Key Words: He holds me here, He . . . of anguish cling to joy.

Collation: 2; white watermarked; 28 x 21.6; unnumbered; none; good.

Contents: Complete; infrequently revised in pencil; an autograph ms. and one typed carbon of this poem.

Dates: Comp. ca. 1933. Pub. ?

188b. Citation: GOD AND MYSELF; t. ms.; ribbon; InU.

Title: GOD AND MYSELF

Key Words: He holds me here, He . . . of anguish cling to joy.

Collation: 1; white watermarked; 27.9 x 21.6; unnumbered; none; good.

Contents: Complete; unrevised.

Dates: Comp. ca. 1933. Pub. ?

189a. Citation: GOD'S COUNTRY; t. ms.; ribbon; InU.

Title: [none]

Key Words: In the sixteenth decade of . . . also are commended to you.

Collation: 86; green; 28.2 x 21.6; numbered, consecutively by groups but not continuously; 25, 46, 51, 55, 64, 65, 71, 72, 83, 86; good.

Contents: Complete; moderately revised in pencil, not in Sinclair's hand; in folder labeled: God's Epic.

Dates: Comp. ca. 1933. Pub. ?

189b. Citation: GOD'S COUNTRY; t. ms.; carbon; InU.

Title: COD'S [sic] EPIC | End Poverty In Civilization

Key Words: In the sixteenth decade of . . . also I commend to you.

Collation: 88; white; 27.9 x 21.7; [1] 2–31, 32–33, 34–43, 43a, 44–87; none; good.

Contents: Complete; infrequently revised in pencil, not in Sinclair's hand; in folder labeled: God's Epic.

Dates: Comp. ca. 1933. Pub. ?

189c. Citation: GOD'S COUNTRY; t. ms.; carbon; InU.

Title: [none]

Key Words: In the sixteenth decade of . . . also I commend to you.

Collation: 73; white watermarked; 27.9 x 21.6; [1] 2–18, 32–33, 34–43, 43a, 44–86; none; good.

Contents: Incomplete; infrequently revised in pencil, not in Sinclair's hand; in folder labeled: God's Epic | Incomplete.

Dates: Comp. ca. 1933. Pub. ?

189d. Citation: GOD'S COUNTRY; t. ms.; carbon; InU.

Title: [none]

Key Words: In the sixteenth decade of . . . also I commend to you.

Collation: 87; white; 27.9 x 21.7; [1] 2–31, 32–33, 34–43, 43a, 44–87; none; good.

Contents: Complete; infrequently revised in pencil, not in Sinclair's hand; in folder labeled: God's Epic.

Dates: Comp. ca. 1933. Pub ?

189e. Citation: GOD'S COUNTRY; t. ms.; ribbon; InU.

Title: GOD'S COUNTRY | The Story of the Reverend John Christian of Mud Hollow

Key Words: The pastor of the consolidated . . . the work of their hands."

Collation: 72; white; 28 x 21.6; 1–72; none; good.

Contents: Complete; infrequently revised in pencil.

Dates: Comp. ca. 1933. Pub. ?

189f. Citation: GOD'S COUNTRY; t. ms., a. ms.; ribbon, carbon, pencil, blue ink; InU.

Title: GOD'S COUNTRY | [GOD SAVES AMERICA (c.o.)] | [GOD'S epic (c.o.)] | The Story of the Rev. John Christian [Carpenter (c.o.)] of Mud Hollow | [And How he Saved America (c.o.)].

Key Words: The pastor of the consolidated . . . the work of their hands."

Collation: 91; white watermarked, misc. sheets; 28 x 21.7, 10.1 x 9.3 to 27.9 x 21.5; continuously numbered with variations; 2, 9, 15, 22, 89; good.

Contents: Complete [?]; moderately revised in pencil.

Dates: Comp. ca. 1933. Pub. ?

189g. Citation: GOD'S COUNTRY; t. ms.; carbon; InU.

Title: [none]

Key Words: Said he: "I left the . . . promotion in the movement, but

Collation: 10; white watermarked; 28 x 21.6; randomly numbered; none; good.

Contents: Incomplete; unrevised; in folder labeled: God's Epic | Extra pages.

Dates: Comp. ca. 1933. Pub. ?

190a. Citation: THE GOLDEN SCENARIO; t. ms., a. ms.; ribbon, blue pencil; InU.

Title: THE GOLDEN SCENARIO

Key Words: According to the 1930 census . . . Love in Arms (original ms.)

Collation: 70; misc. sheets; 29.1 x 16.5 to 27.8 x 21.5; [1] 2–31, 31–32, 33–69, [1]; none; good.

Contents: Complete; moderately revised in pencil.

Dates: Comp. ca. 1931. Pub. ?

190b. Citation: THE GOLDEN SCENARIO; t. ms.; carbon; InU.

Title: THE GOLDEN SCENARIO

Key Words: According to the 1930 census . . . one they have in mind.

Collation: 66; white watermarked; 27.9 x 21.6; 1–66; none; good, punched for two-ring binder.

Contents: Complete; infrequently revised in pencil; in manila folder.

Dates: Comp. ca. 1931. Pub. ?

191. Citation: THE GOLDFISH BOWL; t. ms.; ribbon; InU.

Title: The Gold Fish Bowl.

Key Words: Some of you may recall . . . on ignorantly voting blank checks?

Collation: 6; white watermarked; 28 x 21.7; [1] 2–6; none; good.

Contents: Complete; infrequently revised in pencil, not in Sinclair's hand.

Dates: Comp. ca. 1938. Pub. ?

192. Citation: THE GOLD-SPANGLED BANNER: t. ms., a. ms., print; ribbon, carbon, pencil, print; InU.

Title: [none]

Key Words: 42/1 8/31/32 In accordance with . . . He is content at the last.

Collation: 261; white, misc. sheets; 18.7 x 20.9, 12.4 x 21.6 to 27.9 x 21.7; numbered consecutively by draft but not continuously; 3, 84, 97; good, burned, punched for two-ring binder.

Contents: Complete; infrequently revised in ink, pencil; nine drafts of ms.: no. 1 dated 25 September 1932; no. 2 subtitled: Preliminary Outline by Edgar Selwyn and Upton Sinclair; No. 3 dated 9 September 1932; no. 4 dated 19 September 1932; no. 6 dated 25 September 1932; no. 7 titled: The Gold-Spangled Banner (or the Money-King); page one is a receipt for $2,500 dated 31 August 1932 from Metro-Goldwyn-Mayer Corporation; ms. arranged in two separate folders.

Dates: Comp. ca. August–September 1932. Unpublished.

193. Citation: GOOD BYE, NIPPON; a. ms.; pencil; InU.

Title: Good Bye, Nippon.

Key Words: We love the dainty lady . . . us who have not understood.

Collation: 1; white watermarked; 20.4 x 12.7; 1; 1; good.

Contents: Complete; infrequently revised in pencil.

Dates: Comp. ca. 1951. Pub. ?

194a. Citation: THE GOOSE-STEP; a. ms.; black, green ink, pencil; InU.

Title: [none]

Key Words: Catholic schools: what [?] Joel H. . . . etc. tyranny of its propaganda

Collation: 310; five notebooks, loose sheets; 11.3 x 10.5 to 16.3 x 10.4; unnumbered; all but the last notebook bear extensive notes on the verso; poor.

Contents: Incomplete; infrequently revised in black, blue ink, pencil; notebooks in envelope labeled: Notes for | *The Goosestep* | and | *The Gosling;* they contain notes pertaining to those two books; they are marked A1 to E; in box labeled: Notes.

Dates: Pub. 1922–23 (*Appeal to Reason*), February 1923 (as book).

194b. Citation: The GOOSE-STEP; t. ms.; blue, black ribbon; InU.

Title: [none]

Key Words: Sub-committees continued | *Report on the* . . . to the Academy at Worcester.

Collation: 3; white watermarked, white; 27.9 x 21.5, 27.9 x 21.7; unnumbered; none; good.

Contents: Incomplete; infrequently revised in black ink; folder labeled: Misc. notes; notes on Sub-committee on Academic Freedom and Academic Tenure.

Dates: Pub. 1922–23 (*Appeal to Reason*), February 1923 (as book).

194c. Citation: THE GOOSE-STEP; t. ms., a. ms., print; black, purple ribbon, black, blue, purple carbon, pencil, black, blue ink, print; InU.

Title: [none]

Key Words: I have amused myself by . . . Z mem. board came Fargo,

Collation: 295; misc. sheets; 5.5 x 21.6 to 28.1 x 21.6; unnumbered; 2, 5, 44, 55, 64, 68, 69, 101, 137, 138, 228; poor.

Contents: Incomplete; moderately revised in pencil, blue, black ink, not all in Sinclair's hand; folder labeled: Goose-step? [question mark circled] | Misc. notes.

Dates: Pub. 1922–23 (*Appeal to Reason*), February 1923 (as book).

194d. Citation: THE GOOSE-STEP; t. ms.; carbon; InU.

Title: PROPERTY OF COLUMBIA UNIVERSITY.

Key Words: (From the Report of the . . . owned bonds or shares therein.

Collation: 66; brown; white; 27.9 x 21.5, 28 x 21.6; [1]–17, 17a, 18–22, [1], 24, 1–41; none; poor, crumbling.

Contents: Incomplete; infrequently revised in blue ink; folder contains extensive notes on Columbia University, especially on its financial situation, and is labeled: Goose step [?] notes.

Dates: Pub. 1922–23 (*Appeal to Reason*), February 1923 (as book).

194e. Citation: THE GOOSE-STEP; t. ms.; ribbon, carbon; InU.

Title: "Chapter VI. | *The Socialist Cases* | in the East.

Key Words: The six cases described in . . . for good in the university."

Collation: 115; brown, white; 28.3 x 21.3, 28 x 21.6; consecutively numbered by chapters but not continuously; none; poor, crumbling.

Contents: Incomplete; infrequently revised in blue ink; these notes are concerned with professors fired for various "un-American" causes, i.e., pacifists, socialists; bundles are labeled chapters III–VI; folder labeled: Do not find these chapters in either book, was this published?

Dates: Pub. 1922–23 (*Appeal to Reason*), February 1923 (as book).

194f. Citation: THE GOOSE-STEP; t. ms., a. ms.; ribbon, carbon, pencil; InU.

Title: [none]

Key Words: We have investigated the governing . . . its author will be content.

Collation: 1008; white, misc. sheets; 21.4 x 14 to 27.9 x 21.4; randomly numbered; 17, 48, 49, 50, 51, 52, 53, 54, 55, 56, 57, 60, 61, 65, 66, 67, 76, 78, 84, 85, 90, 98, 102, 105, 106, 109, 117, 120, 121, 123, 145, 158, 166, 168, 170, 174, 184, 229, 241, 247, 249, 253, 258, 267, 279, 292, 295, 297, 300, 304, 310, 323, 326, 332, 336, 338, 340, 342, 343, 344, 348, 407, 413, 428, 429, 450, 455, 456, 470, 476, 478, 561, 569, 594, 604, 608, 616, 619, 675, 678, 679, 681, 684, 697, 717, 726, 728, 736, 740, 764, 784, 826, 827, 832, 885, 889, 900, 910, 995; fair.

Contents: Incomplete; frequently revised in regular, orange pencil, blue black ink, not all in Sinclair's hand; boxes are labeled: Draft Box I; Draft Box II; it appears to be an early draft; chapter LXXXIII is missing; ms. may be a composite of several drafts.

Dates: Pub. 1922–23 (*Appeal to Reason*), February 1923 (as book).

194g. Citation: THE GOOSE-STEP; t. ms., a. ms., print; ribbon, carbon, print; InU.

Title: THE GOOSE-STEP | A Study of American Education

Key Words: Six hundred thousand young people . . . Schools, and entitled "The Goslings."

Collation: 612; brown, white watermarked; 27.9 x 21.3, 27.8 x 21.6; continuously numbered with variations; none; fair, spindled.

Contents: Complete; frequently revised in pencil, a number of pencil notations by the printer; folder labeled: Printer's draft; a portion of the ms. is made up of tear sheets.

Dates: Pub. 1922–23 (*Appeal to Reason*), February 1923 (as book).

194h. Citation: THE GOOSE-STEP; t. ms., a. ms.; black, blue ribbon, carbon, pencil; InU.

Title: [none]

Key Words: Get Veblen, Dewey or James . . . little editor at the Kremlin.

Collation: 61; white, brown; 19.1 x 21.6 to 28 x 21.6; randomly numbered; 3, 24, 25; fair.

Contents: Incomplete; infrequently revised in pencil, black ink; folder labeled: Advertising material | For publication in Goose-step; it contains three groupings: COMMENTS ON CHAPTERS XXXI TO CLOSE OF BOOK, UPTON SINCLAIR | Biographical and Critical Material, and A PROPHET WITHOUT HONOR IN HIS OWN COUNTRY.

Dates: Pub. 1922–23 (*Appeal to Reason*), February 1923 (as book).

195a. Citation: THE GOSLINGS; t. ms.; ribbon; InU.

Title: [none]

Key Words: Wash. bd. controlled by Dist. . . . the gospel of J. C."

Collation: 76; brown, white; 2.1 x 21.8 to 27.8 x 21.6; randomly numbered; none; poor.

Contents: Incomplete; frequently revised in pencil; folder labeled: Misc. notes.

Dates: Pub. ca. 15 February 1924.

195b. Citation: THE GOSLINGS; t. ms.; ribbon, black, purple carbon; InU.

Title: [none]

Key Words: We let them walk around . . . reactionary state you will say.

Collation: 122; brown, white; 27.9 x 21.6, 27.8 x 21.5; randomly numbered; none, fair.

Contents: Incomplete: infrequently revised in regular, blue pencil, black ink; folder contains misc. material that has been tagged and labeled; folder labeled: Goslings | misc various pieces, odd chapters, etc.

Dates: Pub. ca. 15 February 1924.

195c. Citation: THE GOSLINGS; t. ms., a. ms., print; ribbon, black, purple carbon, blue ink, print; InU.

Title: [none]

Key Words: Naturally, we have to begin . . . Spokane Workers' College is dead!

Collation: 155; white, brown; 13.7 x 11 to 28.1 x 21.7; randomly numbered; 59, 60, 63, 64, 103, 109, 110; fair.

Contents: Incomplete; infrequently revised in black ink, pencil; ms. is a collection of misc. notes and chapters, some tagged and labeled and some not.

Dates: Pub. ca. 15 February 1924.

195d. Citation: THE GOSLINGS; t. ms.; ribbon; InU.

Title: THE GOSLINGS | A Study of the American Schools.

Key Words: Life has given you one . . . have or world to gain."

Collation: 683; white, brown; 28.1 x 21.6, 27.9 x 21.5; continuously numbered with variations; none; fair, spindled.

Contents: Complete; moderately revised in pencil; ms. bears printer's notations in regular, red pencil on the verso as well as recto sides of the sheets; box labeled: Printer's copy.

Dates: Pub. ca. 15 February 1924.

195e. Citation: THE GOSLINGS; a. ms.; ink; InU.

Title: [none]

Key Words: [none]

Collation: 1; white watermarked; 20.2 x 17.4; unnumbered; none; good.

Contents: This is the original "Goslings" cover drawing by Art Young.

Dates: Pub. ca. 15 February 1924.

196. Citation: GRAFT IN AMERICA; t. ms.; carbon; InU.

Title: GRAFT IN AMERICA

Key Words: I take it for granted . . . big business and high finance.

Collation: 10; white; 28 x 21.7; [1] 2–5, [1] 2–5; none; good.

Contents: Complete; infrequently revised in pencil, not in Sinclair's hand; three carbons.

Dates: Comp. ca. 1930. Pub. ?

197a. Citation: THE GRAND DUKE LECTURES; t. ms.; ribbon; InU.

Title: THE GRAND DUKE LECTURES | A Comedy in Three Acts

Key Words: Characters in order of appearance . . . the end of the rainbow!

Collation: 122; white; 28 x 21.6; [2] 1–29, 31–121; none; good, punched for two-ring binder.

Contents: Complete; moderately revised in pencil; Harry Clay Blaney, Play Broker, Taft Building, Hollywood, Calif. stamped in red at bottom of page one and page 57 at top.

Dates: Comp. ca. 1935? Unpublished.

197b. Citation: THE GRAND DUKE LECTURES; t. ms., a. ms.; ribbon, pencil; InU.

Title: THE GRAND DUKE LECTURES | A Comedy in Three Acts

Key Words: The drawing-room of the Pott . . . his transports—The Curtain Falls.

Collation: 56; white, green; 27.9 x 21.6; [1] 1a, 2–15, 1–40; 1, 11, 39, 42; good.

Contents: Complete Act I; frequently revised in pencil; in folder labeled: Act I, Earlier Draft.

Dates: Comp. ca. 1935? Unpublished.

197c. Citation: THE GRAND DUKE LECTURES; t. ms., a. ms.; carbon, pencil; InU.

Title: THE GRAND DUKE LECTURES | A Comedy in Three Acts

Key Words: The drawing-room of the Pott . . . his transports—The Curtain Falls.

Collation: 47; white, green; 19.1 x 16 to 28 x 21.7; [1] 1a, 1b, 2, 3a, 3–17, 22–30, 34, 39–40, 40a, 41, 41a, 41b, 42–49, 49a, 51–52, 52; 5, 10, 23, 24, 29, 35, 36, 46; fair, punched for a two-ring binder.

Contents: Complete[?]; moderately revised in pencil, not all in Sinclair's hand; in folder labeled: Act I, Later Draft.

Dates: Comp. ca. 1935? Unpublished.

197d. Citation: THE GRAND DUKE LECTURES; t. ms., a. ms.; carbon, pencil; InU.

Title: [none]

Key Words: Jim: Not yet. | Mrs. Prettyman: . . . land of my boyhood it

Collation: 24; white, green; 28.1 x 21.7, 27.9 x 21.5; randomly numbered; none; good, punched for a two-ring binder.

Contents: Incomplete; moderately revised in pencil, not in Sinclair's hand; in folder labeled: Act I another draft p. 12, 14, 16 of Scene I & Scene II & III.

Dates: Comp. ca. 1935? Unpublished.

197e. Citation: THE GRAND DUKE LECTURES; t. ms., a. ms.; ribbon, pencil; InU.

Title: ACT II

Key Words: A cell of the Pott . . . Adjourn! Out with him! CURTAIN

Collation: 40; green; 27.9 x 21.6; numbered consecutively by scene but not continuously; none; good.

Contents: Complete [?]; frequently revised in pencil; in folder labeled: Act II, Draft of Scences I, II, III.

Dates: Comp. ca. 1935? Unpublished.

197f. Citation: THE GRAND DUKE LECTURES; t. ms.; carbon; InU.

Title: Scene II

Key Words: The Pott reception hall, late . . . from me? (takes her hand).

Collation: 16; white; 28.1 x 21.7; numbered consecutively by scene but not continuously; 1, 2; good, punched for a two-ring binder.

Contents: Incomplete; frequently revised in pencil, not all in Sinclair's hand; in folder labeled: Act II; 2 drafts of Scene II.

Dates: Comp. ca. 1935? Unpublished.

197g. Citation: THE GRAND DUKE LECTURES; t. ms.;
ribbon, carbon; InU.

Title: [none]

Key Words: then it was the chief, . . . said that Zash
is crazy!

Collation: 22; white, green; 28 x 21.7, 27.9 x 21.6;
randomly numbered; 7, 8, 11, 13; good, punched for a
two-ring binder.

Contents: Incomplete; frequently revised in pencil, not
all in Sinclair's hand; in folder labeled: Act II Misc.
pages | where do these go?

Dates: Comp. ca. 1935? Unpublished.

197h. Citation: THE GRAND DUKE LECTURES; t. ms.,
a. ms.; ribbon, pencil; InU.

Title: Scene III

Key Words: The lecture platform, Pottopolis Opera
. . . end of the rainbow! CURTAIN

Collation: 43; misc. sheets; 8.5 x 19.1 to 28 x 21.7;
randomly numbered; 3, 4, 5, 8, 11, 15, 19, 23, 31; fair,
punched for a two-ring binder.

Contents: Incomplete; frenquently revised in pencil,
not all in Sinclair's hand; in folder labeled: Act II | Draft
of Scene III.

Dates: Comp. ca. 1935? Unpublished.

197i. Citation: THE GRAND DUKE LECTURES; t. ms.;
ribbon; InU.

Title: Act III

Key Words: Scene: The Pott drawing-room, immediately
. . . end of the rainbow! | CURTAIN

Collation: 20; green; 27.9 x 21.6; 1–20; none; good.

Contents: Complete; moderately revised in pencil; in folder labeled: Act III.

Dates: Comp. ca. 1935? Unpublished.

198. Citation: GRAPES OF WRATH [A REVIEW]; t. ms.; ribbon; InU.

Title: GRAPES OF WRATH | By John Steinbeck | Reviewed by Upton Sinclair

Key Words: For nearly forty years it . . . has any use for it.

Collation: 4; white watermarked; 28.1 x 21.6; [1] 2–4; none; good.

Contents: Complete; moderately revised in pencil.

Dates: Pub. *Common Sense,* May 1939.

199. Citation: A GREAT AMERICAN PLAY; t. ms.; carbon; InU.

Title: A GREAT AMERICAN PLAY

Key Words: The editor of the Appeal . . . have it ready to hand.

Collation: 2; brown; 27.9 x 21.5; [1] 2; none; good.

Contents: Complete; unrevised; someone has written on page 1 in pencil: Mailed to U. S. 4/14/22; folder labeled: "Appeal to Reason.

Dates: Pub. *Appeal to Reason,* 8 July 1922.

200. Citation: THE GREAT AMERICAN PLAY; t. ms.; carbon; InU.

Title: THE GREAT AMERICAN PLAY. A COMEDY IN FOUR ACTS

Key Words: Scene: The stage is divided . . . The Great American Play! CURTAIN

Collation: 107; white watermarked; 27.8 x 21.4; numbered consecutively by acts but not continuously; none; good.

Contents: Complete; infrequently revised in pencil; bound with two brass studs.

Dates: Comp. ca. 1915. Unpublished.

201a. Citation: GREETINGS FROM UPTON SINCLAIR; a. ms.; pencil; InU.

Title: Greetings from Upton Sinclair

Key Words: In 1913 a young woman . . . But she learned that there

Collation: 1; white; 21.6 x 17.1; unnumbered; 1; fair.

Contents: Complete; infrequently revised in pencil; two different mss. of the same title paper-clipped together.

Dates: Pub. *EPIC News*, 30 August 1937.

201b. Citation: GREETINGS FROM UPTON SINCLAIR; t. ms.; carbon; InU.

Title: GREETINGS FROM UPTON SINCLAIR

Key Words: I am very happy to . . . without exploitation and clear oppression.

Collation: 1; blue; 27.8 x 21.6; unnumbered; none; fair.

Contents: Complete; unrevised, with "TRUD" penciled in blue in one upper right corner; ms. is paper-clipped to another but different "Greetings from Upton Sinclair."

Dates: Pub. *New Leader*, 7 April 1958.

202. Citation: GREETINGS TO THE "NEW MASSES."; t. ms.; carbon; InU.

Title: GREETINGS TO THE "NEW MASSES."

Key Words: Of course I am glad . . . legislative enactments or constitutional amendments.

Collation: 4; white watermarked, blue; 27.8 x 21.6, 28 x 21.6; [1] 2, [1] 2; none; fair.

Contents: Complete; infrequently revised in pencil, not in Sinclair's hand.

Dates: Comp. 1936. Pub. ?

203a. Citation: GREETINGS TO U.S.S.R.; t. ms.; carbon; InU.

Title: [GREETINGS TO U.S.S.R. (c.o. pencil)]

Key Words: The twentieth anniversary of the . . . and for all future time.

Collation: 3; blue; 27.9 x 21.5; [1] 2–3; none; good.

Contents: Complete; infrequently revised in pencil; not in Sinclair's hand.

Dates: Pub. *EPIC News*, 1 November 1937.

203b. Citation: GREETINGS TO U.S.S.R.; t. ms.; carbon; InU.

Title: GREETINGS TO U.S.S.R.

Key Words: The twentieth anniversary of the . . . and for all future time.

Collation: 4; blue; 27.8 x 21.5; [1] 2–4; none; good.

Contents: Complete, unrevised.

Dates: Pub. *EPIC News*, 1 November 1937.

204. Citation: HAM AND EGGS FOR CALIFORNIA; t. ms.; carbon; InU.

Title: HAM AND EGGS FOR CALIFORNIA

Key Words: My comments in "The Progressive" . . . on to some other person.

Collation: 6; white watermarked, green; 28 x 21.6; [1] 2–3, [1] 2–3; good.

Contents: Complete; moderately revised in pencil, not all in Sinclair's hand.

Dates: Comp. 29 August 1938. Pub. ?

205. Citation: HAM AND EGGS PLOWED UNDER; t. ms., a. ms.; ribbon, carbon, pencil; InU.

Title [NO HAM AND EGGS THIS MEAL! (c.o.)] [trip (c.o.)] HAM & EGGS PLOWED UNDER [(w.i. pencil)]

Key Words: I am told that a . . . one, I'm happy to say!

Collation: 7; green, white watermarked; 27.9 x 21.5, 28 x 21.6; [1] 2, a, b, [1] 2–3; 3, 4; good.

Contents: Complete; moderately revised in pencil; original and revised carbon.

Dates: Comp. ca. 1938. Pub. ?

206. Citation: HARD TIMES; t. ms.; carbon; InU.

Title: HARD TIMES

Key Words: As you may know, I . . . and beautiful country after all!

Collation: 4; brown; 27.8 x 21.6; [1] 2–4; none; good.

Contents: Complete; infrequently revised in pencil; note in pencil on page one: Mailed 4-10-22.

Dates: Pub. *Appeal to Reason*, 3 June 1922.

207. Citation: THE HEALTH HUNTERS; t. ms.; ribbon; InU.

Title: THE HEALTH HUNTERS | A Farce Comedy
in Four Acts

Key Words: The first act opens in . . . beefsteak dinner
without further ado.

Collation: 13; white watermarked; 19.3 x 21.5 to 27.9 x
21.6; [1] 2–9, 9a, 10–12; none; good.

Contents: Incomplete; infrequently revised in faded ink,
pencil; insert 7a is apparently missing.

Dates: Comp. ca. 1910. Pub. ?

208a. Citation: THE HEALTH OF LITTLE ALGERNON;
t. ms.; blue carbon; InU.

Title: [none]

Key Words: It was with relief and . . . careful investigation into the causes

Collation: 39; white watermarked; 28 x 20.3; consecutively numbered by chapter but not continuously; none;
fair.

Contents: Incomplete; unrevised.

Dates: Pub. *Physical Culture*, December 1911, January–
June 1912.

208b. Citation: THE HEALTH OF LITTLE ALGERNON;
t. ms.; blue carbon; InU.

Title: [none]

Key Words: the blue line of the . . . harbor's entrance
he could see

Collation: 27; white watermarked; 25.8 x 20.2 to 27.4 x
20.3; consecutively numbered by chapter but not continuously; none; fair.

Contents: Incomplete; unrevised.

Dates: Pub. *Physical Culture*, December 1911, January–
June 1912.

209. Citation: HELL; t. ms., a. ms.; carbon, pencil; InU.

Title: HELL | A Verse Drama and Photoplay

Key Words: Act I: The scene represents . . . Real
Devil! He's Stupidity! | (Curtain)

Collation: 252; white red-lined notebook, misc. sheets;
11.6 x 12 to 22.1 x 12, 27.9 x 21.3; unnumbered or
randomly numbered; 2, 7, 17, 13, 30, 31, 42, 45, 61,
66, 74, 78, 80, 82, 111, 129, 133, 134, 136, 145, 149,
154, 169, 187, 188, 189, 190, 191, 201, 223, 228, 239;
fair.

Contents: Complete; moderately revised in pencil; four
notebooks with one act each; some misc. typed pages.

Dates: Pub. 7 May 1923.

210. Citation: HELP WANTED; t. ms.; carbon; InU.

Title: HELP WANTED

Key Words: The editor and the business . . . how
much are you sorry?

Collation: 5; blue watermarked; 28 x 21.6; [1] 2–5;
none; good.

Contents: Complete; unrevised.

Dates: Comp. ca. 1935–36. Pub. ?

211a. Citation: HERE'S YOUR NEW BABY!; a. ms.; pencil;
InU.

Title: HERE'S YOUR NEW PAPER!

Key Words: The reason for this paper . . . appeals:
¶ "It's up to you!"

Collation: 9; blue watermarked; 27.9 x 21.6; [1] 2–9; 3;
good.

Contents: Complete; moderately revised in pencil.

Dates: Pub. *Upton Sinclair's EPIC News*, 3 June 1935.

211b.Citation: HERE'S YOUR NEW BABY!; t. ms.; ribbon; InU.

Title: HERE'S YOUR NEW [PAPER! (c.o.)] Baby! [(w.i.)]

Key Words: The reason for this issue . . . appeals | "It's up to you!"

Collation: 5; white; 27.9 x 21.5; [1] 2–5; 5; good.

Contents: Complete; moderately revised in pencil.

Dates: Pub. *Upton Sinclair's EPIC News*, 3 June 1935.

211c.Citation: HERE'S YOUR NEW BABY!; t. ms.; carbon; InU.

Title: HERE'S YOUR NEW PAPER!

Key Words: The reason for this paper . . . appeals: "It's up to you!"

Collation: 5; white; 27.9 x 21.5; [1] 2–5; none; good.

Contents: Complete; unrevised.

Dates: Pub. *Upton Sinclair's EPIC News*, 3 June 1935.

212. Citation: HIGH STAKES; t. ms.; ribbon, carbon; InU.

Title: ["The Wheel of Chance" (c.o.)] High Stakes [(w.i. pencil)]

Key Words: Scene of the story: New . . . to produce in the country.

Collation: 11; white watermarked; 28 x 21.8; [1] 2–5, [1] 2–6; none; good.

Contents: Complete; infrequently revised in pencil; the original is revised; the carbon is a copy of the revised text.

Dates: Comp. ca. 1933. Pub. ?

213. Citation: HIRED LIAR!; t. ms.; carbon; InU.

Title: HIRED LIARS! ["s" (c.o.), exclamation point (w.i.)]

Key Words: I can recall the time, . . . shall lift a leg thereto."

Collation: 12; white watermarked, blue watermarked; 28.1 x 21.6, 27.8 x 21.6; [1] 2–6, [1] 2–6; none; good.

Contents: Complete; infrequently revised in pencil, not in Sinclair's hand.

Dates: Comp. ca. 1934–35. Pub. ?

214a. Citation: HIS FIVE WIVES; t. ms.; carbon; InU.

Title: His Second Wife

Key Words: Mary Armstrong was in the . . . about other aspects of marriage.

Collation: 1; white; 27.9 x 21.5; unnumbered; none; good.

Contents: Complete; unrevised.

Dates: Pub. *Physical Culture*, December 1915; January–May, 1916.

214b. Citation: HIS FIVE WIVES; t. ms.; carbon; InU.

Title: His Third Wife

Key Words: Ralph Armstrong had been to . . . not go to the West.

Collation: 11; white; 27.8 x 21.5; [1] 2–11; none; good.

Contents: Complete; infrequently revised in faded ink.
Dates: Pub. *Physical Culture*, December 1915, January–
May 1916.

215. Citation: HISTORY REPEATS ITSELF; t. ms.; ribbon, carbon; InU.
Title: HISTORY REPEATS ITSELF
Key Words: At least, it does under . . . course but you the people.
Collation: 6; white; 27.9 x 21.6; [1] 2–6; none; good.
Contents: Complete; infrequently revised in pencil.
Dates: Pub. *EPIC News*, 11 April 1938.

216. Citation: HOOKED BY A FISH: AND HOW IT FEELS; t. ms.; ribbon; InU.
Title: HOOKED BY A FISH: AND HOW IT FEELS
Key Words: I have a rule, which . . . the course of its work!
Collation: 11; white; 28 x 21.7; [1] 2–7, 8–9, 10–12; none; fair.
Contents: Complete; infrequently revised in pencil.
Dates: Comp. ca. 1930. Pub. ?

217. Citation: HOPES FOR THE OLD PEOPLE; t. ms.; carbon; InU.
Title: HOPES FOR THE OLD PEOPLE
Key Words: Some of you may recall . . . to carry a national election!
Collation: 5; blue watermarked; 28 x 21.6; [1] 2–5; none; good.
Contents: Complete; unrevised.
Dates: Comp. ca. 1935. Pub. ?

218. Citation: HOW I REFORMED THREE GREAT AMERICAN FAMILIES; xerox; print; InU.

Title: HOW I REFORMED THREE GREAT AMERICAN FAMILIES

Key Words: I was asked to tell . . . whether I'm right or not.

Collation: 12; white; 27.9 x 21.6; [1] 2–12; none; good.

Contents: Complete; unrevised.

Dates: Comp. ca. 1961. Recorded several times in 1960s; tapes in Lilly Library.

219. Citation: HOW TO KILL THE TIGER?; t. ms.; carbon; InU.

Title: HOW TO KILL THE TIGER?

Key Words: I don't know who won . . . I can get right now.

Collation: 4; white; 27.8 x 21.5; [1] 2–4; none; good, EPIC letterhead verso.

Contents: Complete; infrequently revised in pencil; signed by Sinclair.

Dates: Pub. *EPIC News*, 27 April 1936.

220. Citation: I AM ASKED TO SAY . . . ; a. ms.; carbon; InU.

Title: [none]

Key Words: I am asked to say . . . true social progress more difficult.

Collation: 1; white; 27.9 x 21.6; unnumbered; none; good.

Contents: Complete; unrevised.

Dates: Comp. ca. 1930s? Pub. ?

221a.Citation: I, CANDIDATE FOR GOVERNOR AND HOW I GOT LICKED; t. ms.; carbon; InU.

Title: I, CANDIDATE FOR GOVERNOR | AND HOW I GOT LICKED

Key Words: This is the story of . . . glad to hear from him!

Collation: 32; white; 28 x 21.7; consecutively numbered but not continuously; none; good.

Contents: Incomplete; infrequently revised in pencil.

Dates: Pub. ca. November 1934.

221b.Citation: I, CANDIDATE FOR GOVERNOR AND HOW I GOT LICKED; t. ms., print; ribbon, black, red carbon, print; InU.

Title: [none]

Key Words: Soon after the EPIC movement . . . and follow along behind us.

Collation: 165; misc. sheets; 27.9 x 21.6 to 28 x 21.6; consecutively numbered by installments but not continuously; 130, 140, 157, 158; fair.

Contents: Incomplete; frequently revised in pencil; Chaps. XIV–XLIII.

Dates: Pub. ca. November 1934.

221c.Citation: I, CANDIDATE FOR GOVERNOR, AND HOW I GOT LICKED; t. ms.; carbon; InU.

Title: UPTON SINCLAIR'S STORY | I, Candidate for Governor, | And How I Got Licked.

Key Words: I am offering the daily . . . End Poverty in California campaign.

Collation: 2; blue watermarked; 27.9 x 21.6; [1] 2; none; good.

Contents: Incomplete; unrevised.

Dates: Pub. ca. November 1934.

222. Citation: IF DEFEATED. t. ms.; carbon; InU.

Title: IF DEFEATED

Key Words: Mr. Merriman, I congratulate you . . . the United States of America.

Collation: 1; white watermarked; 27.8 x 20.2; unnumbered; good.

Contents: Complete; unrevised; paper-clipped to note "If Elected."

Dates: Comp. November 1934. Pub. ?

223. Citation: IF ELECTED; t. ms.; carbon; InU.

Title: IF ELECTED

Key Words: In this victory, let us . . . must obtain and sign—immediately.

Collation: 1; white watermarked; 27.8 x 20.1; unnumbered; none; good.

Contents: Complete; unrevised; paper-clipped to note "If Defeated."

Dates: Comp. November 1934. Pub. ?

224. Citation: IF I LOSE; t. ms.; carbon; InU.

Title: IF I LOSE

Key Words: Our EPIC (End Poverty in . . . of a small privileged class.

Collation: 8; white watermarked; 27.9 x 21.5; [1] 2-4, [1] 2-4; none; good.

Contents: Complete; infrequently revised in pencil.

Dates: Comp. ca. 21 October 1934. Pub. ?

225. Citation: IF I WERE PRESIDENT; t. ms.; carbon; InU.

Title: IF I WERE PRESIDENT.

Key Words: Insofar as the average American . . . by any nation or group.

Collation: 10; white; 28 x 21.6; [1] 2–10; none; good.

Contents: Complete; infrequently revised in pencil, not in Sinclair's hand.

Dates: Comp. ca. 1925. Pub. ?

226. Citation: IF I WIN; t. ms.; carbon; InU.

Title: IF I WIN

Key Words: The victory at the polls . . . shall not perish from California.

Collation: 8; white watermarked; 28 x 21.6; [1] 2–4, [1] 2–4; none; good.

Contents: Complete; infrequently revised in pencil, not all in Sinclair's hand; two carbons; one is revised.

Dates: Comp. ca. 21 October 1934. Pub. ?

227. Citation: I, GOVERNOR OF CALIFORNIA AND HOW I ENDED POVERTY; t. ms., a. ms.; ribbon, carbon, pencil; InU.

Title: I, [THE (c.o.)] GOVERNOR OF CALI-FORNIA AND HOW I ENDED POVERTY. A TRUE STORY OF THE FUTURE [(w.i. pencil)]

Key Words: The beginning of this story . . . are now about to read.

Collation: 179; misc. sheets; 19 x 21.6 to 28 x 21.6; consecutively numbered but not continuously; 1, 3, 7, 8, 9, 10, 14, 17, 19, 28, 29, 53, 67; fair.

Contents: Complete; moderately revised in pencil, not all in Sinclair's hand.

Dates: Pub. 26 December 1933–2 January 1934 (*EPIC News*), ca. December 1933 (as book).

228a. Citation: I HAVE BEEN ASKED . . . ; t. ms.; carbon; InU.

Title: [none]

Key Words: I have been asked by . . . the Atlantic Pact. Upton Sinclair.

Collation: 2; white; 28 x 21.5; [1], 3; none; fair.

Contents: Incomplete; unrevised; signed in blue ink.

Dates: Comp. ca. 1952. Pub. ?

228b. Citation: I HAVE BEEN ASKED . . . ; t. ms.; black, blue carbon; InU.

Title: [none]

Key Words: I have been asked by . . . world in the Atlantic Pact.

Collation: 3; white; 6.6 x 21.7 to 27.8 x 21.5; [1], [1] 2; none; fair.

Contents: Complete; infrequently revised in pencil, blue ink; Sinclair signed on sheet 2 in blue ink.

Dates: Comp. ca. 1952. Pub. ?

229. Citation: IKE; a. ms.; pencil; InU.

Title: Ike

Key Words: It hurts a little to . . . the fire into the furnace.

Collation: 3; yellow; 27.1 x 21.6; [1] 2–3; none; good.

Contents: Complete; infrequently revised in blue ink.

Dates: Comp. ca. 1955. Pub. ?

230. Citation: IKE SPLITS HIS PARTY!; t. ms.; carbon; InU.

Title: IKE SPLITS HIS PARTY!

Key Words: The Texas oil millionaires have . . . did in 1952, and more.

Collation: 3; white; 27.9 x 21.6; [1] 2–3; none; good.

Contents: Complete; unrevised; Harold Lord Varney's article "Eisenhower at Midway" from the *American Mercury* paper-clipped to it.

Dates: Comp. 14 May 1955. Pub. ?

231a. Citation: I KNEW LINCOLN STEFFENS; t. ms.; ribbon; InU.

Title: I KNEW LINCOLN STEFFENS

Key Words: I knew him well. I . . . and it takes courage, too!

Collation: 5; white; 27.9 x 21.5; [1] 2–5; 3; good.

Contents: Complete; frequently revised in blue ink, pencil.

Dates: Comp. ca. 1937. Pub. ?

231b. Citation: I KNEW LINCOLN STEFFENS; t. ms.; carbon; InU.

Title: I KNEW LINCOLN STEFFENS

Key Words: I knew him well. I . . . And it takes courage, too!

Collation: 5; white watermarked; 27.9 x 21.7; [1] 2–5; none; good.

Contents: Complete; unrevised.

Dates: Comp. ca. 1937. Pub. ?

232. Citation: IMMEDIATE EPIC; t. ms., a. ms.; ribbon, carbon, pencil; InU.

Title: Immediate EPIC | The Final Statement of the Plan

Key Words: The book, "I Governor of . . . a voice in their management.

Collation: 146; misc. sheets; 7.5 x 9.9 to 28.1 x 21.7; randomly numbered or consecutively by grouping but not continuously; 7, 25, 37, 56, 57; fair.

Contents: Complete [?]; moderately revised in red, regular pencil, black ink, not all in Sinclair's hand; the ms. is a collection of early drafts and later revisions.

Dates: Pub. ca. August 1934.

233. Citation: IMPROVING CALIFORNIA; t. ms.; carbon; InU.

Title: *IMPROVING CALIFORNIA*

Key Words: We are getting ready for . . . discussion and not of violence.

Collation: 7; white; 28 x 21.6; [1] 2–7; none; good.

Contents: Complete, unrevised.

Dates: Comp. ca. 1963. Pub. ?

234. Citation: IN THE AUGUST 27TH ISSUE; t. ms.; ribbon; InU.

Title: [none]

Key Words: In the August 27th issue . . . slate chosen by the politicians.

Collation: 4; white watermarked; 27.9 x 21.6; 1–4; 2, 3; fair.

Contents: Complete; frequently revised in pencil.

Dates: Comp. ca. 1936. Pub. ?

235. Citation: INCOME; t. ms.; carbon; InU.

Title: INCOME A Review

Key Words: I remember that when I . . . held by the medieval landlord."

Collation: 10; white; 27.9 x 21.5; [1] 2–5, [1] 2–5; none; fair.

Contents: Complete; unrevised.

Dates: Comp. 1915–20? Pub. ?

236. Citation: IN DEFENSE OF ALBERT ABRAMS; t. ms.; carbon; InU.

Title: IN DEFENSE OF ALBERT ABRAMS.

Key Words: In the "Survey" for January . . . the expenses of the investigation.

Collation: 18; white; 28 x 21.6; [1] 2–5, 7–10, [1] 2–5, 7–10; none; good.

Contents: Complete; infrequently revised in pencil, not all in Sinclair's hand.

Dates: Pub. *Survey*, 15 March 1923.

See also: THE ABRAMS DISCOVERY and THE REACTIONS OF ABRAMS.

237. Citation: THE INDIGNANT SUBSCRIBER; t. ms.; ribbon; InU.

Title: THE INDIGNANT SUBSCRIBER

Key Words: (This was one of three . . . off easily). Ha! Ha! Ha!

Collation: 15; white; 27.9 x 21.6; 3, 2–15; none; fair, burned.

Contents: Complete; infrequently revised in blue ink, pencil.

Dates: Pub. *Socialist Review*, January 1910.

238. Citation: THE INDIVIDUAL IN SOCIETY; t. ms.; carbon; InU.

Title: THE INDIVIDUAL IN SOCIETY

Key Words: Some time ago in the . . . of view effective upon me.

Collation: 2; brown; 27.9 x 21.5; [1] 2; none; good.

Contents: Complete; unrevised; someone has written "Mailed 4/18/22" on page 1 in pencil; folder labeled: "Appeal to Reason."

Dates: Pub. *Appeal to Reason*, 24 June 1922.

239. Citation: IN THE ENEMY'S CAMP; t. ms.; carbon; InU.

Title: IN THE ENEMY'S CAMP

Key Words: I read a number of . . . get into the debate free!

Collation: 6; blue watermarked; 28 x 21.7; [1] 2–6; none; good.

Contents: Complete; infrequently revised in pencil.

Dates: Pub. *Upton Sinclair's National EPIC News*, 24 June 1935.

240. Citation: [IN HIS WISCONSIN ADDRESS . . .]; t. ms.; carbon; InU.

Title: [none]

Key Words: In his Wisconsin address a . . . a menace to anybody else.

Collation: 10; white watermarked, blue watermarked; 28 x 21.6, 28.1 x 21.6; [1] 2–5, [1] 2–5; none; good.

Contents: Complete; infrequently revised in pencil; heading on page one: Press rate collect. Hugh Bailie,

General Manager, United Press, New York, N.Y., August 30, 1934.

Dates: Pub. ?

241. Citation: INTERVIEW WITH LUDWIG RENN; t. ms.; carbon; InU.

Title: INTERVIEW WITH LUDWIG RENN

Key Words: One of the oldest stories . . . into the midnight of barbarism.

Collation: 4; blue, white watermarked; 27.8 x 21.5, 27.9 x 21.6; [1] 2, [1] 2; none; good.

Contents: Complete; infrequently revised in pencil.

Dates: Comp. ca. 1936. Pub. ?

242. Citation: INTRODUCING A UNIVERSITY PRESI-DENT; t. ms.; carbon; InU.

Title: INTRODUCING A UNIVERSITY PRESI-DENT

Key Words: From the University of Minnesota . . . enough to hold the crowd!

Collation: 10; white; 28 x 21.6; 1–10; none; good.

Contents: Complete; unrevised.

Dates: Comp. ca. 29 April 1921. Pub. ?

243a. Citation: INTRODUCTION TO INSIDE HITLER; t. ms.; carbon; InU.

Title: INTRODUCTION TO "Inside Hitler."

Key Words: For the writing of an . . . his soul goes marching on!

Collation: 2; green; 27.7 x 21.5; unnumbered; 1; good.

Contents: Complete; infrequently revised in pencil. Foreword to *Inside Hitler*, 1941.

Dates: Pub. 1941.

243b. Citation: INTRODUCTION TO INSIDE HITLER; t. ms.; carbon; InU.

Title: INSIDE HITLER

Key Words: Not long ago I was . . . his soul goes marching on.

Collation: 8; white watermarked; 28 x 21.7; [1] 2–4, [1] 2–4; none; fair.

Contents: Complete; infrequently revised in pencil; two carbons of Foreword to *Inside Hitler*, 1941.

Dates: Pub. 1941.

244a. Citation: INTRODUCTION TO THE LANNY BUDD PICTURE BOOK; t. ms.; carbon; InU.

Title: Introduction to the Lanny Budd picture book

Key Words: The eleven large volumes known . . . alas, they don't all read!

Collation: 4; white; 28 x 21.6; [1] 2–4; none; good.

Contents: Complete; infrequently revised in pencil, blue ink.

Dates: Pub. 1958. To *Lanny Budd Wereld in Beeld*, compiled by Thee De Vries.

244b. Citation: INTRODUCTION TO THE LANNY BUDD PICTURE BOOK; t. ms.; carbon; InU.

Title: Introduction to the Lanny Budd picture book

Key Words: The eleven large volumes known . . . the methods of majority consent.

Collation: 5; white; 28 x 21.6; [1]–5; none; good.

Contents: Complete; infrequently revised in pencil, blue ink.

Dates: Pub. 1958. To *Lanny Budd Wereld in Beeld*, compiled by Thee De Vries.

245. Citation: I PULL POLITICAL WIRES; t. ms.; ribbon, carbon; InU.

Title: I PULL POLITICAL WIRES

Key Words: I am going to tell . . . Party in our Golden State.

Collation: 34; green, white watermarked; 28 x 21.6, 28 x 21.7; 1–12, [1] 2–11, [1] 2–11;11; good.

Contents: Complete; infrequently revised in pencil, not all in Sinclair's hand; an original copy plus a revised copy and carbon.

Dates: Comp. ca. 1939. Pub. ?

246. Citation: I SAW RED FOR A NICKEL; t. ms.; ribbon; InU.

Title: I SAW RED FOR A NICKEL

Key Words: You pay the equivalent of . . . but I had seen red.

Collation: 3; white; 32.4 x 20.4; [1] 2–3; none; good.

Contents: Complete; infrequently revised in ink, unidentified hand.

Dates: Comp. ca. 1953. Pub. ?

247. Citation: IS CAPITALISM WORTH IT?; t. ms.; ribbon; InU.

Title: IS CAPITALISM WORTH IT?

Key Words: Capitalism is a word that . . . to support him against the

Collation: 9; white, white watermarked; 28 x 21.7, 27.9 x
21.6; 1–9; none; fair.

Contents: Incomplete; moderately revised in pencil.

Dates: Comp. ca. 1949. Pub. ?

248. Citation: THE ISLAND OF KINGS; t. ms.; ribbon,
purple carbon; InU.

Title: THE ISLAND OF KINGS

Key Words: To J. F. Kerensky, Minister . . . YOURS
FOR THE SOCIAL REVOLUTION,

Collation: 8; white watermarked, brown; 27.9 x 21.8,
27.8 x 21.6; [1] 2–4, [1] 2, [1], 3; none; fair.

Contents: Complete; moderately revised in pencil.

Dates: Comp. ca. 1917. Pub. ?

249a. Citation: THE ISLAND OF MANHATO; t. ms.; ribbon; InU.

Title: THE ISLAND OF MANHATO | A STORY

Key Words: The sun was setting, and . . . are that
scrapes the sky!"

Collation: 7; white; 27.9 x 21.6; [1] 2–7; none; good.

Contents: Complete; moderately revised in pencil.

Dates: Comp. ca. 1952. Pub. ?

249b. Citation: THE ISLAND OF MANHATO; t. ms.; ribbon; InU.

Title: THE ISLAND OF MANHATO

Key Words: The sun was setting and . . . are that
scrape the sky!"

Collation: 6; white; 27.9 x 21.6; [1] 2–6; none; good.

Contents: Complete; infrequently revised in green ink.

Dates: Comp. ca. 1952. Pub. ?

250a. Citation: IS THIS JACK LONDON?; t. ms.; ribbon; InU.

Title: IS THIS JACK LONDON? | His "Spirit" Talks with Upton Sinclair

Key Words: My friend Jack London has . . . verdict upon their alleged phenomena.

Collation: 17; green; 27.9 x 21.6; 1–9, 11–18; 15; fair.

Contents: Complete; frequently revised in pencil.

Dates: Pub. *Occult Review*, December, 1930–January 1931.

250b. Citation: IS THIS JACK LONDON?; t. ms., a. ms.; carbon, pencil; InU.

Title: IS THIS JACK LONDON? | His "Spirit" Talks with Upton Sinclair

Key Words: My friend Jack London has . . . that you have "gone spooky!"

Collation: 20; white, green watermarked; 28 x 21.7, 27.9 x 21.6; 1–7, 7a, 8–10, 12–14, 14a, 11, 15–16, 18, 20; 7, 18, 19, 20; fair.

Contents: Complete; moderately revised in pencil.

Dates: Pub. *Occult Review*, December 1930–January 1931.

250c. Citation: IS THIS JACK LONDON?; t. ms.; carbon; InU.

Title: IS THIS JACK LONDON? | His "Spirit Talks with Upton Sinclair

Key Words: My friend Jack London has . . . that you have "gone spooky"!

Collation: 17; white; 28 x 21.6; 1–17; none; fair, corner torn out.

Contents: Complete; infrequently revised in pencil, blue ink, unidentified hand.

Dates: Pub. *Occult Review*, December 1930–January 1931.

250d. Citation: IS THIS JACK LONDON?; t. ms.; carbon; InU.

Title: IS THIS JACK LONDON? His "Spirit" Talks with Upton Sinclair

Key Words: My friend Jack London has . . . that you have "gone spooky"!

Collation: 17; white; 28 x 21.6; 1–17; none; good.

Contents: Complete; infrequently revised in pencil, blue ink, unidentified hand.

Dates: Pub. *Occult Review*, December 1930–January 1931.

251a. IT HAPPENED TO DIDYMUS; t. ms.; ribbon; InU.

Title: What DIDYMUS DID (Whether You Believe It Or Not)

Key Words: As some of you know . . . self do nothing." THE END

Collation: 135; white; 28 x 19.6 to 28 x 21.7; [1] 2, [1] 2, [1] 2, 115–129, [130], [1] 2–44, 44a, 44b, 45–95, 95a, 95b, 96–108, [1]; 40, 44, 96, 99, 135; good.

Contents: Complete; moderately revised in pencil; complete ms. plus some misc. revised sheets, prefaces, etc.

Dates: Pub. ca. 24 March 1958 (as *What Didymus Did*, 1953, England).

251b. Citation: IT HAPPENED TO DIDYMUS; t. ms.; carbon; InU.

Title: WHAT DIDYMUS DID | (Whether You Believe It Or Not)

Key Words: The first time I met . . . Temple is full of them."

Collation: 112; white; 28 x 21.7; [1] 2-44, 44a, 44b, 45-109, 1; none; good.

Contents: Complete; unrevised.

Dates: Pub. ca. 24 March 1958 (as *What Didymus Did*, 1953, England).

252. Citation: IT HAS BEEN YOUR FATE; t. ms.; ribbon, carbon; InU.

Title: [none]

Key Words: It has been your fate . . . they will follow him through.

Collation: 10; white watermarked; 28 x 21.6; [1] 2-5, [1] 2-5; none; good.

Contents: Complete; infrequently revised in pencil; ribbon copy with a carbon.

Dates: Comp. ? Pub. ?

253. Citation: [IT IS MY DELIBERATE OPINION . . .]; t. ms.; ribbon, carbon; InU.

Title: [none]

Key Words: It is my deliberate opinion . . . United States is that the

Collation: 20; white watermarked; 28.1 x 21.6; [1] 2-9, [1] 2-9, [1], [1]; none; good.

Contents: Complete; infrequently revised in pencil.

Dates: Comp. 22 April 1939. Pub. ?

254. Citation: [IT IS MY PLEASURE . . .]; t. ms.; carbon; InU.

Title: [none]

Key Words: It is my pleasure today . . . a new, more beautiful world.

Collation: 6; white watermarked; 27.9 x 21.6; 1–6; 5; fair.

Contents: Complete; infrequently revised in pencil, not all in Sinclair's hand.

Dates: Comp. ca. 1942. Pub. ?

255. Citation: "I WILL NOT LET THE PEOPLE DOWN!"; t. ms.; ribbon, carbon; InU.

Title: "I Will Not Let the People Down!"

Key Words: "I will not let the . . . the Unemployed! Never forget that!

Collation: 7; white watermarked; 28 x 21.6; [1] 2–4, [1] 2–3; none; good.

Contents: Complete; moderately revised in pencil, not all in Sinclair's hand; original plus carbon of revised typescript.

Dates: Pub. EPIC News, 23 May 1938.

256a. Citation: JACK LONDON; t. ms.; carbon; InU.

Title: JACK LONDON

Key Words: Jack London has been dead . . . generous as Mother Nature herself.

Collation: 15; white watermarked; 28.1 x 21.6; [1] 2–15; none; good.

Contents: Complete; infrequently revised in blue, black ink; not in Sinclair's hand.

Dates: Pub. New Age, 1 March 1917.

256b. Citation: JACK LONDON; t. ms.; carbon; InU.

Title: JACK LONDON

Key Words: Jack London has been dead . . . generous as Mother Nature herself.

Collation: 15; white watermarked; 28 x 21.6; [1] 2–15; none; fair.

Contents: Complete; unrevised.

Dates: Pub. *New Age*, 1 March 1917.

257. Citation: THE JEW; t. ms.; ribbon; InU.

Title: THE JEW

Key Words: Patient, persevering, pitiful slaves; Heroic . . . no man can rise above.

Collation: 1; white watermarked; 28.1 x 21.6; unnumbered; none; good.

Contents: Complete poem; infrequently revised in blue ink in unidentified hand.

Dates: Comp. 1930s. Pub. ?

258a. Citation: JIMMIE HIGGINS; t. ms., a. ms.; ribbon, carbon, ink; InU.

Title: JIMMIE HIGGINS GOES TO WAR | A Novel

Key Words: "Comrade Higgins, have you got . . . are true and righteous altogether."

Collation: 389; brown, white; 19.1 x 12.3 to 37.7 x 21.6; numbered consecutively by chapter but not continuously; 1, 24, 78, 189, 194, 200, 212, 216, 222, 242, 251, 252, 260, 262, 279, 280, 306, 311, 332, 351, 374, 377, 380, 383; fair.

Contents: Complete; frequently revised in pencil, faded ink; ms. in box labeled: early complete draft.

Dates: Pub. 1918–19 (*Upton Sinclair's*), 1919 (as book).

258b. Citation: JIMMIE HIGGINS; t. ms.; ribbon, carbon InU.

Title: JIMMIE HIGGINS GOES TO WAR | A Novel

Key Words: (Synopsis of the first installment . . . a girl out to dinner!

Collation: 42; brown, white watermarked; 27.8 x 21.6 27.9 x 21.5; randomly numbered; 4, 5, 10; fair.

Contents: Incomplete; frequently revised in pencil, black ink; folder labeled: Chapt. III-V | Chapt. VII, sec| 6 (1) page), | Chapt. XXII sec. 1 and part | of sec. 2, | part of sec. 3; the first chapter III–V seems to be the copy for the serialization; box labeled: later partial drafts and misc.

Dates: Pub. 1918–19 (*Upton Sinclair's*), 1919 (as book).

258c. Citation: JIMMIE HIGGINS; t. ms.; ribbon, black, blue carbon; InU.

Title: CHAPTER TWELVE. | *Jimmie Higgins Meets a Patriot.*

Key Words: The country, it seemed, was . . . that red cavern running blood.

Collation: 146; brown, misc. sheets; 27.7 x 21.7, 27.7 x 21.6 to 28 x 21.6; 1–16, [2], 17–98, 98a, 99–143; 43, 96, 128, 137, 139; fair, punched for two-ring binder.

Contents: Incomplete; infrequently revised in pencil, blue ink; these last three folders contain the latest draft of Chapters XII to XXIII, part V, third from last paragraph; box labeled: later partial drafts and misc.

Dates: Pub. 1918–19 (*Upton Sinclair's*), 1919 (as book).

258d. Citation: JIMMIE HIGGINS; t. ms.; black, blue carbon; InU.

Title: CHAPTER FOURTEEN. | *Jimmie Higgins Takes to the Road.*

Key Words: Jimmie Higgins was wandering down . . . when the Yanks come home!

Collation: 223; brown, misc. sheets; 28 x 21.4, 28 x 21.7 to 28.1 x 21.8; numbered consecutively by chapter but not continuously; none; fair, punched for two-ring binder.

Contents: Incomplete; infrequently revised in blue, black ink; these seven folders contain carbons of the earlier drafts of Chapters XIV–XXII, sec. 1 and 2; the chapters are in various stages of revision; box labeled: later partial drafts and misc.

Dates: Pub. 1918–19 (*Upton Sinclair's*), 1919 (as book).

258e. Citation: JIMMIE HIGGINS; a. ms.; blue ink; InU.

Title: [none]

Key Words: was in distress of mind . . . and would hardly have been

Collation: 13; brown, lined notebook; 25.6 x 20.2, 22.2 x 14.9; randomly numbered; none; poor, crumbling.

Contents: Incomplete; frequently revised in faded ink; folder labeled: *Jimmie Higgins* | Misc. pages.

Dates: Pub. 1918–19 (*Upton Sinclair's*), 1919 (as book).

258f. Citation: JIMMIE HIGGINS; t. ms., a. ms.; ribbon, carbon, ink; InU.

Title: JIMMIE HIGGINS GOES TO WAR | a Story

Key Words: Jimmie Higgins is the fellow . . . Jimmie Higgins Votes for Democracy."

Collation: 11; brown, misc. sheets; 27.8 x 21.6, 28 x 21.4 to 28.1 x 21.8; unnumbered; none; fair.

Contents: Incomplete; infrequently revised in faded ink; there are three pieces in the folder: a title page with introduction, a table of contents, and a SCENARIO OF THE REMAINDER OF "JIMMIE HIGGINS GOES TO WAR."

Dates: Pub. 1918–19 (*Upton Sinclair's*), 1919 (as book).

258g. Citation: JIMMIE HIGGINS; t. ms.; ribbon; InU.

Title: *JIMMIE HIGGINS* | Based on the novel by Upton Sinclair

Key Words: 1. Empire Machine Shops, the . . . win the world. | the end.

Collation: 6; white watermarked; 27.9 x 21.6; [1]–2, [3], 4–6; none; good.

Contents: Complete; infrequently revised in pencil, black ink; ink not in Sinclair's hand; ms. is apparently not by Upton Sinclair but rather a Scenario by I. Babel based on Sinclair's novel.

Dates: Pub. 1918–19 (*Upton Sinclair's*), 1919 (as book).

259. Citation: THE JOB OF CHANGING AMERICA; t. ms.; ribbon, carbon; InU.

Title: THE [ART (c.o.)] JOB OF CHANGING AMERICA

Key Words: The job I have in . . . they will do about it.

Collation: 18; white, white watermarked; 28 x 21.6; [1] 2–4, 4a, 5–8, [1] 2–9; 1; good.

Contents: Complete; frequently revised in pencil.

Dates: Comp. ca. 1962. Pub. ?

260a. Citation: JOHN D: AN ADVENTURE; t. ms., a. ms.; ribbon, carbon, pencil; InU.

Title: JOHN D | A Mellow-drammer with Mellow-dee

Key Words: Act I; Scene I | The . . . drinking in the [indistinguishable word]—making

Collation: 182; white, misc. sheets; 28 x 21.6 to 28.1 x 21.5, 33 x 21.6; numbered consecutively by group but not continuously; 119, 144; good.

Contents: Complete; moderately revised in pencil; ms. in three states: autograph original with revision, typed original with revisions, typed carbons without revisions; each state is later than the preceding one.

Dates: Pub. *Wilshire's Magazine*, January 1910.

260b. Citation: JOHN D: AN ADVENTURE; t. ms.; carbon; InU.

Title: John D | A Mellow-drammer with Mellow-dee

Key Words: Act I: Scene I. | The . . . but John the most. Curtain.

Collation: 37; white; 28 x 21.6; [1] 2–35, [2]; none; good.

Contents: Complete; infrequently revised in pencil; bound together in upper left corner with a brass stud.

Dates: Pub. *Wilshire's Magazine*, January 1910.

261. Citation: JOHN D. ROCKEFELLER, I AM SORRY; a. ms.; pencil; InU.

Title: [none]

Key Words: John D. Rockefeller, I am . . . about your theory of gardening?

Collation: 1; brown; 22 x 11.7; unnumbered; none; fair.

Contents: Complete; infrequently revised in pencil.

Dates: Comp. ca. 1914. Pub. ?

262. Citation: THE JUNGLE; a. ms.; blue ink; InU.

Title: THE JUNGLE

Key Words: It was four o'clock when . . . she turned and began to

Collation: 2; white; 28 x 21.5; [1] 2; 1, 2; good.

Contents: Incomplete; infrequently revised in blue ink. Written out by Sinclair for Lilly Library; verso note explains circumstances. Copy of pp. 1–2 of the novel.

Dates: Comp. 1957.

263. Citation: KEEP OUR PAPER—HELP *NATIONAL EPIC*; t. ms.; carbon; InU.

Title: KEEP OUR PAPER

Key Words: The editor of the EPIC . . . are going to get it.

Collation: 4; white watermarked, blue watermarked; 28 x 21.6; [1] 2, [1] 2; none; fair.

Contents: Complete; infrequently revised in pencil, not in Sinclair's hand.

Dates: Pub. *Upton Sinclair's National EPIC News*, 14 October 1935.

264a. Citation: KING COAL; t. ms., a. ms., print; ribbon, blue ink, print; InU.

Title: *KING COAL* | A Novel

Key Words: The town of Pedro stood . . . these bruises on my back.

Collation: 74; brown watermarked, misc. sheets; 27.8 x 21.4, 28 x 21.6 to 28 x 21.7; [3], [1]–19, [11], 20–28, [6], 33–34, [1], 31, [5], 35–40, [6], 42–46; 46, 49; fair.

Contents: Incomplete; frequently revised in pencil, blue, black ink; ms. has been tagged and labeled: ms.

has been punched to be bound by two brass studs one of which is missing; folder numbered 1.

Dates: Pub. 1915–17 (in part), 1917 (as book).

264b. Citation: KING COAL; t. ms.; carbon; InU.

Title: *KING COAL* | A Novel | by | UPTON SIN-CLAIR | *BOOK ONE* | THE DOMAIN OF KING COAL

Key Words: The town of Pedro stood . . . these bruises on my back!"

Collation: 104; white; 27.8 x 21.7; [4], 1–3, 3a, 3b, 4–40, 40a, 41–58, 58a, 59–69, 69a, 70–94, [1]; none; good.

Contents: Incomplete; infrequently revised in blue, brown ink; blue ink not in Sinclair's hand; ms. is tagged and labeled; ms. is bound with two brass studs in a wrapper; folder numbered 2.

Dates: Pub. 1915–17 (in part), 1917 (as book).

264c. Citation: KING COAL; t. ms., a. ms.; ribbon, black, purple carbon, pencil, blue ink; InU.

Title: [none]

Key Words: Old King Coal was a . . . if they could!" sniffed Mary.

Collation: 134; white watermarked, brown; 27.9 x 21.7 to 28 x 21.6, 27.8 x 21.4; randomly numbered; 16, 17, 18, 29, 30, 31, 58, 60, 67, 68, 69, 98, 101, 102, 121; fair, punched for two-ring binder.

Contents: Incomplete; frequently revised in pencil, blue, black ink; folder labeled: Misc. drafts of various portions of Book One; folder numbered 3.

Dates: Pub. 1915–17 (in part), 1917 (as book).

264d. Citation: KING COAL; t. ms., a. ms.; blue ribbon, carbon, pencil; InU.

Title: KING COAL | *Book One*

Key Words: The town of Pedro stood . . . these bruises on my back!"

Collation: 125; brown, white watermarked; 13.3 x 21.6 to 28 x 21.5; continuously numbered with variations; 1, 7, 15, 26, 30, 39, 46, 49, 50, 55, 69, 75, 79, 81, 88, 103, 105; fair, punched for two-ring binder.

Contents: Complete; frequently revised in pencil, black ink; this folder contains an early draft of Book One; folder has been tagged and labeled: Many passages deleted | in printed version; apparently it is a complete draft; folder numbered 4.

Dates: Pub. 1915–17 (in part), 1917 (as book).

264e. Citation: KING COAL; t. ms.; ribbon, carbon; InU.

Title: *KING COAL* | A Novel

Key Words: The town of Pedro stood . . . smile on the pit-boss's face.

Collation: 89; white watermarked, brown; 17.5 x 21.6 to 28 x 21.6; [4],1–16, 18–23, 23a, 24–30, 31 and 32, 33–54, 55 and 56, 57–68, 68a, 69–77, 77a, [78]–84, [1]; 39, 45, 48; good.

Contents: Incomplete; infrequently revised in pencil, faded ink; ms. is bound with two brass studs in a brown wrapper; tagged and labeled: Incomplete carbon copy of | printer's copy; Book I | M.C.S. on cover; folder numbered 5.

Dates: Pub. 1915–17 (in part), 1917 (as book).

264f. KING COAL; t. ms.; ribbon, carbon; InU.

Title: *BOOK ONE* | THE DOMAIN OF KING COAL

Key Words: The town of Pedro stood . . . bargain the two shook hands.

Collation: 101; white watermarked, brown; 28 x 21.6, 27.8 x 21.4; [2], 1–15, 16 and 17, 18–23, 23a, 24–30, 31 and 32, 33–54, 55 and 56, 57–68, 68a, 69–77, 77a, 78–98, [1]; none; fair, punched for two-ring binder, spindled.

Contents: Complete; infrequently revised in black ink, bears the printer's notations in blue, regular pencil, red ink; ms. has a brown outer wrapper labeled: Complete printer's draft; folder numbered 6.

Dates: Pub. 1915–17 (in part), 1917 (as book).

264g.Citation: KING COAL; t. ms.; carbon; InU.

Title: *KING COAL* | A Novel

Key Words: The town of Pedro stood . . . now occupied in holding him.

Collation: 87; white watermarked; 28 x 21.7; [3], 1–8, 10–79, 81–85, 86, 87 and 88; none; good, punched for two-ring binder.

Contents: Incomplete; infrequently revised in pencil, black ink; ms. is tagged and labeled: Corrected partial printer's draft; folder numbered 7.

Dates: Pub. 1915–17 (in part), 1917 (as book).

264h.Citation: KING COAL; t. ms., a. ms.; carbon, pencil; InU.

Title: [none]

Key Words: Book I (changes to be . . . a blunder now and then.

Collation: 11; brown, white watermarked; 27.9 x 21.6, 22.2 x 21.5 to 27.8 x 21.6; randomly numbered; 1, 2, 3, 5, 6, 7, 9; fair.

Contents: Incomplete; infrequently revised in pencil; folder labeled: Notes in Book I; it is a misc. collection of sheets; sheet number one indicates that they may be corrections for the proof sheets.

Dates: Pub. 1915–17 (in part), 1917 (as book).

264i. Citation: KING COAL; a. ms.; ink, pencil; InU.

Title: [none]

Key Words: Hal had not seen him . . . her pessimism in all industry.

Collation: 45; misc. sheets; 4.4 x 21.6 to 28 x 21.7; randomly numbered; 16, 18, 20, 22, 27, 32, 34, 35, 38, 40, 41; fair.

Contents: Incomplete; frequently revised in black ink, pencil; folder labeled: Notes for Book 2.

Dates: Pub. 1915–17 (in part), 1917 (as book).

264j. Citation: KING COAL; t. ms., a. ms.; ribbon, carbon, pencil; InU.

Title: "KING COAL" | BOOK TWO

Key Words: The first thing Hal did . . . college professors," snapped the marshall.

Collation: 89; brown, white watermarked; 28 x 21.5, 27.9 x 21.7; 21, 21–23, 25–71, [72], 73–79, 79, 80, 80, 80a, 80b, 83–84, 96–99, 101–104, 106–107, 101–107, 107, 114–118; 1, 2, 3, 7, 15, 35, 43, 50, 51, 52, 61, 62, 66, 84, 85; fair, punched for two-ring binder.

Contents: Incomplete; infrequently revised in pencil, black ink; folder labeled: Partial revised later draft.

Dates: Pub. 1915–17 (in part), 1917 (as book).

264k. Citation: KING COAL; t. ms., a. ms.; carbon, ink; InU.

Title: KING COAL | Book Two.

Key Words: Hal was now started upon . . . a few seats behind him.

Collation: 131; white, white watermarked; 28 x 21.6, 27.9 x 21.6 to 28.1 x 21.6; [2], 1–13, 13a, 13b, 14–73, 73a, 74–81, 81a, 81aa, 82–84, 84a, 84b, 85–121, 1; 8, 11, 40; good.

Contents: Complete; infrequently revised in pencil, blue, black ink; this is a later draft; not in Sinclair's hand; ms. is bound with two brass studs in a brown wrapper; folder labeled: Craig's Corrections; numbered 4.

Dates: Pub. 1915–17 (in part), 1917 (as book).

264l. Citation: KING COAL; t. ms.; ribbon, carbon; InU.

Title: *BOOK TWO* | THE SERFS OF KING COAL

Key Words: Hal was now started upon . . . a few seats behind him.

Collation: 129; white, white watermarked; 27.8 x 21.4, 27.9 x 21.6 to 28 x 21.7; [1], 1–13, 13a, 14–58, 58a, 58b, 58c, 59–73, 73a, 74–85, 85a, 85b, 86–121; none; good, punched for two-ring binder.

Contents: Complete; infrequently revised in blue, black ink; this ms. is a later draft, apparently complete, of Book Two; folder numbered 5.

Dates: Pub. 1915–1917 (in part), 1917 (as book).

264m. Citation: KING COAL; t. ms.; carbon; InU.

Title: KING COAL | *Book Two*

Key Words: Hal was now started upon . . . a few seats behind him.

Collation: 129; white, white watermarked; 28 x 21.6, 27.9 x 21.6 to 28 x 21.6; [2], 1–13, 13a, 14–81, 81a, 81aa, 82–84, 84a, 84b, 85–121, 1; none; good.

Contents: Complete; infrequently revised in blue, black ink; blue ink revisions not in Sinclair's hand; this is a revised later draft; ms. is bound in a brown wrapper with two brass studs; folder labeled: 6 – final.

Dates: Pub. 1915–17 (in part), 1917 (as book).

264n. Citation: KING COAL; t. ms.; ribbon; InU.

Title: *BOOK TWO* | THE SERFS OF KING COAL

Key Words: Hal was now started upon . . . a few seats behind him.

Collation: 126; white watermarked; 28 x 21.6; 99–224; none; fair, spindled, punched for two-ring binder.

Contents: Complete; infrequently revised in black ink; folder is labeled: Printer's copy; printer's notation in blue, black pencil; folder numbered 7.

Dates: Pub. 1915–17 (in part), 1917 (as book).

264o. Citation: KING COAL; t. ms., a. ms.; ribbon, carbon, ink; InU.

Title: *BOOK THREE* | THE HENCHMEN OF KING COAL

Key Words: It was Hal's intention to . . . said the Coal King's son.

Collation: 146; white watermarked; 27.9 x 21.6 to 28 x 21.7; [1], 1–49, 49a, 50–52, [1]–19, 21a, 22–31, 31a, 31–32, 32a, 33–39, 1–52; 58, 65, 66, 69, 71, 72, 75, 76, 79, 86, 91, 94, 95; fair.

Contents: Incomplete; infrequently revised in pencil, blue, black ink; folder labeled: Early draft; part of the ms. has been bound with a brass stud and part by two studs; the balance is not bound; folder numbered 1.

Dates: Pub. 1915–17 (in part), 1917 (as book).

264p. Citation: KING COAL; t. ms., a. ms.; ribbon, carbon, pencil, ink; InU.

Title: [none]

Key Words: and Hal hurried to the . . . even so, it was cruel!

Collation: 69; brown, misc. sheets; 19 x 17.8 to 28 x 21.8; 1a, 2–3, [1], 10, 8, [1], 9–23, 25–27, 27a, 27b, 27c, 28–47, 47a, 48–49, 49a, 50–52, 53a, 53a2, [9], 21, 25, 88a; 2, 5, 6, 17, 22, 25, 30, 32, 33, 37, 48, 50, 57, 67, 68; fair, punched for a two-hole binder.

Contents: Incomplete; frequently revised in pencil, black ink; folder labeled: Revised portion of early draft of book three; ms. is tagged and labeled; folder numbered 2.

Dates: Pub. 1915–17 (in part), 1917 (as book).

264q. Citation: KING COAL; t. ms.; carbon; InU.

Title: *Book Three* | THE HENCHMEN OF KING COAL

Key Words: It was Hal's intention to . . . the pieces of her "man"!

Collation: 99; white watermarked; 28 x 21.6; [1], 1–8, 8a, 9–35, 35a, 36–79, 79a, 79b, 80–94; none; good.

Contents: Incomplete; infrequently revised in blue ink; folder labeled: Later draft; it has been bound in a brown wrapper with two brass studs; folder numbered 3.

Dates: Pub. 1915–17 (in part), 1917 (as book).

264r. Citation: KING COAL; t. ms., a. ms.; ribbon, carbon, pencil; InU.

Title: *KING COAL* | A Novel | by | UPTON SINCLAIR | *BOOK THREE* | THE HENCHMEN OF KING COAL

Key Words: It was Hal's intention to . . . the pieces of her "man"!

Collation: 108; white watermarked, brown; 21.5 x 14 to 29.3 x 22.8; [4], 1–8, 8a, 9–35, 35a, 36–76, [3], 77–79,

79a, 79b, 80–90, a p 91, 91–92, a p 93, 93–94, [1]; 9, 10, 11, 15, 18, 83, 84, 85, 91; good.

Contents: Incomplete; infrequently revised in pencil, blue ink, blue ink not in Sinclair's hand; ms. labeled: Later draft; it has been bound in a brown wrapper with two brass studs; folder numbered 4.

Dates: Pub. 1915–17 (in part), 1917 (as book).

264s. Citation: KING COAL; t. ms.; carbon; InU.

Title: *BOOK THREE* | THE HENCHMEN OF KING COAL

Key Words: It was Hal's intention to . . . the pieces of her "man"!

Collation: 93; white watermarked; 27.9 x 21.6; [1], 1–92; none; good.

Contents: Complete; infrequently revised in pencil, black ink; folder labeled: Printer's copy (carbon copy); it has been bound in a brown folder with two brass studs; tagged and labeled; folder numbered 5.

Dates: Pub. 1915–17 (in part), 1917 (as book).

264t. Citation: KING COAL; t. ms.; carbon; InU.

Title: *BOOK THREE* | THE HENCHMEN OF KING COAL

Key Words: It was Hal's intention to . . . the pieces of her "man"!

Collation: 97; white watermarked; 28 x 21.6; [1], 1–10, 10a, 11–49, 49a, 50–51, 51a, 52–53, 53a, 54–69, 70 and 71, 72–88, 88a, 89–92; none; good.

Contents: Complete; infrequently revised in black ink, not all in Sinclair's hand; folder labeled: Printer's copy (carbon); ms. is bound in a brown wrapper with two brass studs; folder numbered 6.

Dates: Pub. 1915–17 (in part), 1917 (as book).

264u. Citation: KING COAL; t. ms.; ribbon; InU.

Title: *Book Three* | THE HENCHMEN OF KING COAL

Key Words: It was Hal's intention to . . . the pieces of her "man"!

Collation: 97; white watermarked; 28.1 x 21.6; 225–321; none; good, spindled, punched for a two-hole binder.

Contents: Complete; infrequently revised in black ink; it also bears the printer's notations in black, blue pencil; folder labeled: Printer's copy; folder numbered 7.

Dates: Pub. 1915–17 (in part), 1917 (as book).

264v. Citation: KING COAL; a. ms.; pencil; InU.

Title: [none]

Key Words: But now that Hal had . . . unconcerned, [?] how *sure* she was!

Collation: 41; brown, white watermarked; 27.8 x 21.4, 28.1 x 21.8; randomly numbered; 7, 10, 11, 25, 26, 27, 28, 31, 36, 37, 38, 39, 40; fair.

Contents: Incomplete; moderately revised in pencil; folder labeled: Notes in B[oo]k 3; ms. contains criticism and revision of Book 3; part of the ms. has been fastened together with a brass stud.

Dates: Pub. 1915–17 (in part), 1917 (as book).

264w. Citation: KING COAL; t. ms., a. ms.; ribbon, purple carbon, ink; InU.

Title: [none]

Key Words: The pit of death was . . . of moisture in his eyes.

Collation: 119; white watermarked; 25.3 x 21.5 to 27.9 x 21.7; continuously numbered with variations; 9, 10, 11, 13, 16, 23, 27, 29, 30, 31, 32, 33, 36, 38, 39, 42, 43, 44, 48, 56, 57, 58, 62, 63, 64, 65, 69, 70, 71, 73,

74, 75, 81, 82, 83, 87, 88, 100, 102, 103, 105, 106, 108, 109, 111, 112, 113, 115, 117; fair, punched for a two-ring binder.

Contents: Incomplete; frequently revised in pencil, black ink, not all in Sinclair's hand; folder labeled: Incomplete early draft; one section has been bound by a brass stud; ms. has been tagged and labeled; folder numbered 1.

Dates: Pub. 1915–17 (in part), 1917 (in book).

264x. Citation: KING COAL; t. ms.; carbon; InU.

Title: King Coal | *Book Four* | THE WILL OF KING COAL

Key Words: The pit of death was . . . the people, for the people.

Collation: 140; white watermarked; 28.1 x 21.7; [1], 1–14, 14a, 14b, 15–122, 1–15; 21, 35, 42, 45, 76; good.

Contents: Incomplete; infrequently revised in pencil, blue ink; blue ink not in Sinclair's hand; folder labeled: Complete revised early draft; it has been tagged and labeled and is bound in a brown wrapper with two brass studs; folder numbered 2.

Dates: Pub. 1915–17 (in part), 1917 (as book).

264y. Citation: KING COAL; t. ms.; carbon; InU.

Title: King Coal | *Book Four* | THE WILL OF KING COAL

Key Words: The pit of death was . . . the people, for the people.

Collation: 140; white watermarked; 28 x 21.6; [1], 1–14, 14a, 14b, 15–122, 1–15; none; good.

Contents: Incomplete; infrequently revised in blue, black ink, not in Sinclair's hand; ms. labeled: Corrected revised early draft; ms. is bound in a brown wrapper by two brass studs; folder numbered 3.

Dates: Pub. 1915–17 (in part), 1917 (as book).

264z. Citation: KING COAL; t. ms.; ribbon; InU.

Title: KING COAL | BOOK FOUR | THE WILL OF KING COAL

Key Words: The pit of death was . . . of moisture in his eyes.

Collation: 129; white watermarked, brown; 28 x 21.6, 27.8 x 21.5; [1], 1–14, 14a, 14b, 15–119, 119a, 120–125; 13, 21, 30, 34, 35, 53, 59; good, punched for a two-ring binder.

Contents: Incomplete; frequently revised in black ink; ms. is a later draft; tagged and labeled; folder numbered 4.

Dates: Pub. 1915–17 (in part), 1917 (as book).

264aa. Citation: KING COAL, t. ms.; carbon; InU.

Title: *King Coal* | *Book Four* | THE WILL OF KING COAL

Key Words: The pit of death was . . . the people, for the people.

Collation: 122; white watermarked; 22.3 x 21.7 to 28 x 21.7; [1], 1, 2 and 3, 4–13, 13a, 14–15, 17–52, 53 and 54, 55–110, 1–13; none; good.

Contents: Incomplete; infrequently revised in pencil, black ink; black ink revisions not in Sinclair's hand; ms. labeled: Later draft; ms. is bound in a brown wrapper by two brass studs; folder numbered 5.

Dates: Pub. 1915–17 (in part), 1917 (as book).

264bb. Citation: KING COAL; t. ms.; carbon; InU.

Title: *King Coal* | *Book Four* | THE WILL OF KING COAL

Key Words: The pit of death was . . . the people, for the people.

Collation: 125; white watermarked; 28 x 21.6; [1], 1, 2 and 3, 4–13, 13a, 14–16, 16a, 16b, 17–52, 53 and 54, 55–110, 1–13; none; good.

Contents: Incomplete; infrequently revised in black ink, not all in Sinclair's hand; this folder is labeled: Revised later draft; ms. is bound in brown wrappers by two brass studs; folder numbered 6.

Dates: Pub. 1915–17 (in part), 1917 (as book).

264cc. Citation: KING COAL; t. ms., a. ms.; ribbon, carbon, pencil, ink; InU.

Title: [none]

Key Words: —that when they do wrong . . . call Jeff Cotton a son-of-a——!"

Collation: 17; white watermarked, misc. sheets; 28 x 21.6, 27.8 x 21.6 to 28 x 21.5; randomly numbered; 5, 7, 9, 11, 16; good, punched for a two-ring binder.

Contents: Incomplete; frequently revised in pencil, black ink; folder labeled: Misc. drafts of various sections of Book IV; ms. has been tagged and labeled.

Dates: Pub. 1915–17 (in part), 1917 (as book).

264dd. Citation: KING COAL; a. ms.; pencil, ink; InU.

Title: [none]

Key Words: I can't help wondering why . . . necessary," said Hal. "Why not?"

Collation: 29; misc. sheets; 15.3 x 21.6 to 28 x 21.7; randomly numbered; 4, 6, 8, 14, 16, 17, 18, 19, 20, 22, 23, 24, 25, 26; fair.

Contents: Incomplete; frequently revised in pencil, black ink; folder labeled: Notes on Book IV.

Dates: Pub. 1915–17 (in part), 1917 (as book).

264ee.Citation: KING COAL; t. ms., a. ms.; ribbon, carbon, ink; InU.

Title: KING COAL | BOOK FOUR | THE WILL OF | KING COAL

Key Words: Please do this title page . . . OF KING COAL IS DONE.

Collation: 19; white watermarked; 27.8 x 21.5, 27.9 x 21.4; not numbered; none; good, punched for a two-ring binder.

Contents: Incomplete; infrequently revised in black ink; ms. consists of ribbon copies and carbons of the title page, contents and individual book headings.

Dates: Pub. 1915–17 (in part), 1917 (as book).

264ff.Citation: KING COAL, a. ms.; pencil; InU.

Title: [none]

Key Words: Book I 97a here in . . . believe I would," said Ha.

Collation: 32; cardboard; 9.6 x 6.2; randomly numbered; 1–20, 22–27, 29–31; good.

Contents: Incomplete; infrequently revised in pencil; these cards are apparently notations for corrections written in the ms.; they bear book numbers and in many cases page numbers.

Dates: Pub. 1915–17 (in part), 1917 (as book).

264gg.Citation: KING COAL; t. ms.; black, purple ribbon, black, purple carbon; InU.

Title: [none]

Key Words: "He's not such a bad . . . a few seats behind him.

Collation: 152; white watermarked, misc. sheets; 17.1 x 21.6 to 28.1 x 21.7; randomly numbered; 20, 21, 27, 35, 41, 42, 56, 61, 67, 68, 72, 74, 78, 79, 80, 83, 84, 86, 87, 105, 109, 113, 117, 122, 123, 136, 138, 143, 147, 149, 150, 151; fair, punched for two-ring binder.

Contents: Incomplete; frequently revised in black, blue ink, pencil; this folder is tagged and labeled: Partial early draft.

Dates: Pub. 1915–17 (in part), 1917 (as book).

264hh.Citation: KING COAL; t. ms., a. ms.; ribbon, black, blue carbon, pencil, ink; InU.

Title: [none]

Key Words: When they set fire to . . . I'd sell meself to some

Collation: 259; white watermarked, brown; 7.4 x 21.8 to 28 x 21.7; randomly numbered; 4, 7, 8, 10, 37, 39, 43, 48, 53, 55, 56, 59, 61, 62, 71, 86, 87, 90, 93, 107, 109, 110, 116, 119, 120, 122, 123, 127, 128, 129, 130, 132, 136, 170, 195, 247, 251; fair, punched for a two-ring binder.

Contents: Incomplete; frequently revised in black, blue ink, pencil; they are drafts and notes for *King Coal*; much of the ms. has been tagged and labeled; folder labeled: Miscellaneous drafts of various portions.

Dates: Pub. 1915–17 (in part), 1917 (as book).

264ii.Citation: KING COAL; t. ms.; carbon; InU.

Title: [none]

Key Words: turn into a living thing . . . sealed?" cried Hal, in consternation.

Collation: 31; white watermarked; 28 x 21.5; 86–99, 95–111; 6, 9, 29; good, punched for two-ring binder.

Contents: Incomplete; infrequently revised in pencil, black ink; folder labeled: Partial draft (carbon of / printer's draft with corrections); ms. has been tagged and labeled.

Dates: Pub. 1915–17 (in part), 1917 (as book).

264jj.Citation: KING COAL; t. ms.; carbon; InU.

Title: [none]

Key Words: This business of conspiracy was . . . pity for Mary had involve[d] . . .

Collation: 5; white watermarked, brown; 28 x 19.6 to 28 x 21.6, 27.8 x 21.5; randomly numbered; 4; fair.

Contents: Incomplete; frequently revised in pencil, ink; ms. seems to be a misc. collection of loose pages; ms. has been tagged and labeled.

Dates: Pub. 1915–17 (in part), 1917 (as book).

264kk.Citation: KING COAL; a. ms.; blue ink; InU.

Title: Introduction to | King Coal.

Key Words: Upton Sinclair is a writer . . . so many, still unknown world.

Collation: 12; white lined notebook paper; 25.6 x 20.4; [1]–12; none; good, punched for two-ring binder.

Contents: Complete; infrequently revised in pencil; this ms. contains the introduction to the Dutch edition of *King Coal* by Frederik van Eeden and the Foreword from the Artist by H. Hegenbrock.

Dates: Pub. 1915–17 (in part), 1917 (as book).

264ll.Citation: KING COAL; t. ms.; black, purple ribbon, carbon; InU.

Title: *KING COAL* | An introduction to Upton Sinclair's new (not yet published) novel, | By Dr. Georg Brandes

Key Words: Upton Sinclair is one of . . . felt the air about him.

Collation: 15; white watermarked, white laid; 25.3 x 20.3, 27.8 x 21.4; [1]–8, [1]–7; 3; fair.

Contents: Complete; infrequently revised in black, faded ink, pencil; not all in Sinclair's hand; this ms. consists of an original and the carbons of the corrected t. ms.; the carbons have not been revised; misc. pages of Sinclair's ms. tagged and labeled.

Dates: Pub. 1915–17 (in part), 1917 (as book).

264mm.Citation: KING COAL; t. ms., a. ms.; ribbon, carbon, blue, black ink; InU.

Title: [none]

Key Words: The winter does not believe . . . in favor of the strikers.

Collation: 138; white watermarked; 28 x 21.4 to 28 x 21.6; randomly numbered; none; fair, punched for a two-ring binder.

Contents: Incomplete; infrequently revised in blue, black ink; folder labeled: Postscript—various drafts.

Dates: Pub. 1915–17 (in part), 1917 (as book).

264nn.Citation: KING COAL; t. ms., a. ms.; ribbon, carbon, pencil, ink; InU.

Title: [none]

Key Words: The girl's countance was as . . . in books I & II.

Collation: 139; white watermarked, brown; 21.5 x 17.2 to 28 x 21.5; randomly numbered; 1, 5, 8, 14, 15, 21, 26, 28, 31, 38, 39, 41, 43, 44, 45, 46, 47, 48, 49, 57, 58, 60, 62, 63, 64, 66, 67, 68, 69, 75, 76, 82, 84, 90, 93, 94, 95, 100, 107, 110, 113, 116, 119, 123, 124, 125, 126, 130, 133, 135, 139; poor.

Contents: Incomplete; frequently revised in pencil, ink; folder labeled: Revision of orig. ms. of King Coal by M.C.S. & U.S.

Dates: Pub. 1915–17 (in part), 1917 (as book).

264oo.Citation: KING COAL; a. ms., print; pencil, print; InU.

Title: [none]

Key Words: You say I must write . . . want you to understand that.

Collation: 291; white watermarked, brown; 14.3 x 21.6 to 32.1 x 21.7; randomly numbered; 1, 2, 6, 7, 8, 10, 14, 15, 26, 27, 28, 29, 32, 39, 49, 53, 54, 5a, 65, 66, 70, 71, 75, 77, 78, 79, 85, 86, 87, 92, 96, 116, 133, 134, 135, 144, 158, 191, 193, 198, 199, 200, 202, 203, 206, 216, 217, 222, 223, 228, 230, 238, 239, 240, 241, 247, 250, 252, 253, 256, 259, 266, 268, 273, 277, 278, 280, 282, 287, 289, 290, 291; good.

Contents: Incomplete; moderately revised in pencil; folder labeled: Mrs. Sinclair's comments and criticisms on *King Coal.*

Dates: Pub. 1915–17 (in part), 1917 (as book).

265. Citation: KING EDWARD AND DEMOCRACY; t. ms.; carbon; InU.

Title: KING EDWARD AND DEMOCRACY

Key Words: Some people may find it . . . them and to demand time.

Collation: 17; white watermarked, blue; 28 x 21.6, 28 x 21.5; [1] 2–6, [1] 2–6, [1] 2–5; none; fair.

Contents: Complete; infrequently revised in pencil; three carbons in various states.

Dates: Comp. ca. December 1936. Pub. ?

266. Citation: A KING AND A REBEL; t. ms.; carbon; InU.

Title: A KING AND A REBEL

Key Words: My friends and publishers, Farrar . . . to the field of economics.

Collation: 5; blue; 28 x 21.6; [1] 2–5; none; fair.

Contents: Complete; infrequently revised in pencil, not in Sinclair's hand.

Dates: Pub. *EPIC News,* 14 December 1936.

267. Citation: [LADIES AND GENTLEMEN: I DO]; t. ms.; carbon; InU.

Title: [none]

Key Words: LADIES AND GENTLEMEN: I DO . . . our theatres. I thank you.

Collation: 2; blue watermarked; 27.8 x 21.5; [1] 2; none; good.

Contents: Complete; infrequently revised in pencil.

Dates: Comp. 23 January 1935. Pub. ?

268. Citation: THE LADY FROM BALTIMORE; t. ms.; carbon; InU.

Title: THE LADY FROM BALTIMORE

Key Words: As I sit down to . . . this book goes to press.

Collation: 17; white; 28 x 21.6; 1–17; none; good.

Contents: Complete; infrequently revised in pencil.

Dates: Comp. ca. December 1936. Pub. 1936.

269. Citation: LADY POETS; t. ms.; carbon; InU.

Title: *Lady Poets*

Key Words: There is, as you may . . . we no more are here?

Collation: 22; white; 28 x 21.7; 1–11, [1] 131, 132, 132a, 133–139; none; good.

Contents: Complete; moderately revised in pencil.

Dates: Comp. ca. 1927? Pub. ?

270. Citation: LAND OF ORANGE GROVES AND JAILS; t. ms., a. ms.; ribbon, pencil; InU.

Title: LAND OF ORANGE GROVES AND JAILS

Key Words: Southern California is proud of . . . It is its natural manure."

Collation: 10; green; 27.9 x 21.6; [1] 2–10; 4, 5, 6, 9, 10; good.

Contents: Complete; frequently revised in pencil.

Dates: Pub. *Open Forum*, 23 November 1929.

271. Citation: THE LAYING ON OF HANDS; t. ms.; ribbon; InU.

Title: *The Laying On of Hands*

Key Words: About three years ago I . . . use a little strychnine too!"

Collation: 21; brown; 28.3 x 21.4; [1] 2–21; none; good.

Contents: Complete; frequently revised in pencil.

Dates: Pub. *Hearst's International Magazine*, April 1914.

272a. Citation: LEAGUE FOR CREEPING SOCIALISM; t. ms., a. ms.; ribbon, carbon, pencil; InU.

Title: LEAGUE FOR CREEPING SOCIALISM

Key Words: During the recent presidential elections . . . give it up," I said.

Collation: 8; white watermarked, white; 27.9 x 21.6, 20.3 x 12.7; randomly numbered; 3, 4, 5, 6, 7, 8; good.

Contents: Complete; moderately revised in pencil, blue ink.

Dates: Comp. ca. 1920. Pub. ?

272b. Citation: LEAGUE FOR CREEPING SOCIALISM; t. ms., a. ms.; ribbon, carbon, pencil; InU.

Title: LEAGUE FOR CREEPING SOCIALISM

Key Words: During the recent American Spectacle, . . . she said, "I mean socialism."

Collation: 26; brown, misc. sheets; 13.7 x 22.6, 27.6 x 21.3 to 27.9 x 21.7; numbered consecutively by group but not continuously; 1, 3, 4, 6, 12, 13; good.

Contents: Complete; infrequently revised in pencil, blue ink, original copy with carbon.

Dates: Comp. ca. 1920. Pub. ?

273. Citation: LEONARD LYONS HAS ASKED ME; t. ms.; carbon; InU.

Title: [none]

Key Words: Leonard Lyons has asked me . . . adopted
to our uncertain times.

Collation: 4; white; 28 x 21.5; [1] 2–4; none; good.

Contents: Complete; unrevised.

Dates: Comp. ca. 1947. Pub. ?

274a. Citation: LETTERS TO JUDD; t. ms.; ribbon, pencil;
InU.

Title: LETTERS TO JUDD: An American Working-
man

Key Words: Judd is an old carpenter . . . you to join
our ranks.

Collation: 142; green; 14 x 21 to 28 x 21.6; consecutively numbered by chapter but not continuously; 8,
12, 16, 19, 27, 35, 37, 43, 45, 46, 50, 51, 60, 61, 65, 66,
69, 71, 72, 79, 80, 82, 83, 85, 87, 114, 120, 124, 131,
132, 138, 139, 142; good.

Contents: Complete; frequently revised in pencil.

Dates: Pub. 1 April 1926.

274b. Citation: LETTERS TO JUDD; t. ms., a. ms.; carbon,
pencil; InU.

Title: [none]

Key Words: ruin a business man and . . . richer and
the poor poorer.

Collation: 18; white, misc. sheets; 28.1 x 21.6; randomly numbered; 13; good.

Contents: Incomplete; moderately revised in pencil.

Dates: Pub. 1 April 1926.

274c. Citation: LETTERS TO JUDD; t. ms., a. ms.; carbon,
pencil; InU.

Title: Letter III

Key Words: My dear Judd: How does . . . has done to cause it!

Collation: 8; white, green; 27.9 x 21.5, 28.1 x 21.8; 1, 1a, 2, 2a, 2b–5; none; good.

Contents: Complete; moderately revised in pencil.

Dates: Pub. 1 April 1926.

274d. Citation: LETTERS TO JUDD; a. ms.; pencil; InU.

Title: JUDD

Key Words: This booklet was published in . . . ownership of the same big

Collation: 7; white watermarked; 21.6 x 13.9; randomly numbered; 2, 4, 6, 8, 10, 12; good.

Contents: Complete, moderately revised in pencil.

Dates: Pub. 1 April 1926.

274e. Citation: LETTERS TO JUDD; t. ms.; carbon; InU.

Title: LETTERS TO JUDD

Key Words: (This booklet was published in . . . one of his hunting trips.

Collation: 4; white; 28 x 21.6; 1–4; none; good.

Contents: Complete; unrevised.

Dates: Pub. 1 April 1926.

275a. Citation: LETTERS TO PERCY; t. ms.; ribbon, carbon; InU.

Title: LETTERS TO [FREDERICK (c.o.)] PERCY [(w.i. pencil)]

Key Words: When the Spanish novelist, Blasco . . . and waste of human life?

Collation: 117; white watermarked, green; 28 x 21.6, 28 x 21.7; consecutively numbered but not continuously; 74, 113, 116; good.

Contents: Complete; moderately revised in pencil.

Dates: Comp. ca. 1930? Pub. ?

275b. Citation: LETTERS TO PERCY; t. ms.; ribbon, carbon; InU.

Title: LETTERS TO PERCY

Key Words: When the Spanish novelist, Blasco . . . the same right to act.

Collation: 44; white watermarked; 27.9 x 21.6; randomly numbered; none; fair.

Contents: Incomplete (Preface only); infrequently revised in pencil.

Dates: Comp. ca. 1930. Pub. ?

276. Citation: LETTER TO AN APPEASER; t. ms.; carbon, InU.

Title: LETTER TO AN "APPEASING" [ing (c.o.); er (w.i. pencil)] [EDITOR (c.o.)]

Key Words: I have your letter in . . . unless and until that happens.

Collation: 12; white watermarked; 28 x 21.6; [1] 2–6, [1] 2–6; none; good.

Contents: Complete; infrequently revised in pencil.

Dates: Comp. ca. 1939. Pub. ?

277a. Citation: A LETTER TO THE CHICAGO CONFERENCE; t. ms.; carbon; InU.

Title: A LETTER TO THE CHICAGO CONFERENCE

Key Words: Dear Friends: I regret very . . . discussions of our national problem.

Collation: 6; blue watermarked; 28 x 21.7; [1] 2–6; none; good.

Contents: Complete; infrequently revised in pencil.

Dates: Pub. *Upton Sinclair's National EPIC News*, 29 July 1935.

277b. Citation: A LETTER TO THE CHICAGO CONFERENCE; t. ms.; carbon; InU.

Title: A LETTER TO THE CHICAGO CONFERENCE

Key Words: Dear Friends: I regret very . . . discussions of our national problem.

Collation: 12; white watermarked; 28 x 21.6; [1] 2–6, [1] 2–6; none; good.

Contents: Complete; two copies infrequently revised in pencil.

Dates: Pub. *Upton Sinclair's National EPIC News*, 29 July 1935.

278. Citation: [LETTER TO PRAVADA]; a. ms.; blue ink; InU.

Title: [none]

Key Words: Thank you for your invitation . . . of peace among all nations.

Collation: 3; yellow; 28 x 21.4; 1–3; none; good.

Contents: Complete; infrequently revised in pencil.

Dates: Comp. ca. 1925–30. Pub. ?

279. Citation: LETTER TO THE SOUTH; t. ms.; carbon; InU.

Title: LETTER TO THE SOUTH

Key Words: The writer of this letter . . . while we practice Council hate?

Collation: 3; white; 27.9 x 21.6; [1] 2–3; none; good.

Contents: Complete; unrevised.

Dates: Comp. ca. 1956. Pub. ?

280. Citation: LIFE IN AMERICA; t. ms.; carbon; InU.

Title: LIFE IN AMERICA

Key Words: I have been asked to . . . pay to grow it. Consequently

Collation: 12; white watermarked; 28 x 21.6; [1] 2–11, [1]; none; good.

Contents: Complete; infrequently revised in pencil; one complete carbon with an additional first page.

Dates: Comp. ca. October 1935. Pub. ?

281a. Citation: LIMBO ON THE LOOSE; t. ms.; ribbon; InU.

Title: LIMBO ON THE LOOSE | A Midsummer's Night's Dream

Key Words: In a remote portion of . . . ability to do it right!

Collation: 35; white, white watermarked; 27.9 x 21.6, 27.8 x 21.6; [1] 2–35; 6, 10, 13, 15, 21, 22, 33, 34; good.

Contents: Incomplete; moderately revised in pencil, not all in Sinclair's hand. Revised version of *The Way Out—What Lies Ahead for America* (1933).

Dates: Pub. 1948.

281b. Citation: LIMBO ON THE LOOSE; t. ms.; carbon; InU.

Title: LIMBO ON THE LOOSE

Key Words: In a remote portion of . . . that place also was vacant!

Collation: 22; white; 28 x 21.6; 1–22; none; good.

Contents: Complete; infrequently revised in pencil; Pamphlet; 1948, penciled in the upper right corner. Revised version of *The Way Out—What Lies Ahead for America* (1933).

Date: Pub. 1948.

282. Citation: THE LITERARY RADICAL; t. ms.; carbon; InU.

Title: THE LITERARY RADICAL

Key Words: First let us decide what . . . our money." I am prepared.

Collation: 7; white; 28 x 21.7; [1] 2–7; none; good.

Contents: Complete; infrequently revised in pencil.

Dates: Pub. *Writers' 1932 Year Book and Market Guide.*

283. Citation: A LITTLE CHILD SHALL LEAD THEM; t. ms.; carbon; InU.

Title: THE PECULIAR FEEBLENESS OF SOCIAL DEMOCRATS

Key Words: The cause of democratic socialism . . . Well, it can't be done.

Collation: 7; white; 27.9 x 21.3; [1] 2–7; none; good.

Contents: Complete; infrequently revised, in unidentified hand.

Dates: Pub. *Progressive*, April 1953.

284. Citation: LITTLE HALLS FOR RADICALS; t. ms.; carbon; InU.

Title: LITTLE HALLS FOR RADICALS

Key Words: The touchiest problem with all . . . "radicals" take part in athletics!

Collation: 7; white; 27.9 x 21.6; 1–7; none; good.

Contents: Complete; infrequently revised in pencil.

Dates: Comp. May, 1921. Pub. ?

285a. Citation: LITTLE STEEL; t. ms., a. ms.; ribbon, pencil; InU.

Title: [none]

Key Words: anybody get you excited. That's . . . a school of business administration.

Collation: 10; misc. sheets; 10.5 x 21.6 to 28 x 21.5; randomly numbered; none; good.

Contents: Incomplete; frequently revised in pencil; ms. is a partial, early draft.

Dates: Pub. ca. September 1938.

285b. Citation: LITTLE STEEL; t. ms.; ribbon; InU.

Title: LITTLE STEEL A Story

Key Words: It was eight o'clock of . . . fella fo' you." THE END.

Collation: 336; green, misc. sheets; 18.7 x 21.6 to 27.9 x 21.5; numbered consecutively by chapters but not continuously; 4, 7, 9, 18, 82, 92, 99, 109, 120, 131, 132, 163, 169, 209, 217, 271, 275; fair.

Contents: Incomplete; frequently revised in pencil; an early draft; missing Chap. 8 Part X.

Dates: Pub. ca. September 1938.

285c. Citation: LITTLE STEEL; t. ms.; ribbon, carbon; InU.

Title: LITTLE STEEL

Key Words: It was eight o'clock of . . . fella fo' you." The End.

Collation: 324; brown, white watermark; 28 x 21.6, 27.9 x 21.5; continuously numbered with variations; none; fair, spindled, punched for a two-ring binder.

Contents: Complete; moderately revised in pencil, red ink, red ink not in Sinclair's hand; it also bears regular, pencil markings of printer; ms. is printer's copy.

Dates: Pub. ca. September 1938.

286. Citation: LITTLE WORLD WAR IN A GARDEN; t. ms.; carbon; InU.

Title: LITTLE WORLD WAR IN A GARDEN

Key Words: There is distress in our . . . catch the spiders?" says C,

Collation: 10; green; 28 x 21.7; [1] 2–10; 6; good.

Contents: Complete; frequently revised in pencil.

Dates: Comp. ca. 1936. Pub. ?

287. Citation: LIZZIEVILLE; t. ms.; carbon; InU.

Title: LIZZIEVILLE

Key Words: Now all you niggers, sit . . . de grub to come eroun'!

Collation: 3; white watermarked; 28 x 21.7; unnumbered; none; fair.

Contents: Complete; unrevised; two copies of poem; beneath title: copyright, 1927.

Dates: Comp. 1927. Pub. ?

288. Citation: LOSING; t. ms.; carbon; InU.

Title: LOSING

Key Words: In some two hundred speeches . . . and give us its support.

Collation: 1; blue watermarked; 28 x 21.7; [1]; **none;** good.

Contents: Complete; infrequently revised in pencil; in upper right corner: Election Statements by U.S.

Dates: Comp. ca. 1934. Pub. ?

289. Citation: A LOST LEADER; t. ms.; carbon; InU.

Title: A LOST LEADER

Key Words: One morning recently I sat . . . and the American Liberty League.

Collation: 12; white watermarked; 27.9 x 21.6; [1] 2–6, [1] 2–6; none; good.

Contents: Complete; infrequently revised in pencil, not in Sinclair's hand; two carbons; one revised, the other not.

Dates: Pub. *EPIC News*, 14 March 1938.

290a. Citation: LOVE IN ARMS; t. ms.; ribbon; InU.

Title: LOVE IN ARMS | A Play in Three Acts

Key Words: Mrs. Ogden of the Ogden . . . while the curtain slowly falls).

Collation: 75; green, white watermarked; 28 x 21.6, 28.1 x 21.7; consecutively numbered by act but not continuously; 8, 32, 40, 50, 60, 72; good.

Contents: Complete; moderately revised in pencil.

Dates: Comp. ca. 1936. Unpublished.

290b. Citation: LOVE IN ARMS; t. ms.; carbon; InU.

Title: LOVE IN ARMS | A Play in Three Acts

Key Words: Mrs. Ogden of the Ogden . . . while the curtain slowly falls).

Collation: 82; white watermarked; 28 x 21.6; [1] 2–63, 63a, 64–75, 75a, 76–80; 14; good, punched for two-ring binder.

Contents: Complete; infrequently revised in pencil.

Dates: Comp. ca. 1936. Unpublished.

291. Citation: LOVE IN HANDCUFFS; t. ms.; carbon; InU.

Title: LOVE IN HANDCUFFS | Outline of a Motion Picture Story

Key Words: The story represents an effort . . . adore, embrace shyly and hesitatingly.

Collation: 8; white watermarked; 27.8 x 21.6; [1], 1a, [1], 1–4, 19; none; fair, stained and repaired, punched for three-ring binder.

Contents: Incomplete; unrevised.

Dates: Comp. ca. 1932. Pub. ?

292a. Citation: LOVE'S PILGRIMAGE; t. ms., a. ms.; purple carbon, pencil; InU.

Title: [none]

Key Words: fare of the book. "Here . . . matrons of the summer population.

Collation: 173; brown, white; 18.9 x 20.2 to 31.7 x 20.3; 2, 2a, 2b, 3–105, 6–46, 48–72, [73]; 9, 12, 20, 78, 92, 133, 137, 167; poor.

Contents: Incomplete; frequently revised in pencil, faded ink; ms. is labeled: Part I; Books I & II: late version, very minor changes.

Dates: Pub. March 1911.

292b. Citation: LOVE'S PILGRIMAGE; t. ms.; ribbon, purple carbon; InU.

Title: [none]

Key Words: Oh, if I might only . . . *are you going to do?*

Collation: 115; white legal paper, white watermarked; 32 x 20.4, 26.6 x 20.3 to 32 x 20.5; continuously numbered with variations; none; fair.

Contents: Incomplete; frequently revised in black ink, pencil; ms. labeled: Part I Book III.

Dates: Pub. March 1911.

292c. Citation: LOVE'S PILGRIMAGE; a. ms.; pencil; InU.

Title: BOOK IV | [THE (c.o.)]

Key Words: It was early one November . . . sup- | pose I should become | domestic!"

Collation: 135; brown lined; 11.2 x 20.3 to 26.9 x 19.7; 1–50, 50a, 50b, 51–100, 101 and 202, 3–34; 17, 33, 63, 69, 71, 72, 73, 85, 118; poor.

Contents: Incomplete; moderately revised in pencil; ms. is labeled: Part I, Book IV and V | late version, very minor changes.

Dates: Pub. March 1911.

292d. Citation: LOVE'S PILGRIMAGE; t. ms.; carbon; InU.

Title: [none]

Key Words: To my English Readers: | Five . . . reading of every young girl.

Collation: 14; white watermarked; 27.9 x 21.4; [1]–7, [1]–7; none; fair.

Contents: Complete; unrevised; ms. consists of two carbons of the introduction to *Love's Pilgrimage*; it is tagged and labeled: Intro. | (not in | print).

Dates: Pub. March 1911.

292e. Citation: LOVE'S PILGRIMAGE; t. ms.; ribbon; InU.

Title: *REPORT* | LOVE'S PILGRIMAGE | (*UPTON SINCLAIR*)

Key Words: The manuscript submitted contains six . . . an objection could be sustained.

Collation: 16; white; 26.6 x 18.9; [1]–16; none.

Contents: Complete; unrevised; folder is labeled: pre-publication report; report contains synopsis of novel plus some extracts.

Dates: Pub. March 1911.

293a. Citation: LOVE'S PROGRESS; t. ms.; black, blue ribbon, carbon; InU.

Title: LOVE'S PROGRESS, | A Novel by Upton Sinclair, | Author of THE JUNGLE, LOVE'S PIL-GRIMAGE, etc.

Key Words: It is not an easy . . . could never atone to them.

Collation: 793; white watermarked, white; 26.8 x 20.3 to 28.1 x 21.7, 26.6 x 20.3; randomly numbered; none; good, charred slightly.

Contents: Complete; moderately revised in black, blue ink, pencil; an early draft of ms., arranged in five manila folders: Folder #1 Books I–IV, Folder #2 Books V–VIII, Folder #3 Books IX–XI, Folder #4 Books XII–XIV, Folder #5 miscellaneous pages.

Dates: Comp. ca. 1911. Unpublished.

293b. Citation: LOVE'S PROGRESS; t. ms.; black, blue ribbon, carbon; InU.

Title: LOVE'S PROGRESS | A Novel by Upon Sin-clair, | Author of THE JUNGLE, LOVE'S PILGRIM-AGE, etc.

Key Words: The man sat in a . . . former things are passed away.' "

Collation: 518; white, white watermarked; 26.6 x 20.3 to 26.7 x 20.4, 23.2 x 21.6 to 28.1 x 21.7; randomly numbered; none; good.

Contents: Complete (save for a few pages); moderately revised in black, blue ink, pencil; a later draft of ms., arranged in three manila folders: Folder #1 I–IV, Folder #2 Books V–IX, Folder #3 Books X–XIV.

Dates: Comp. ca. 1911. Unpublished.

293c. Citation: LOVE'S PROGRESS; t. ms., a. ms.; black, blue carbon, pencil; InU.

Title: [none]

Key Words: The man sat in a . . . said, and that was all.

Collation: 513; white, misc. sheets; 26.7 x 20.3, 10.7 x 14.1 to 28.1 x 21.5; randomly numbered; none; poor, ms. is badly waterstained, stain grows increasingly severe until the last one-third of ms. is nearly illegible, spindled.

Contents: Complete (save for a few pages); moderately revised in black, blue ink, pencil; carbon of later draft, arranged in three manila folders; Folder #1 Books I–IV, Folder#2 Books V–IX, Folder #3 Books X–XIV.

Dates: Comp. ca. 1911. Unpublished.

294. Citation: THE MACHINE; t. ms.; blue carbon; InU.

Title: THE MACHINE

Key Words: Characters: (in order of appearance.) . . . door and stands watching. "Well?"

Collation: 13; white; 26.7 x 20.3; [2] 2–12; none; fair.

Contents: Complete; infrequently revised in pencil, hand unidentified.

Dates: Pub. 12–26 March 1911, 1912.

See also: SYNOPSIS OF METROPOLIS-MONEY-CHANGERS-MACHINE.

295a. Citation: THE MAGIC HUNTERS; t. ms.; carbon; InU.

Title: THE MAGIC HUNTERS | Outline of Scenario for movie or T-V story, dealing with the | cave paintings of Altamira, in Spain.

Key Words: On the Spanish side of . . . doctor would perform his incantations.

Collation: 2; white; 27.9 x 21.5; [1] 2; none; good.

Contents: Incomplete; infrequently revised in ink.

Dates: Comp. ca. 1950s? Pub. ?

295b. Citation: THE MAGIC HUNTERS; t. ms.; ribbon; InU.

Title: THE MAGIC HUNTERS | Outline of Scenario for movie or T-V story, dealing with the | cave paintings of Altamira, in Spain.

Key Words: On the Spanish side of . . . perform his incantations. All this

Collation: 2; white; 27.8 x 21.5; [1] 2; none; good.

Contents: Incomplete; infrequently revised in ink.

Dates: Comp. ca. 1950s? Pub. ?

296a. Citation: MAKING DEMOCRACY WORK; t. ms.; carbon; InU.

Title: MAKING DEMOCRACY WORK

Key Words: I am going to set . . . white or brown or black.

Collation: 3; white; 28 x 21.7; [1] 2–3; none; good.

Contents: Complete; infrequently revised in pencil.

Dates: Pub. *Common Sense*, September 1934.

296b. Citation: MAKING DEMOCRACY WORK; t. ms.; carbon; InU.

Title: MAKING DEMOCRACY WORK

Key Words: I am going to set . . . and poverty through uncounted ages.

Collation: 3; white; 28 x 21.7; [1] 2–3; none; good.

Contents: Complete; unrevised.

Dates: Pub. *Common Sense*, September 1934.

297a. Citation: MAKING OUR MINDS WORK; t. ms.; carbon; InU.

Title: MAKING OUR MINDS WORK: | Experiences in Mental Healing.

Key Words: Note to the Editor: This . . . the moral forces within us.

Collation: 54; white watermarked; 28 x 21.6; [1] 1–53; none; good.

Contents: Complete; infrequently revised in pencil.

Dates: Comp. ca. 18 April 1935. Pub. ?

297b. Citation: MAKING OUR MINDS WORK; t. ms.; carbon; InU.

Title: GOD AS SUGGESTION

Key Words: We have seen that the . . . the moral forces within us.

Collation: 41; white watermarked; 28 x 21.6; 13–53; none; good.

Contents: Incomplete; infrequently revised in pencil.

Dates: Comp. ca. 18 April 1935. Pub. ?

297c. Citation: MAKING OUR MINDS WORK; t. ms.; ribbon; InU.

Title: [none]

Key Words: planting of the idea of . . . the moral forces within us.

Collation: 40; white watermarked; 28 x 21.6; 14–53; none; good.

Contents: Incomplete; infrequently revised in pencil.

Dates: Comp. ca. 18 April 1935. Pub. ?

297d. Citation: MAKING OUR MINDS WORK; t. ms., a. ms.; ribbon, pencil; InU.

Title: MAKING OUR MINDS WORK: | Experiences in Mental Healing.

Key Words: Instructions for copying arti–cles from . . . the impression goes to work.

Collation: 4; white, blue; 16.2 x 21.6, 14 x 21.6; unnumbered; none; good, part on postal telegram form.

Contents: Complete; infrequently revised in pencil; appear to be corrections and additions to the ms.

Dates: Comp. ca. 18 April 1935. Pub. ?

298a. Citation: MAMMONART; t. ms., a. ms.; ribbon, carbon, pencil, ink; InU.

Title: [none]

Key Words: This is a long | critique . . . of megalomania, let me add.

Collation: 54; misc. sheets; 13.9 x 21.6 to 28.3 x 21.7; unnumbered; 3, 4, 7, 8, 9, 10, 15, 17, 35, 36, 37, 38, 39, 41, 42, 43, 44, 45, 46, 47, 48, 49; fair.

Contents: Incomplete; infrequently revised in black ink, pencil; ms. is a collection of notes and correction sheets for *Mammonart*; there are two notebooks of Sinclair's notes, correction sheets and carbons, and two sheets of misc. notes.

Dates: Pub. 1924–25, 1925.

298b.Citation: MAMMONART; t. ms., print; ribbon, print; InU.

Title: [none]

Key Words: Julius II died and Leo . . . and many another major prophet!

Collation: 172; white, green; 27.9 x 21.6, 27.9 x 21.5; 77–159, 269–271, 271a, 272–302, 302a, 303–338, 339–340, 340–353, 353a, 354–355; 88; fair, spindled.

Contents: Incomplete; infrequently revised in pencil and bears pencil notations of the printer; ms. is labeled: Mammonart | Chap. XXXI, p. 86 of book – LXXX.

Dates: Pub. 1924–25, 1925.

298c.Citation: MAMMONART; t. ms.; carbon; InU.

Title: CHAPTER [LVII (c.o.)] | THE ANGEL OF REVOLT.

Key Words: Percy Bysshe Shelley was born . . . find space for that | letter!

Collation: 16; white; 28 x 21.5; 254–265, 265a, 266–268; none; good.

Contents: Incomplete; infrequently revised in pencil, not all in Sinclair's hand; it also bears printing notations in pencil; ms. is labeled: Mammonart | Chap. LVIII– | LIX | carbon.

Dates: Pub. 1924–25, 1925.

298d. Citation: MAMMONART; t. ms.; ribbon; InU.

Title: CHAPTER LXXXVII. | HEADACHES AND DYSPEPSIA.

Key Words: We left the French novel . . . of generous and eager support.

Collation: 133; white; 28 x 21.6; 382–407, 407a, 408–443, 443a, 444–470, 470a, 471–511; none; good, spindled.

Contents: Incomplete; infrequently revised in pencil and bears the printer's notations in pencil; ms. is labeled: Mammonart | Chap. LXXXVII–CVIII.

Dates: Pub. 1924–25, 1925.

298e. Citation: MAMMONART; t. ms.; ribbon; InU.

Title: CHAPTER CX. | THE REBEL IMMORTAL.

Key Words: Henry James remarks somewhere that . . . the very best bourgeois style."

Collation: 9; white; 27.9 x 21.6; 520–528; none; good.

Contents: Incomplete; infrequently revised in pencil and bears the pencil notations; ms. labeled: Mammonart | CX–CXI (end of bk[)].

Dates: Pub. 1924–25, 1925.

299. Citation: [MANHATTAN, THY TOWERS AND TEMPLES]; a. ms.; pencil; InU.

Title: [none]

Key Words: Manhattan, thy towers and temples . . . fleeting and fragile than thee?

Collation: 1; white lined; 12.6 x 20.4; unnumbered; none; good.

Contents: Complete; unrevised; dated by Sinclair in note at bottom: (about 1906, probably)

Dates: Comp. ca. 1906. Pub. ?

300a. MARIE ANTOINETTE; t. ms., a. ms.; ribbon, carbon, pencil; InU.

Title: Outline Sketch of [quotation marks c.o.] DOOM: A DRAMA OF MARIE ANTOINETTE AND HER LOVER [quotation marks c.o.]

Key Words: Scene 1: Time, 1790. Place, . . . the scope of a drama.

Collation: 38; misc. sheets; 9.3 x 16.5 to 27.9 x 21.7; 1, 16, 2–17, [1], 18–32, 1a, A for 1a, A, 1b; 9, 11, 14, 16, 20, 24, 27, 29, 36, 37; good.

Contents: Complete; moderately revised in pencil; ms. is an outline sketch for "Marie Antoinette." Published in 1948 as *Marie and Her Lover*.

Dates: Pub. ca. July 1939.

300b. Citation: MARIE ANTOINETTE; t. ms., a. ms.; ribbon, pencil; InU.

Title: [Outline Sketch of (c.o.)] | DOOM: A DRAMA OF MARIE ANTOINETTE AND HER LOVER | In Three Acts [(w.i. pencil)]

Key Words: For a long time the . . . The outrage of the poor.

Collation: 146; misc. sheets; 21.5 x 14.5 to 27.9 x 21.7; numbered consecutively within each act but not continuously; 3, 7, 36, 63, 79, 97, 99, 144; fair.

Contents: Complete; frequently revised in pencil; ms. is tagged and labeled: Late draft, complete. Published in 1948 as *Marie and Her Lover*.

Dates: Pub. ca. July 1939.

300c. Citation: MARIE ANTOINETTE; t. ms.; ribbon; InU.

Title: PREFACE

Key Words: For a long time the . . . The outrage of the poor.

Collation: 144; white watermarked; 28 x 21.7; consecutively numbered within each act but not continuously; none; good, punched for two-ring binder.

Contents: Complete; infrequently revised in pencil; ms. has been tagged and labeled: Final copy, complete. Published in 1948 as *Marie and Her Lover*.

Dates: Pub. ca. July 1939.

301. Citation: THE MARSEILLAISE IN THE TOMBS; t. ms.; carbon; InU.

Title: THE MARSEILLAISE IN THE TOMBS

Key Words: First comes the settler with . . . the fury of that song.

Collation: 2; white; 13.9 x 21.6; unnumbered; none; good.

Contents: Complete; unrevised; two copies of poem.

Dates: Pub. *International Socialist Review*, July 1914.

302. Citation: McADOO AND OUR PRISONERS; t. ms.; carbon; InU.

Title: McADOO AND OUR PRISONERS

Key Words: Nearly three years ago I . . . your hands." | (They did so.).

Collation: 10; brown; 27.8 x 21.5; [1] 2–10; none; good.

Contents: Complete; unrevised; folder labeled: Appeal to Reason; note in pencil on page one: Mr. S took copy with him.

Dates: Pub. *Appeal to Reason*, 29 April 1922.

303. Citation: ME AND HAM FISH; t. ms.; carbon; InU.

Title: ME AND HAM FISH

Key Words: The Honorable Hamilton Fish, jr., . . .
hour week is no rem

Collation: 10; white; 27.5 x 21.2; unnumbered; none;
good.

Contents: Incomplete; infrequently revised in pencil.

Dates: Comp. ca. July 1935. Pub. ?

304. Citation: ME AND MAIN STREET; t. ms.; carbon;
InU.

Title: ME AND MAIN STREET

Key Words: Every once in a while . . . in a state of
nature.

Collation: 2; brown; 27.9 x 21.5; [1] 2; none; good.

Contents: Complete; unrevised; "Mailed 4/18/22" penciled on page 1, not in Sinclair's Hand; folder labeled:
"Appeal to Reason."

Dates: Pub. *Appeal to Reason*, 24 June 1922.

305. Citation: THE MEANING OF GRAFT; t. ms.; ribbon;
InU.

Title: Chapter XVII | THE MEANING OF GRAFT.
| (Investigates the corruption of government, its causes,
| its consequences, and the remedy therefor.)

Key Words: In the first decade of . . . they please!
Ten years ago

Collation: 86; brown; 9.6 x 21.7 to 28 x 21.6; randomly
numbered; 24; good, punched for two-ring binder.

Contents: Incomplete; infrequently revised in pencil;
contents includes following: Chapter XVII "The Meaning of Graft," Chapter XXI "The Question of Violence,"

Chapter XXII "Violence and Propaganda," Chapter XIII "Democracy or Empire," Chapter XIV "Working Versus Owning," Chapter XXV "The Problem of Propaganda," Chapter XXX "The Socialist Party," Chapter XXI "The Transition Stage," Chapter XXIX "The Labor Unions," Chapter XXVI "The Public Bank"; in manila folder labeled: Found with *Book of Society* mss (Not in book in any form).

Dates: Comp. ca. 1920–21. Pub. ?

See: THE BOOK OF LIFE

306. Citation: MEANING OF MOVEMENT TO END POVERTY IN CALIFORNIA [THE MEANING OF EPIC]; t. ms.; carbon; InU.

Title: THE MEANING OF EPIC

Key Words: The meaning of our movement . . . this seems clear to me.

Collation: 8; white watermarked, green; 28 x 21.6; [1] 2–4, [1] 2–4; none; good.

Contents: Complete; infrequently revised in pencil.

Dates: Pub. *Literary Digest*, 13 October 1934.

307. Citation: ME—MILLIONAIRE; t. ms.; ribbon; InU.

Title: ME—MILLIONAIRE

Key Words: You will recall how during . . . the organized greed of California.

Collation: 3; white watermarked; 28.1 x 21.6; [1] 2–3; none; good.

Contents: Complete; moderately revised in pencil.

Dates: Comp. ca. 1935. Pub. ?

308. Citation: MEMORIES OF EDWARD MACDOWELL;
t. ms.; ribbon; InU.

Title: MEMORIES OF EDWARD MACDOWELL

Key Words: Yesterday the postman brought a . . . so
many in one lifetime.

Collation: 11; brown, white; 27.9 x 21.5, 28 x 21.4; [1]
2–11; none; good.

Contents: Complete; infrequently revised in pencil.

Dates: Pub. *The Sackbut*, December 1925; also *American Mercury*, January 1926.

309. Citation: MEMORIES OF A MUCKRAKER; t. ms.;
carbon; InU.

Title: MEMORIES OF A MUCKRAKER

Key Words: I have been asked to . . . a new school
of muckrakers!

Collation: 8; white; 27.9 x 21.6; [1] 2–4, [1] 2–4; none;
good.

Contents: Complete; unrevised; "Printed in Exposé Feb.
56 Upton Sinclair" written in blue ink on page one of
each of the carbons.

Dates: Pub. *Exposé*, February 1956.

310. Citation: MEMORIES OF A MUCKRAKER; t. ms.;
ribbon, carbon; InU.

Title: MEMORIES OF A MUCKRAKER

Key Words: I have been asked to . . . a new school
of muckrakers!

Collation: 12; white; 27.9 x 21.6, 28 x 21.5; [1] 2–4,
[1] 2–4, [1] 2–4; none; good.

Contents: Complete; infrequently revised in pencil.

Dates: Pub. *Exposé*, February 1956.

311a. Citation: MENTAL RADIO; a. ms., print; pencil, ink, print; InU.

Title: [none]

Key Words: Dead Blacktower . . . | motion—the thing . . . paper & considered | drawing | it.

Collation: 48; misc. sheets; 6.3 x 14 to 55.7 x 39.5; unnumbered; 9, 12, 17, 18, 19, 26, 30, 32, 33, 35, 38, 42, 43, 46, 47; poor.

Contents: Incomplete; infrequently revised in pencil; ms. contains writing other than Sinclair's; folder labeled: MENTAL RADIO | 1927-1929 MISC | (BOOK COVER EXP'S).

Dates: Comp. 1927–29. Pub. 2 March 1930.

311b. Citation: MENTAL RADIO; a. ms.; pencil, ink; InU.

Title: [none]

Key Words: Exps. with brother "Bob" | July . . . "Concentrated on bald head" | U.S.

Collation: 65; misc. sheets, envelopes; 5.2 x 7.6 to 27.8 x 21.5; unnumbered; 3, 4, 6, 8, 9, 11, 13, 16, 17, 18, 19, 20, 30, 32, 34, 38, 39, 47, 48, 51, 53, 56, 62, 64; poor.

Contents: Incomplete; infrequently revised in black ink, pencil; it is impossible to be accurate on the various handwriting, but not all of it is Sinclair's; ms. labeled: MENTAL RADIO | EXP'S: 1928; this box and two that follow contain the experimental data that went into the book; they have been grouped and dated.

Dates: Comp. 1927–29. Pub. 2 March 1930.

311c. Citation: MENTAL RADIO; a. ms.; pencil, ink; InU.

Title: [none]

Key Words: 1st series | lock [?] tried | move . . . y spred out v shape.

Collation: 129; misc. sheets, envelope; 7.1 x 7.8 to 27.8 x 21.5; unnumbered; 1, 11, 17, 28, 35, 36, 65, 67, 68, 71, 74, 80, 83, 84, 86, 87, 92, 94, 95, 98, 99, 100, 102, 103, 106, 110, 112, 115, 116, 119, 120, 121, 123, 124, 125, 126, 128, 129; poor.

Contents: Incomplete; infrequently revised in pencil; it is in several different hands; folder labeled: MENTAL RADIO | EXP'S: 1929, Jan.–Feb. 2.

Dates: Comp. 1927–29. Pub. 2 March 1930.

311d. Citation: MENTAL RADIO; a. ms.; pencil, ink; InU.

Title: [none]

Key Words: Percipients No. 1 is halfway between . . . place (all visor of cap).

Collation: 120; misc. sheets, envelopes; 13.4 x 8.2 to 27.9 x 21.4; unnumbered; 12, 18, 21, 23, 30, 33, 45, 46, 52, 60, 69, 71, 72, 74, 104, 120; poor.

Contents: Incomplete; infrequent revisions in black ink, pencil; the notes bear the markings of several different hands; folder labeled: MENTAL RADIO | EXP'S: 1929, Feb. 6–11.

Dates: Comp. 1927–29. Pub. 2 March 1930.

311e. Citation: MENTAL RADIO; a. ms.; pencil, ink; InU.

Title: [none]

Key Words: "There is a flower basket . . . of [?] one end of egg.

Collation: 135; misc. sheets, envelopes; 3.2 x 9.8 to 21.5 x 15.8; unnumbered; 1, 3, 4, 27, 30, 48, 78, 106, 112, 123, 135; poor.

Contents: Incomplete; infrequently revised in black ink, pencil; ms. bears handwriting other than Sinclair's; folder labeled: MENTAL RADIO | EXP'S: 1929, Feb. 12–15.

Dates: Comp. 1927–29. Pub. 2 March 1930.

311f. Citation: MENTAL RADIO; a. ms.; ink, pencil; InU.

Title: [none]

Key Words: failure (but something living) | "Golf
. . . dog— | muzzle maybe pig | snort

Collation: 180; misc. sheets, envelopes; 10.8 x 7.8 to
23.7 x 10.8; unnumbered; 1, 20, 42, 68, 72, 73, 83, 87,
90, 91, 112, 129, 130, 144, 149, 150, 165, 180; poor.

Contents: Incomplete; infrequently revised in black ink,
pencil; notes in Sinclair's hand and others; folder labeled:
MENTAL RADIO | EXP'S: 1929, Feb. 16–28.

Dates: Comp. 1927–29. Pub. 2 March 1930.

311g. Citation: MENTAL RADIO; a. ms.; pencil, ink; InU.

Title: [none]

Key Words: (failure) Mrs. S. says that . . . living
thing | 4. only mgts [?] discovery [?]?

Collation: 124; misc. sheets, envelopes; 7.2 x 5.5 to
27.9 x 21.4; unnumbered; 3, 7, 16, 27, 28, 31, 62, 63,
64, 70, 89, 99, 116; poor.

Contents: Incomplete; infrequently revised in black
ink, pencil; ms. bears other handwriting than Sinclair's;
folder labeled: MENTAL RADIO | EXP'S: 1929,
MAR–APRIL.

Dates: Comp. 1927–29. Pub. 2 March 1930.

311h. Citation: MENTAL RADIO; a. ms.; pencil, ink; InU.

Title: [none]

Key Words: "May be profile of a . . . rosette | Daddy
Long Legs Spider.

Collation: 86; misc. sheets, envelopes; 7.5 x 9.9 to 21.5 x
15.5; unnumbered; 1, 15, 16, 24, 33, 40, 41, 72; poor.

Contents: Incomplete; infrequently revised in black ink,
pencil; some of the notations are in hands other than

Sinclair's; folder labeled: MENTAL RADIO | EXP'S: 1929, Aug–Nov.

Dates: Comp. 1927–29. Pub. 2 March 1930.

311i. Citation: MENTAL RADIO; a. ms., print; pencil, ink, print; InU.

Title: [none]

Key Words: Another variation of method | Pers. . . . it is foliage around him.

Collation: 54; misc. sheets, envelopes; 7.2 x 9.9 to 29.8 x 21.9; unnumbered; 1, 11, 16, 20, 26, 33, 43, 44, 46; poor.

Contents: Incomplete; infrequently revised in black ink, pencil; ms. bears handwriting other than Sinclair's; folder labeled: MENTAL RADIO | EXP'S: 1930, Jan.–May.

Dates: Comp. 1927–29. Pub. 2 March 1930.

311j. Citation: MENTAL RADIO; a. ms.; pencil, ink; InU.

Title: [none]

Key Words: 5 trials of which 2 . . . until all had been done.

Collation: 68; misc. sheets, envelopes; 13.9 x 10.5 to 27.8 x 21.5; unnumbered; 1, 2, 3, 4, 5, 6, 9, 10, 11, 12, 15, 24, 25, 37, 46, 48, 68; poor.

Contents: Incomplete; infrequently revised in black ink, pencil; ms. bears notations in other than Sinclair's hand; folder labeled: MENTAL RADIO | EXP'S: 1930, July–Aug.

Dates: Comp. 1927–29. Pub. 2 March 1930.

311k. Citation: MENTAL RADIO; a. ms.; pencil, ink; InU.

Title: [none]

Key Words: Bell & | flame of | light . . . legs of something" | partial success.

Collation: 17; misc. sheets; 7.7 x 12.6 to 21.6 x 14.3; unnumbered; none; poor.

Contents: Incomplete; infrequently revised in black ink, pencil; ms. bears notations in a hand other than Sinclair's; folder labeled: MENTAL RADIO | EXP'S: 1931 [sic].

Dates: Comp. 1927–29. Pub. 2 March 1930.

311l. Citation: MENTAL RADIO; a. ms.; pencil, ink; InU.

Title: [none]

Key Words: 1. Fox | Guns. | Horn with notes . . . in strange way. The mouthpiece.

Collation: 111; misc. sheets, envelopes; 9.8 x 7.3 to 23.7 x 10.3; unnumbered; 1, 17, 24, 35, 50, 93, 109, 110, 111; poor.

Contents: Incomplete; infrequently revised in black ink, pencil; ms. bears handwriting other than Sinclair's; folder labeled: MENTAL RADIO | EXP'S: DATE UN-KNOWN.

Dates: Comp. 1927–29. Pub. 2 March 1930.

311m. Citation: MENTAL RADIO; a. ms.; pencil; InU.

Title: [none]

Key Words: Lamb chop- | -eating- | -angel: | the . . . Drawings by US | (to try).

Collation: 121; misc. sheets, envelopes; 5 x 7.1 to 15.5 x 11.5; unnumbered; 16, 25, 66; poor.

Contents: Incomplete; infrequently revised in pencil; folder labeled: MENTAL RADIO | EXP'S: TO TRY.

Dates: Comp. 1927–29. Pub. 2 March 1930.

311n. Citation: MENTAL RADIO; t. ms., a. ms.; ribbon, carbon, pencil, ink; InU.

Title: [none]

Key Words: Jan. 31 aft nap | Dreamed . . . and Feoder are to sign.

Collation: 85; misc. sheets, envelopes; 10.2 x 4.5 to 27.9 x 21.5; unnumbered; 1, 2, 3, 4, 6, 7, 11, 13, 14, 15, 16, 22, 24, 29, 32, 35, 37, 40, 42, 44, 46, 48, 50, 51, 52, 53, 54, 56, 57, 58, 72, 74, 75, 76, 82, 85; poor.

Contents: Incomplete; infrequently revised in black ink, pencil; most of the ms. is Mrs. Sinclair's hand; there are, however, notes by Sinclair as well as others; folder labeled: MENTAL RADIO | re Craig's Dreams.

Dates: Comp. 1927–29. Pub. 2 March 1930.

3110. Citation: MENTAL RADIO; a. ms.; pencil, green ink; InU.

Title: [none]

Key Words: When I did these experiments . . . on top of — another" (over).

Collation: 30; misc. sheets; 7.2 x 9.8 to 27.8 x 21.6; unnumbered; 1, 2, 3, 4, 5, 6, 7, 8, 9, 10, 11, 12, 13, 14, 15, 16, 17, 18, 19, 20, 22, 25, 26, 30; fair.

Contents: Incomplete; infrequently revised in pencil; Sinclair does not seem to have contributed to these notes; folder labeled: MENTAL RADIO | re EXP'S | NOTES BY MCS.

Dates: Comp. 1927–29. Pub. 2 March 1930.

311p. Citation: MENTAL RADIO; photographs, positives (black and white), negatives; InU.

Title: [none]

Key Words: [none]

Collation: 32 positives, 282 negatives, misc. positives and negatives (black and white); 5.3 x 7.9 to 10.9 x 12.2 (pos), 4 x 6.9 to 10.9 x 14.2 (neg); numbered by figures; none; good.

Contents: These photos and negatives are photographs of Mary Craig Sinclair's experiments, primarily of the drawings used in them and a few of manuscript pages of her notes; numbers appear later in book versions; housed in box labeled: Telepathy negatives.

Dates: Comp. 1927–29. Pub. 2 March 1930.

311q. Citation: MENTAL RADIO; t. ms., a. ms.; ribbon, pencil; InU.

Title: [none]

Key Words: Note a for page 4 . . . paper | and enclose in envelopes.

Collation: 17; misc. sheets; 21.5 x 11.7 to 21.5 x 15.6; randomly numbered; 2, 4; poor.

Contents: Incomplete; moderately revised in pencil, some of the notes are not by Sinclair; folder labeled: MENTAL RADIO | PARTS OF BOOK MS; misc. collection.

Dates: Comp. 1927–29. Pub. 2 March 1930.

311r. Citation: MENTAL RADIO; t. ms., a. ms., print; carbon, pencil, ink, print; InU.

Title: [none]

Key Words: Mary Craig Sinclair, wife of . . . Subsequent to the *book* | U.S.

Collation: 61; misc. sheets, envelopes; 7.2 x 9.9 to 35.8 x 23.5; unnumbered; 3, 4, 24, 27, 32, 44; poor.

Contents: Incomplete; infrequently revised in pencil; folder labeled: MENTAL RADIO | MISC; it appears to be a collection of experiments and notes; some have been tagged and labeled.

Dates: Comp. 1927–29. Pub. 2 March 1930.

311s. Citation: MENTAL RADIO; t. ms., a. ms.; ribbon, carbon, pencil; InU.

Title: [none]

Key Words: Orchestra leader who had come . . . was taking a nap. She

Collation: 68; misc. sheets; 29.4 x 15.6 to 28.2 x 21.6; randomly numbered; 6, 10, 11, 15, 18, 19, 25, 26, 27, 28, 40, 47, 56, 57, 58, 63, 65, 67; good.

Contents: Incomplete; moderately revised in pencil, black ink; ms. is a collection of misc. sheets from *Mental Radio*; many of the groupings have been tagged and labeled.

Dates: Comp. 1927–29. Pub. 2 March 1930.

311t. Citation: MENTAL RADIO; t. ms.; carbon; InU.

Title: MIND-READING HAPPENS | And Here are the Proofs

Key Words: When I was a small . . . for most | certainly it happens.

Collation: 199; white; 27.9 x 21.6; continuously numbered with variations; none; good.

Contents: Incomplete; unrevised; ms. labeled as probably a middle version; it does contain the photo-illustrations and the text; they have been pasted in and numbered; some of the sheets have been tagged and labeled.

Dates: Comp. 1927–29. Pub. 2 March 1930.

311u. Citation: MENTAL RADIO; t. ms., a. ms., print; carbon, faded ink, print; InU.

Title: MENTAL RADIO | DOES IT WORK AND HOW? | BY UPTON SINCLAIR | with an introduction by professor William McDougall. | 278 illustrations

Key Words: Mr. Upton Sinclair needs no . . . to read on her trip.

Collation: 209; misc. sheets; 25.4 x 20.3 to 28.1 x 21.7; [1], 1–4, [1], 5–208; none; poor.

Contents: Complete; moderately revised in pencil, not in Sinclair's hand; the printer has made notations in blue and purple pencil and has renumbered the ms; folder labeled: Printer's copy; many of the pictures have been removed and have damaged the sheets; pages [1] and 1–4, [1] appear to be the pages from the London, T. Werner Laurie edition; they contain the usual publishing information plus a list of books by Sinclair available from Laurie.

Dates: Comp. 1927–29. Pub. 2 March 1930.

311v. Citation: MENTAL RADIO; t. ms.; carbon; InU.

Title: FOREWORD

Key Words: I contemplated a statement introducing . . . And now, to the text.

Collation: 10; white; 28 x 21.7; 1–5, 1–5; none; good.

Contents: Complete; unrevised; two carbons of the Foreword.

Dates: Comp. 1927–29. Pub. 2 March 1930.

311w. Citation: MENTAL RADIO; t. ms., mimeo; ribbon, mimeo; InU.

Title: FOREWORD

Key Words: I contemplated a statement introducing . . . without head. Albert Einstein.

Collation: 6; white; 28 x 21.7; 1–5 [1]; none; good.

Contents: Complete; infrequently revised in pencil; Foreword with mimeographed statement from Albert Einstein.

Dates: Comp. 1927–29. Pub. 2 March 1930.

311x. Citation: MENTAL RADIO; t. ms.; carbon; InU.

Title: MENTAL RADIO | Does it happen? And what does it mean?

Key Words: Pulitzer Prize-Winning novelist, author . . . in capital letters: TELEPATHY HAPPENS.

Collation: 3; tan; 28 x 21.7; [1]–3; none; good.

Contents: Complete; unrevised; ms. consists of what appears to be a promotion sheet.

Dates: Comp. 1927–29. Pub. 2 March 1930.

See: EXPLAIN THIS TO ME and MIND READING HAPPENS

312. Citation: A MESSAGE TO THE CZECH PEOPLE; t. ms.; carbon; InU.

Title: A MESSAGE TO THE CZECH PEOPLE

Key Words: I sit in my quiet . . . forces of freedom and truth.

Collation: 2; white; 28 x 21.6; [1] 2; good.

Contents: Complete; unrevised.

Dates: Comp. 8 July 1953. Pub. ?

313a. Citation: THE METROPOLIS; t. ms.; ribbon; CSt.

Title: SCENARIO OF VOL. 1 OF PROPOSED NOVEL

Key Words: The hero is a Southerner . . . himself. That he is in

Collation: 3; white; 28 x 21.7; [1] 2–3; good.

Contents: Complete; unrevised; apparently an early draft.

Dates: Pub. 14 March 1908.

See also: SYNOPSIS OF METROPOLIS—MONEY-CHANGERS—MACHINE.

313b. Citation: THE METROPOLIS; t. ms.; carbon; InU.

Title: THE METROPOLIS [underscored three times]

Key Words: Just three years ago there . . . object in making these prices.

Collation: 3; white watermarked; 27.5 x 21.4; 1–3; none; good.

Contents: Incomplete; unrevised.

Dates: Pub. 14 March 1908.

314a. Citation: THE MILLENNIUM; t. ms.; ribbon, carbon; InU.

Title: Preface to "The Millennium." ["'s (w.i. black ink)]

Key Words: "The plot of "The Millennium" . . . the food tablets for himself.

Collation: 104; brown, white; 28 x 21.6, 27.8 x 21.6; some unnumbered, others numbered consecutively but not continuously by groups; none; good.

Contents: Incomplete; infrequently revised in pencil, black, faded ink; folder labeled: Millennium | Misc. | None in printed version; some of the materials included are: Preface to The Millennium, a synopsis by Hunter Kimbrough, COMMENTARY ON "MILLENNIUM" SCRIPT, Notes for First Part of Scenario, "Millennium," "MILLENNIUM" A Scenario by Upton Sinclair, SUGGESTIONS ABOUT THE CHARACTERS | OF THE MILLENNIUM, and Synopsis of "The Millennium" | by Upton Sinclair.

Dates: Comp. 1907–8. Pub. 1914, 1924.

314b. Citation: THE MILLENNIUM; t. ms.; ribbon, black, blue carbon; InU.

Title: The Milleneum [sic] or [w.i. pencil] | THE CHOSEN PEOPLE. | A comedy in four acts.

Key Words: Scene: —Foreground is the entrance . . .
you find? (see next page).

Collation: 170; white, white laid paper; 26.6 x 20.3,
26.9 x 20.4; numbered consecutively by acts but not
continuously; 169; fair, punched for a two-ring binder.

Contents: Incomplete; infrequently revised in pencil;
folder labeled: Millennium | (in play form); all but the
final loose sheets are bound by act with two brass studs.

Dates: Comp. 1907–8. Pub. 1914, 1924.

314c. Citation: THE MILLENNIUM; t. ms.; carbon; InU.

Title: THE MILLENNIUM: A STORY | By Upton
Sinclair | Author of the "Jungle," "Sylvia," etc.

Key Words: It was shortly before the . . . Sarita! Come,
Helen—my wife!

Collation: 124; white laid paper, white; 26.7 x 20.6,
27.8 x 21.5; [1]–3, 3–14, [15–16], 17–53, 54aa, 54–66,
68–114; none; poor, spindled.

Contents: Incomplete; moderately revised in pencil,
black ink; ms. labeled: Early, incomplete draft, p. 7–90
(printed) | [Chapt. I–IX].

Dates: Comp. 1907–8. Pub. 1914, 1924.

314d. Citation: THE MILLENNIUM; t. ms.; black, blue
ribbon; InU.

Title: "THE MILLENNIUM" A COMEDY IN
FOUR ACTS

Key Words: Act 1: The opening ball upon . . . arms
and Eloise in Reggie's.)

Collation: 157; blue, misc. sheets; 20.5 x 14.2, 27.9 x
21.7 to 28 x 21.6; consecutively numbered by act but
not continuously; none; good, spindled.

Contents: Complete; infrequently revised in black ink;
an early draft; page one is blue cloth bound paper, title

page: Selwyn and Company, Authors' Representatives, 1451 Broadway, New York City at top, followed by title.

Dates: Comp. 1907–8. Pub. 1914, 1924.

314e. Citation: THE MILLENNIUM; t. ms.; carbon; InU.

Title: "THE MILLENNIUM" A COMEDY IN FOUR ACTS

Key Words: Act 1: The opening ball upon . . . arms and Eloise in Reggie's.)

Collation: 67; white watermarked; 27.9 x 21.5; consecutively numbered by act but not continuously; none; good, spindled.

Contents: Complete; unrevised; carbon of later draft.

Dates: Comp. 1907–8. Pub. 1914, 1924.

314f. Citation: THE MILLENNIUM; t. ms.; carbon; InU.

Title: *THE MILLENNIUM* A FARCE COMEDY OF THE FUTURE

Key Words: CAST: BILLY KINGDOM, Handsome young . . . generation lived happily forever afterwards.

Collation: 22; white; 27.8 x 21.5; unnumbered; 11; fair.

Contents: Incomplete; infrequently revised in blue ink, not in Sinclair's hand; ms. consists of two carbons of the same material.

Dates: Comp. 1907–8. Pub. 1914, 1924.

314g. Citation: THE MILLENNIUM; t. ms.; black, blue carbon; InU.

Title: THE MILLENNIUM | A comedy in four Acts.

Key Words: Scene: —Foreground is the entrance . . . seeds of wrong destroy! | CURTAIN.

Collation: 147; white, misc. sheets; 26.7 x 20.4, 26.6 x 20.4 to 28.5 x 22; numbered consecutively by acts but not continuously; none; fair, punched for two-ring binder.

Contents: Complete; infrequently revised in pencil, black ink, not in Sinclair's hand; folder labeled: *Millennium* | Play Form; the title page has the label: THE LITERARY AGENCY OF LONDON; it was apparently an agent's copy; it appears to be a complete ms.

Dates: Comp. 1907–8. Pub. 1914, 1924.

314h. Citation: THE MILLENNIUM; t. ms.; black ribbon; InU.

Title: THE MILLENNIUM [A Story (c.o.)] | A Comedy of the Year 2000 [(w.i. pencil)]

Key Words: This Little farce comedy of . . . reigned forever after! | THE END.

Collation: 184; brown; 28 x 21 to 28 x 21.9; [2], 1–89, 90–100, 101–134, 135–136, 137–183; none; poor, punched for two-ring binder.

Contents: Complete; moderately revised in pencil; black ink notes not in Sinclair's hand; perhaps they along with some pencil notations belong to the printers, as this appears to be a complete printer's copy; ms. labeled: Final complete draft. | almost no corrections.

Dates: Comp. 1907–8. Pub. 1914, 1924.

315. Citation: MILLIONS DANCE; t. ms.; carbon; InU.

Title: MILLIONS DANCE

Key Words: Scene of the Story: New . . . to produce in the country.

Collation: 5; white watermarked; 27.9 x 21.6; [1] 2–5; none; fair, stained, repaired.

Contents: Complete; unrevised.

Dates: Comp. ca. 1930–32. Pub. ?

316. Citation: MIND IS A FORCE; t. ms.; carbon; InU.

Title: *MIND IS A FORCE*

Key Words: Here, in the peace and . . . seed ye can move mountains."

Collation: 2; white watermarked; 28 x 21.7; [1] 2; none; good.

Contents: Complete; unrevised.

Dates: Comp. ca. 1954. Pub. ?

317. Citation: MIND READING HAPPENS; t. ms., a. ms.; ribbon, pencil, ink; InU.

Title: TELEPATHY | MIND-READING HAPPENS | And Here Are the Proofs.

Key Words: When I was a small . . . swirling scarf tied around head."

Collation: 100; white, green; 21.8 x 13.8 to 28.2 x 21.6, 21.7 x 13.8 to 27.9 x 21.4; continuously numbered with variations; none; good.

Contents: Complete; frequently revised in pencil.

Dates: Comp. ca. 1930. Pub. ?

See: MENTAL RADIO

318. Citation: MOBILIZING THE MOVIES; t. ms.; carbon; InU.

Title: MOBILIZING THE MOVIES

Key Words: I do not suppose I . . . American Legion convention as follows:

Collation: 4; blue watermarked; 27.9 x 21.6; [1] 2–3, [1]; 4; good.

Contents: Incomplete; moderately revised in pencil; essay incomplete but includes a press statement on the verso of sheet four.

Dates: Pub. *Upton Sinclair's National EPIC News*, 19 August 1935.

319. Citation: THE MONEY-CHANGERS; t. ms.; carbon; InU.

Title: THE MONEY CHANGERS

Key Words: Allan Montague is the grandson . . . of the money-changers. Happy ending!

Collation: 23; white watermarked; 28.5 x 21.6; [1] 2–23; none; good.

Contents: Complete; infrequently revised in pencil, black ink.

Dates: Pub. 19 September 1908.

See also: SYNOPSIS OF METROPOLIS-MONEY CHANGERS-MACHINE.

320a. Citation: MONEY WRITES!; t. ms.; carbon; InU.

Title: [XXVII (c.o.)] | *The Critic-Caste*

Key Words: Every successful artist becomes host . . . wrought in the new Russia!

Collation: 61; white; 27.9 x 21.7 to 28 x 21.6; 121–129, 140–147, 144–169, 140–143, 156–196; none; fair.

Contents: Incomplete; infrequently revised in pencil, not in Sinclair's hand; folder labeled: *Money Writes* | Misc. pages.

Dates: Pub. ca. 1 November 1927.

320b. Citation: MONEY WRITES!; t. ms., a. ms.; carbon, pencil; InU.

Title: INDEX Money Writes [(w.i. pencil)]

Key Words: During the days when I . . . wrought in the new Russia!

Collation: 46; white, watermarked green; 27.6 x 21.5 to 27.9 x 21.7; [1]–4, 1–24, 24a, 25–30, 30a, 31–33, 34–35, 36–40; 5, 6, 15, 43; fair.

Contents: Incomplete; infrequently revised in pencil; folder labeled: *Money Writes* (Chaps. XXX–XXXVI | Holograph).

Dates: Pub. ca. 1 November 1927.

320c. Citation: MONEY WRITES!; t. ms.; ribbon, carbon; InU.

Title: VII | *Incense to Mammon*

Key Words: Ruling-classes have existed for a . . . masses can achieve their freedom.

Collation: 100; white; 28 x 21.6; 64–96, 98–139, 144–168; none; fair, spindled.

Contents: Incomplete; infrequent revisions in pencil, not all in Sinclair's hand; portions of the ms. were printer's copy and bear printer's notations in pencil; folder labeled: *Money Writes* | Chaps. XVII–XXXV | Typewritten | Incomplete.

Dates: Pub. ca. 1 November 1927.

320d. Citation: MONEY WRITES!; t. ms., a. ms.; carbon, pencil; InU.

Title: [none]

Key Words: insert footnote galley 32 | *My . . . me as merely a reporter,

Collation: 2; brown; 27.9 x 21; unnumbered; 1; poor.

Contents: Incomplete; infrequently revised in pencil; folder labeled: *Money Writes* | galley proof addition; the second sheet is a carbon of the first.

Dates: Pub. ca. November 1927.

321. MORAL NEW ZEALAND; t. ms.; ribbon; InU.

Title: MORAL NEW ZEALAND

Key Words: Some time ago I received . . . feed them through the nose.

Collation: 2; brown; 27.8 x 21.6; [1] 2; none; good.

Contents: Complete; infrequently revised in pencil; someone has written on page 1 in pencil: Mailed to U.S. 4/14/22; folder labeled: "Appeal to Reason."

Dates: Pub. *Appeal to Reason*, 6 May 1922.

322. Citation: MOST HAUNTED HOUSE; t. ms.; ribbon; InU.

Title: MOST HAUNTED HOUSE | A Motion Picture Scenario

Key Words: This story is based upon . . . can't forget that shattered glass!

Collation: 38; white, white watermarked; 27.9 x 21.6, 28 x 21.6; 1–38; 4, 15; good.

Contents: Complete; frequently revised in pencil; in manila folder labeled: Most haunted house.

Dates: Comp. ca. 1947. Unpublished.

323a. Citation: MOUNTAIN CITY; t. ms., a. ms.; ribbon, pencil; InU.

Title: Mountain City | A Novel

Key Words: The great transcontinental railroad tracks . . . man in America!" The End.

Collation: 426; green, misc. sheets; 27.9 x 21.6; numbered consecutively in groups but not continuously; 40, 41, 71, 72, 78, 85, 113, 118, 127, 128, 176, 177, 189, 199, 213, 223, 268, 296, 303, 353, 365; good.

Contents: Complete; frequently revised in pencil; folder labeled: Mountain City | Earlier draft | complete.

Dates: Pub. 21 February 1930.

323b. Citation: MOUNTAIN CITY; t. ms.; ribbon; InU.

Title: MOUNTAIN CITY | A NOVEL

Key Words: The great transcontinental railroad tracks . . . man in America! | The End.

Collation: 367; white; 28 x 21.8; 1–12, 20–235, 235a, 236–305, 305a, 305b, 306–338, 338a, 339–370; none; fair, spindled.

Contents: Incomplete; infrequently revised in pencil; bears printer's notations in regular, orange pencil; folder labeled: Mountain City | A draft | (Printer's | copy) | Lacks pp. 13–19.

Dates: Pub. 21 February 1930.

323c. Citation: MOUNTAIN CITY; t. ms., a. ms.; ribbon, pencil; InU.

Title: [none]

Key Words: clean white collars and beautiful . . . did it become really (over)

Collation: 8; green, white; 27.9 x 21.6, 28 x 21.7; randomly numbered; 8; good.

Contents: Incomplete; infrequently revised in pencil; folder labeled: *Mountain City* | Misc. pages. | Not the pages missing | from Printer's copy.

Dates: Pub. 21 February 1930.

324. Citation: MR. AND MRS. FRANKLIN SMITH; t. ms.; carbon; InU.

Title: [none]

Key Words: Mr. & Mrs. Franklin Smith . . . second, Elvira was a woman.

Collation: 8; white; 27.8 x 21.5; [1] 2–8; none; good.

Contents: Complete (story); infrequently revised in pencil.

Dates: Comp. ? Pub. ?

325. Citation: MRS. DILLING ENTERTAINS; t. ms.; carbon; InU.

Title: MRS DILLING ENTERTAINS

Key Words: For the most part I . . . and so I become sad.

Collation: 12; white watermarked, blue; 28 x 21.6; [1] 2–6, [1] 2–6; none; good.

Contents: Complete; infrequently revised in pencil.

Dates: Pub. *EPIC News,* 16 November 1936.

326a. Citation: MR. UPTON SINCLAIR LEWIS [BROWNE]; t. ms.; ribbon; InU.

Title: MR. UPTON SINCLAIR LEWIS BROWNE

Key Words: Mr. James A. Michener has . . . box of persimmons, Mr. Lewis."

Collation: 2; yellow; 28 x 21.5; [1] 2; none; good.

Contents: Complete; moderately revised in blue ink, pencil.

Dates: Pub. *Harper's Magazine,* March 1961.

326b. Citation: MR. UPTON SINCLAIR LEWIS [BROWNE]; t. ms.; carbon; InU.

Title: MR. UPTON-SINCLAIR-LEWIS-BROWNE

Key Words: Mr. James A. Michener has . . . box of persimmons, Mr. Lewis."

Collation: 2; white; 28 x 21.7; unnumbered; none; good.

Contents: Complete; infrequently revised in blue ink.

Dates: Pub. *Harper's Magazine,* March 1961.

326c. Citation: MR. UPTON SINCLAIR LEWIS; t. ms.; carbon; InU.

Title: [none]

Key Words: Lewis Browne, American scholar, author
. . . has never been known before."

Collation: 9; white; 28 x 21.7; 2–10; none; good.

Contents: Incomplete; infrequently revised in pencil.

Dates: Pub. *Harper's Magazine*, March 1961.

327a. Citation: MUCKRAKERS; t. ms.; ribbon; InU.

Title: PREFACE TO "THE MUCKRAKERS"

Key Words: I believe that I am . . . scare away my half-million subscribers?"

Collation: 9; white; 28 x 21.7; [1] 2–9; none; good.

Contents: Complete; moderately revised in blue ink.

Dates: Comp. ca. 1962. Unpublished.

327b. Citation: MUCKRAKERS; t. ms.; carbon; InU.

Title: PREFACE TO "THE MUCKRAKERS"

Key Words: I believe that I am . . . scare away my half-million subscribers?"

Collation: 9; white; 28 x 21.7; [1] 2–9; none; good.

Contents: Complete; infrequently revised in blue ink.

Dates: Comp. ca. 1962. Unpublished.

328. Citation: MUSIC MADE VISIBLE; t. ms.; purple carbon; InU.

Title: MUSIC MADE VISIBLE: | An Account of the Dalcroze System of Eurhythmics

Key Words: I suppose that everyone who . . . alone great art can spring.

Collation: 19; white watermarked, brown; 25.5 x 20.3 to 26 x 20.3, 26.4 x 21; [2], [1] 2–16 [1]; none; good.

Contents: Complete; infrequently revised in faded ink; also included with the ms. in a pocket in the front cover of The Paget Literary Agency binder, 12 photographs and 2 sheets apparently of explanations in German, all illustrating the article; bound in brown wrappers with three brass studs.

Dates: Comp. ca. 1913–15. Pub. ?

329. Citation: MY ANTI-HEADACHE DIET [NO MORE HEADACHES!]; t. ms.; black, red ribbon, black carbon; InU.

Title: NO MORE HEADACHES!

Key Words: For almost half a century . . . benefit of it to others.

Collation: 39; white watermarked, misc. sheets; 28 x 21.5, 28 x 21.6; [1] 2–7, [1] 2–7, [1] 2–6, [1] 2–7, [1] 2–6, [1] 2–6; none; good.

Contents: Complete; infrequently revised in pencil, ink; in manila folder labeled: Upton Sinclair Writings; revised original, carbons of revisions; original and carbon of further revisions.

Dates: Pub. *Harper's Magazine*, December 1963.

330. Citation: MY AUTOBIOGRAPHY BY CHARLES CHAPLIN, A REVIEW; t. ms.; ribbon, carbon; InU.

Title: MY AUTOBIOGRAPHY BY CHARLES CHAPLIN

Key Words: Here is something that comes . . . lucky as to be able.

Collation: 8; white, yellow; 28 x 21.7; [1] 2–3, [1] 2–3, [1] 2; none; good.

Contents: Complete; infrequently revised in pencil; review by Sinclair of the Chaplin book; revised original and carbon plus carbon of reviewed typed copy.

Dates: Comp. ca. 1964. Pub. ?

331. Citation: MY BATTLE; t. ms.; carbon; InU.

Title: MY BATTLE

Key Words: In my novels which have . . . now to the first adventure!

Collation: 14; white watermarked; 28 x 21.6; [1] 2–4, [1] 2–3, [1] 2–4, [1] 2–3; none; good.

Contents: Complete; infrequently revised in pencil, ink, unidentified hand.

Dates: Comp. ca. 1945. Pub. ?

332. Citation: MY CAUSE; t. ms.; carbon; InU.

Title: My Cause

Key Words: I, Upton Sinclair, would-be singer and . . . and the cost, so long.

Collation: 4; white watermarked; 28 x 21.6; [1] 2–4; none; good.

Contents: Incomplete; unrevised.

Dates: Pub. *Independent*, 14 May 1903.

333a. Citation: MY COUSIN MRS. SIMPSON; t. ms.; ribbon; InU.

Title: MY COUSIN MRS. SIMPSON

Key Words: As I sit down to . . . that the story of little

Collation: 4; white watermarked, green; 28 x 21.6; [1] 2–3 [1]; none; good.

Contents: Incomplete; infrequently revised in pencil.

Dates: Comp. ca. December 1936. Pub. ?

333b. Citation: MY COUSIN MRS. SIMPSON; t. ms.; carbon; InU.

Title: MY COUSIN MRS. SIMPSON

Key Words: As I sit down to . . . woman from Biddle street, Baltimore.

Collation: 22; white watermarked; 27.9 x 21.6; [1] 2, 2a, 3–10, 10a, 11–20; none; good.

Contents: Complete; infrequently revised in pencil.

Dates: Comp. ca. December 1936. Pub. ?

333c. Citation: MY COUSIN MRS. SIMPSON; t. ms.; ribbon, carbon; InU.

Title: MY COUSIN MRS. SIMPSON

Key Words: As I sit down to . . . to life in our imaginations.

Collation: 55; white watermarked, misc. sheets; 14.8 x 21.6 to 28 x 21.5, 28 x 21.6; randomly numbered; 2, 3, 5, 6, 11, 17; good.

Contents: Complete; moderately revised in pencil.

Dates: Comp. ca. December 1936. Pub. ?

See: WALLY FOR QUEEN

334. Citation: MY DEAR TED COOK; t. ms.; carbon; InU.

Title: [none]

Key Words: My dear Ted Cook: My . . . yours, I pull my own.

Collation: 1; white; 28 x 21.7; unnumbered; none; fair.

Contents: Complete (poem); unrevised.

Dates: Comp. 1920s. Pub. ?

335a. Citation: MY FRIENDS, THE PEOPLE OF JAPAN;
t. ms.; carbon; InU.

Title: MY FRIENDS THE [parentheses & crossings-
out in pencil] OF JAPAN (w.i. pencil)

Key Words: I have been honored with . . . our civilization hope to survive.

Collation: 6; white; 27.9 x 21.6; [1] 2–6; none; good.

Contents: Complete; frequently revised in pencil.

Dates: Pub. *Unity,* September–October 1955.

335b. Citation: MY FRIENDS, THE PEOPLE OF JAPAN;
t. ms.; carbon; InU.

Title: MY FRIENDS, THE PEOPLE OF JAPAN

Key Words: I have been honored with . . . for con-
cessions. But their pledged

Collation: 5; white; 28.1 x 21.7; [1] 2–5; none; fair.

Contents: Incomplete; unrevised.

Dates: Pub. *Unity,* September–October 1955.

335c. Citation: MY FRIENDS, THE PEOPLE OF JAPAN;
t. ms.; ribbon, carbon; InU.

Title: MY FRIENDS, THE PEOPLE OF JAPAN

Key Words: I have been honored with . . . our civilization hope to survive.

Collation: 12; white watermarked; 28.1 x 21.8; [1] 2–6,
[1] 2–6; none; good.

Contents: Complete; unrevised; signed on last page of
both copies in blue ink; upper left bears address and
date: Monrovia, Calif. | May, 1955.

Dates: Pub. *Unity,* September–October 1955.

1 Sinclair's checklist for readers of the manuscript of *O Shepherd, Speak!*
This practice was followed for all volumes in the Lanny Budd series. Reproduced
by courtesy of the Lilly Library, Indiana University.

bered it. Kate was married to a civil engineer, Walter was
ill—and so on.

At last I saw my childhood playmate off in a high-powered
military car, with a chauffeur in khaki and a guard to ride at
his side, both with holsters at their belts; most imposing. It
was fine local color for a novelist—and incidentally it was a
knockout for the American Legion chiefs of Santa Barbara.
Since I was cousin-in-law to the commander-in-chief of this
military district, it was impossible to prevent my speaking in
favor of the public ownership of water power in California!

VII

To return to childhood days: my summers were spent at
the country home of the Bland family, or with my mother at
summer resorts in Virginia. My father would be "on the
road," and I remember his letters, from which I learned the
names of all the towns in Texas, and the merits of the leading
hotels. If my father was "drinking," we stayed in some low-
priced boarding-house if he was keeping his pledges, we
stayed at one of the springs hotels. My earliest memory of
these hotels is of a "fancy-dress ball, for which my mother
had fixed me up as a baker, with a white coat and long trousers
and a round cap. That was all right, except that I was sup-
posed to carry a wooden tray with rolls on it, which interfered
with my play. Another story was told to me recently by one
of the victims, whom I happened to meet. I had whooping-
cough, and the other children were forbidden to play with
me; this seemed to me injustice, so I chased them and coughed

2 Sinclair's revisions of a copy of *American Outpost,* the text of which was
substantially incorporated into *The Autobiography of Upton Sinclair.* Reproduced
by courtesy of the Lilly Library, Indiana University.

#11. One of the charms of Mary Burke was this fact
that close beneath the surface of her wit lay all the melancholy
of her race; some of the things she said made one think of old
folk-songs. And her features reflected this quality of hers;
Her grey eyes, were real close and steady, set under sharply defined dark brows, which did not at all match her hair. Her lips
also were sharply defined, and straight, almost without curves, so that
it seemed as if her mouth had been painted in carmine upon her
face. These features gave her, when she stared at you, an
aspect vivid and startling, bold, with a touch of defiant
monkery. But then she would smile, and the red lips would curve
into gentler lines, and the grey eyes would become wistful, and
seemingly darker in color. A winsome Irish lass, indeed, thought
Hal

asked her name, and she told him,
well know the truth," she added, "'Tis
'Red Mary', along of this hair."

answered, "'Twas a red rose I saw up on the mountain."

"Ah!" she cried. "'Tis a fine, soothin' tongue ye
have with ye, Mr. Smith! It must be a joy to your friends!
But why should ye bring it to a place like North Valley?"

"'Tis the meals I have to have," he answered, "The

3 Revised typescript of *King Coal*. The extensive revisions suggest the difficulties Sinclair faced with this novel. Reproduced by courtesy of the Lilly Library, Indiana University.

Crauder: Held up John Mc ormick and ᴹelvin Adams pres of rwy Caths
believe frame up--rich say get him before he gets us.   Indict Allen for
taking money from client, embezzlement, produced man to testify.

Cookley free man, and rich.   ᴸittle public opinion but
much public sentiment   Dan Coakley bartender, St car conductor, re-
porter lawyer built up machine wit politicians and judges made-up evidence more potent than real, truth is not mighty in law.   Man killed
by merchants auto, damage suit, chauf. operator, went out of way, picked
up girls, drunk, frame evidence.

Lawrence strike, dynamite Wood case, leaders of bar, include Coakley
ᴱmerson ᴹotor cases, demonstration car, stock-selling scheme, 5000 pay to
bribe dist atty--came out in N.Y trial.   Long standing feud bet
Godfrey L Cabot and Felletier, Cᵁs petition ignored.   Miskawan
Manor case ith movies, indict Fierce and Allen. Fonzi case Coakley as
counsel. C disbarred   Scandal reached Palmer Complete record of
charges in ᴬass Reports. ᴶim Reed of ᴹo defend Pell.

15 yrs ago most conspicuous Cath layman. Handsome young bachelor
last days, yellow, skin baggy.   Herric financed crew to Oxford.
George Crocker wealthy B lawyer, blue blood, relatives quarreled with
wife, left her power over money, with right to select which child got
money. Family smarted fought will. "Soft spot in canteloupe." Jury
"things not left to mercy of chance."   Will broken; one of sons in-
dicted for bribery, the "bagman."

Hotel with double set of books, man paid $40,000 to hush up; sue
Coakley to get it back, C say had no case in equite, not clean hands
judge decide in C's favor and then go supr court. Fell. made campaign to
get Crocker then he engage Coakley (partner) and Pell drop case.

How many old people got any good at home? Insolence of behavior
Rouge lips in public. Screwed down safety valves girls fling arms around
boy's neck in restaurant ᴸaughter drank cocktail hit her with base
ball bat   Horrified use to park corsets for dance, now not wear any

4 Typescript version of field notes for *Boston*. Reproduced by courtesy of the
Lilly Library, Indiana University.

336a. Citation: MY INTERVIEW WITH MUSSOLINI;
t. ms.; ribbon; InU.

Title: MY INTERVIEW WITH MUSSOLINI

Key Words: My Interview with Mussolini was . . .
uses he makes of it.

Collation: 7; green watermarked; 27.9 x 21.6; 1–7;
none; good.

Contents: Complete; moderately revised in pencil.

Dates: Pub. *Forward*, 14 March 1936.

336b. Citation: MY INTERVIEW WITH MUSSOLINI;
t. ms.; ribbon, carbon; InU.

Title: MY INTERVIEW WITH MUSSOLINI

Key Words: My interview with Mussolin was . . .
use he makes of it.

Collation: 21; white watermarked; 28.1 x 21.6; [1] 2–7,
[1] 2–7, [1] 2–7; none; good.

Contents: Complete; three copies infrequently revised
in pencil.

Dates: Pub. *Forward*, 14 March 1936.

336c. Citation: MY INTERVIEW WITH MUSSOLINI;
t. ms.; carbon; InU.

Title: MY INTERVIEW WITH MUSSOLINI

Key Words: My interview with Mussolini was . . .
use he makes of it.

Collation: 9; white watermarked; 28.1 x 21.6; [2] 2–7,
[1]; none; good.

Contents: Complete; infrequently revised in pencil; in
cover labeled: Article Department: from Brandt &
Brandt, 101 Park Avenue, New York.

Dates: Pub. *Forward*, 14 March 1936.

337. Citation: MY KIND OF WORLD; t. ms.; carbon; InU.

Title: MY KIND OF WORLD

Key Words: Yes, I can tell Mr. . . . you about it in words.

Collation: 3; blue; 27.9 x 21.6; [1] 2–3; none; good.

Contents: Complete; infrequently revised in pencil.

Dates: Comp. ca. 1934. Pub. ?

338a. Citation: MY LIFETIME IN LETTERS; t. ms.; ribbon; InU.

Title: [My (c.o.)] LIFE IN LETTERS | As Lived by Upton Sinclair.

Key Words: In the course of sixty-three . . . to all men, and women!

Collation: 3; white; 28 x 21.6; [1] 2–3; 1; good.

Contents: Complete; frequently revised in pencil; preface.

Dates: Pub. ca. 15 February 1960.

338b. Citation: MY LIFETIME IN LETTERS; mimeo; mimeo; InU.

Title: LIFE IN LETTERS

Key Words: In the course of sixty-three . . . as a sort of envoi.

Collation: 3; white; 28 x 21.7; [1] 2–3; none; good.

Contents: Complete; infrequently revised in pencil; preface.

Dates: Pub. ca. 15 February 1960.

338c. Citation: MY LIFETIME IN LETTERS; t. ms.; ribbon, carbon; InU.

Title: ACKNOWLEDGMENTS

Key Words: When I set out to . . . forever "arrayed for mutual slaughter."

Collation: 36; white; 28 x 21.7; unnumbered; 5; good.

Contents: Incomplete; infrequently revised in pencil; there are also miscellaneous jottings in green, blue ink, not in Sinclair's hand; folder labeled: Sinclair MSS | Writings | My lifetime in letters; there is a carbon of the acknowledgements and copies of several of the letters; ms. has been tagged and labeled.

Dates: Pub. ca. 15 February 1960.

338d. Citation: MY LIFETIME IN LETTERS; t. ms.; mimeo; carbon, mimeo; InU.

Title: LIFE IN LETTERS | Edited by Upton Sinclair

Key Words: In the course of sixty-three . . . estimate by about 163. Upton).

Collation: 414; white; 27.8 x 21.6; continuously numbered with variations; none; good.

Contents: Complete; infrequently revised in pencil, blue ink; ms. is boxed and contains copies of the letters used in the volume.

Dates: Pub. ca. 15 February 1960.

338e. Citation: MY LIFETIME IN LETTERS; t. ms., a. ms.; print; ribbon, carbon, pencil, blue ink, print; InU.

Title: LIFE IN LETTERS

Key Words: In the course of sixty-five . . . both. Faithfully yours Lewis Mumford

Collation: 1876; white, white watermarked; 9.4 x 12.6 to 28 x 21.6, 27.9 x 21.5; randomly numbered; 13, 25, 230, 379, 383–386, 404; good, rust and water stains.

Contents: Complete; moderately revised in blue, green ink, pencil; arranged in four boxes labeled: MY LIFE-TIME IN LETTERS I, II, III, and IV.

Dates: Pub. ca. 15 February 1960.

338f. Citation: MY LIFETIME IN LETTERS; t. ms., a. ms.; ribbon, carbon, pencil, blue ink; InU.

Title: [none]

Key Words: Introduction | Harry Sinclair Lewis, January . . . we are all in French.

Collation: 410; misc. sheets; 8.9 x 16.8 to 28 x 21.6; randomly numbered; 284; good.

Contents: Incomplete; moderately revised in pencil, blue, green ink; there are also some notations in pencil but they are apparently printer's or editor's notations; box labeled: MY LIFETIME IN LETTERS | (copy); it is a copy with many carbons of the text with a contents and foreword.

Dates: Pub. ca. 15 February 1960.

338g. Citation: MY LIFETIME IN LETTERS; t. ms., p. proof; black, brown ribbon, print; InU.

Title: Introduction

Key Words: In the course of sixty-five . . . *days after President Roosevelt's death.*

Collation: 473; misc. sheets; 8.9 x 12.5 to 28 x 21.6; [1], 1–344, [345], 346–440, [2], 441–470; none; good.

Contents: Complete; infrequently revised in blue, green, and red ink and in blue, red, regular pencil; most of the notations appear to be printer's corrections, not in Sinclair's hand; box labeled: MY LIFETIME IN | LETTERS MSS; it is apparently a complete printer's copy.

Dates: Pub. ca. 15 February 1960.

338h. Citation: MY LIFETIME IN LETTERS; g. proof; print; MoU.

Title: [none]

Key Words: In the course of sixty-five . . . *days after President Roosevelt's death.*

Collation: 138; white; 72 x 16; 1–470 [3–5 pages per galley]; good, some staining.

Contents: Complete (save for front and back matter); moderately revised in pencil in Sinclair's hand and infrequent copy-editing in blue, red pencil; each galley stamped at top "AUTHORS PROOF | Galley No. _____ | JOB No. _____ | RACK _____"; lower right-hand corner initialed by various persons, sometimes by stamp, sometimes in pencil.

Dates: Pub. ca. 15 February 1960.

338i. Citation: MY LIFETIME IN LETTERS; t. ms.; ribbon, carbon; InU.

Title: LIFE IN LETTERS | Edited by Upton Sinclair

Key Words: In the course of sixty-four . . . the subtitle . | Best wishes, | Floyd.

Collation: 1002; white; 27.8 x 21.6 to 28 x 21.6; continuously numbered with variations; none; good.

Contents: Incomplete; infrequently revised in pencil; box contains a later draft of the letter copies; there are four double sheets of comparisons with the published copy.

Dates: Pub. ca. 15 February 1960.

339. Citation: MY LIFE AND DIET; t. ms.; carbon; InU.

Title: MY LIFE IN DIET

Key Words: Some thirty years ago I . . . character. (I knock on wood!)

Collation: 5; yellow; 28 x 21.6; [1] 2–5; none; good.

Contents: Complete; infrequently revised in pencil.

Dates: Pub. *Physical Culture*, November 1924.

340. Citation: MY MOST INSPIRING MOMENT; t. ms.; carbon; InU.

Title: MY MOST INSPIRING MOMENT

Key Words: I was born in Baltimaore ["a" c.o.] . . . a new kind of matchmaking.

Collation: 6; yellow; 28 x 21.6; [1] 2–3, 5, 2, 2; none; good.

Contents: Incomplete; unrevised.

Dates: Comp. ca. 1962. Pub. ?

341. Citation: NATIONAL HOOKUP ADDRESS; t. ms.; carbon; InU.

Title: National Hookup | Address by | Upton Sinclair | over KHJ at & | 7:45 P.M. | Aug. 29, 1934

Key Words: I have been asked to . . . now are patches of weeds.

Collation: 5; white; 27.8 x 21.5; [1] 2–5; none; good.

Contents: Complete; infrequently revised in pencil; note in upper right corner of page one: Return to Gus Inglis.

Dates: Pub. ?

342. Citation: NATURE IS CRUEL, NATURE IS; a. ms.; blue ink; InU.

Title: [none]

Key Words: Nature is cruel, nature is . . . look and cry O Devil!

Collation: 1; white; 18.9 x 14.7; unnumbered; none; good.

Contents: Complete (poem); infrequently revised in pencil, blue ink.

Dates: Comp. ? Pub. ?

343. Citation: NATURE STUDY; t. ms., a. ms.; carbon, pencil; InU.

Title: *Nature Study*

Key Words: The chickadees, high in the . . . a doggie underneath the trees.

Collation: 3; white watermarked; 27.8 x 21.5; unnumbered; 1; good.

Contents: Complete; unrevised; one original, two carbons; verso of page one is a t. ms. letter from John Tibby, Associate Editor; on Letterhead: American Institute of Public Opinion, 152 West 42nd Street, New York City to Sinclair at Station A, Pasadena; letter dated January 19, 1937.

Dates: Comp. 19 January 1937. Pub. ?

344a. Citation: THE NEW DEAL; t. ms.; carbon; InU.

Title: SCENARIO | THE NEW DEAL | by Upton Sinclair | Outline for a motion picture scenario

Key Words: (The following is a brief . . . renewed pledges of the president.

Collation: 5; blue watermarked; 27.9 x 21.6; 1–5; none; good.

Contents: Complete; infrequently revised in pencil.

Dates: Comp. ca. 1938. Unpublished.

344b. Citation: THE NEW DEAL; t. ms.; carbon; InU.

Title: SCENARIO | THE NEW DEAL | by Upton Sinclair | Outline for a motion picture scenario.

Key Words: The following is a brief . . . renewed pledges of the President.

Collation: 5; white watermarked; 28 x 21.5; 1–5; none; fair, stained.

Contents: Complete; infrequently revised in pencil in unidentified hand.

Dates: Comp. ca. 1938. Unpublished.

345. Citation: NEWS SUPPRESSION; t. ms.; carbon; InU.

Title: NEWS SUPPRESSION

Key Words: One of the most useful . . . you can get hold of.

Collation: 1; brown; 27.8 x 21.5; unnumbered; none; good.

Contents: Complete; unrevised; note in pencil: Mailed 4-10-22.

Dates: Comp. ca. 10 April 1922. Pub. *Appeal to Reason?*

346. Citation: THE NEW SUN; t. ms.; carbon; InU.

Title: THE NEW SUN by Taro Yashima | number of pages: 310 | publisher: Henry Holt & Co.

Key Words: In the endless stream of . . . the millions of humble Japanese.

Collation: 2; white watermarked; 28 x 21.6; [1] 2; none; good.

Contents: Complete; infrequently revised in ink; signed by Sinclair.

Dates: Comp. ? (Book published 1943.)

347. Citation: NO PASARAN!; t. ms.; ribbon; InU.

Title: NO PASARAN! | (THEY SHALL NOT PASS) | A Novel of the Battle of Madrid

Key Words: Dear Friend: Like every lover . . . the dinner-table of his family!

Collation: 210; green, misc. sheets; 24 x 21.6 to 28 x 21.6, 27.9 x 21.6 to 28 x 21.6; consecutively numbered by chapter but not continuously, or randomly numbered; 12, 53, 84, 96, 107, 120, 130, 135, 181, 183, 207; good, spindled.

Contents: Complete; frequently revised in pencil.

Dates: Pub. ca. February 1937.

348. Citation: THE NOBEL PRIZE FOR LITERATURE; t. ms.; carbon; InU.

Title: The Nobel Prize for Literature

Key Words: (In the autumn of 1931 . . . himself received the Nobel prize.

Collation: 4; white; 28 x 21.6; unnumbered; none; good.

Contents: Complete; infrequently revised in pencil.

Dates: Comp. ca. 1931. Pub. ? See pamphlet, 1931.

349. Citation: NORMAN THOMAS: A BIOGRAPHY BY HARRY FLEISCHMAN; t. ms.; ribbon, carbon; InU.

Title: NORMAN THOMAS: A Biography by Harry Fleischman

Key Words: I was well pleased when . . . multi-millionaires and utterly destitute millions.

Collation: 5; yellow; 28 x 21.5; [1] 3, [1] 2–3; none; good.

Contents: Complete; infrequently revised in blue ink; a review of the Fleischman book.

Dates: Pub. Book, 1964.

350. Citation: NOTES FOR DEMOCRATIC PLATFORM; t. ms.; carbon; InU.

Title: NOTES FOR DEMOCRATIC PLATFORM

Key Words: We, the representatives of the . . . not perish from our State.

Collation: 10; white watermarked; 28 x 21.6; [1] 2–10; none; good.

Contents: Complete; infrequently revised in pencil.

Dates: Comp. ca. 1934? Pub. ?

351. Citation: NOTES ON LITERATURE; t. ms.; ribbon; InU.

Title: Notes on Literature.

Key Words: Purpose of art, repres. and . . . Russia. Disordered souls—Strindberg, M. Williams.

Collation: 22; brown; 28 x 21.6; 1–22; none; fair.

Contents: Complete; moderately revised in pencil; notes for *Mammonart* (1925)?

Dates: Comp. ca. 1924.

352. Citation: THE NOVELIST AS A SOCIAL COM-MENTATOR; t. ms.; carbon; InU.

Title: THE NOVELIST AS A SOCIAL COMMEN-TATOR

Key Words: They didn't have novelists in . . . an industrial and financial empire.

Collation: 2; yellow; 28 x 21.6; [1] 2; none; good.

Contents: Complete; infrequently revised in pencil.

Dates: Comp. ca. 1960. Pub. ?

353. Citation: A NUMBER OF THINGS; t. ms.; carbon; InU.

Title: A NUMBER OF THINGS.

Key Words: The poet tells us that . . . two days, but already friends.

Collation: 31; brown; 24.7 x 21.6 to 28.1 x 21.6; [1]
2–5, [1] 2–4, [1] 2, [1] 2, 10a, 10a–11, 1–3, [1] 2–
11, [1]; 11; good.

Contents: Incomplete; infrequently revised in pencil;
eight articles: "A Number of things," "Breaking the
Money Trust," "The Land of the Free," "The Case of
Gale," "The History of Revolution," "The High Cost of
Justice," "Hard Times," "The White Terror in Journal-
ism" [incomplete]; in manila folder labeled: Found with
Book of Society mss Not in Book Were these published
in "Appeal"? Sinclair mss. unidentified.

Dates: Comp. ca. 1919. Pub. See *Book of Life.*

354. Citation: OF THE LATE MR. JOSEF STALIN; t.
ms., a. ms.; ribbon, carbon, pencil; InU.

Title: Of the Late Mr. Josef Stalin

Key Words: Just half a century ago . . . resources of
a dozen nations.

Collation: 10; white, white watermarked; 20.5 x 12.7,
28 x 21.7 to 28.1 x 21.7; [1] 2–3, [1] 2–3, [1] 2, [1] 2;
none; good.

Contents: Complete; infrequently revised in pencil and
blue ink. Autograph, typed original plus revised and
unrevised carbons.

Dates: Comp. ca. 1953. Pub. ?

355. Citation: "O GOD, MY FATHER, AND . . . ; t. ms.;
ribbon; InU.

Title: [none]

Key Words: "O God, my Father, and . . Guide to
Poverty's end. Amen."

Collation: 1; white; 28 x 21.6; unnumbered; none; good.

Contents: Complete; infrequently revised in pencil.

Dates: Comp. ca. 1934. Pub. ?

356. Citation: [OH COME YOU LORDS AND]; a. ms.; pencil; InU.

Title: [none]

Key Words: O come you lords and . . . [unreadable, conjecturally the last three words are: mourn all graves]

Collation: 1; white watermarked; 22.7 x 11.3; unnumbered; 1; poor.

Contents: Complete [?]; unrevised; verso is a receipt form for money and clothing for prisoners on their commitment to New Castle County Workhouse.

Dates: Comp. ca. 1911. Pub. ?

357. Citation: [OH, THE GOVERNOR OF ARKANSAW]; a. ms.; pencil; InU.

Title: [none]

Key Words: Oh, the governor of Arkansaw . . . deed it was too raw.

Collation: 1; white; 28 x 21.6; unnumbered; none; good.

Contents: Complete (poem); moderately revised in pencil.

Dates: Comp. ? Pub. ?

358a. Citation: OIL!; a. ms.; pencil; InU.

Title: Notes | for | Oil!

Key Words: 1912 Chap I drive 4000 . . . Pasadena, reward will be | paid.

Collation: 53; white ruled notebook; 14.6 x 9; unnumbered; 1, 5, 6, 7, 32, 33; good.

Contents: This notebook contains jottings for *Oil!* and *Money Writes!* according to a library note; from sheet 32 to the end the notebook entries run from the back to the front; notice has been taken of this in entering the verso notations.

Dates: Pub. 1926, 1927.

358b. Citation: OIL!; t. ms.; ribbon, carbon; InU.

Title: [none]

Key Words: was nothing but gambling anyhow . . . certain of the pre-Elizabethan dramatists.

Collation: 22; white, green; 28 x 21.6, 27.8 x 21.3; randomly numbered; 18, 21; fair.

Contents: Incomplete; moderately revised in pencil; folder contains miscellaneous sheets from *Oil!*

Dates: Pub. 1926, 1927.

358c. Citation: OIL!; t. ms.; carbon; InU.

Title: Preface to "Oil!"

Key Words: People ask me, which is . . . its author will be pleased.

Collation: 2; brown; 28.1 x 21.6; [1]–2; none; good.

Contents: Complete; unrevised.

Dates: Pub. 1926, 1927.

358d. Citation: OIL!; t. ms., a. ms.; ribbon, carbon, pencil; InU.

Title: *OIL!* | A Novel

Key Words: This novel, published three years . . . forced to follow along (over).

Collation: 14; misc. sheets; 27.9 x 21.5 to 28.3 x 22; randomly numbered; 14; good, punched for a two-ring binder.

Contents: Incomplete; moderately revised in pencil; a synopsis of *Oil!*

Dates: Comp. ca. 1930. Unpublished.

358e. Citation: OIL!; t. ms., a. ms.; ribbon, pencil; InU.

Title: Preface for a new Hungarian edition of "Oil!" 1957

Key Words: This novel was published thirty . . . and exploit labor. THE END.

Collation: 822; misc. sheets; 11.2 x 21.5 to 27.9 x 21.5; numbered consecutively within each chapter but not continuously; 8, 9, 15, 21, 23, 24, 29, 41, 43, 72, 81, 94, 95, 107, 117, 118, 119, 122, 153, 164, 187, 190, 193, 194, 195, 198, 216, 230, 242, 245, 252, 254, 255, 259, 267, 274, 283, 303, 308, 320, 356, 358, 359, 360, 365, 372, 373, 383, 389, 458, 468, 513, 514, 571, 579, 665, 684, 692, 712, 720, 752, 764, 773, 786; good.

Contents: Incomplete; moderately revised in pencil; ms. is a draft, apparently a complete one except for title page, introduction, and contents page; ms. has been tagged and labeled.

Dates: Comp. Preface: 1957. Pub. Preface: 1957; novel, 1926, 1927.

359a. Citation: OIL! A PLAY; t. ms., a. ms.; ribbon, black, blue carbon, blue ink; InU.

Title: OUTLINE SKETCH OF "OIL"

Key Words: "Act I: Scene I—The Watkins . . . Ruth and Bunny and Eli.

Collation: 99; misc. sheets; 27.8 x 21.5 to 28 x 21.6; numbered continuously within groupings but not consecutively; 14; good.

Contents: Complete; infrequently revised in pencil; ms. contains general synopsis and early draft material of the play "Oil!"

Dates: Pub. ca. November–December 1929.

359b. Citation: OIL! A PLAY; t. ms., a. ms.; ribbon, carbon, pencil; InU.

Title: OIL! A Play in Four Acts

Key Words: Characters in order of appearance . . . machinery continues to roar.) | *CURTAIN*.

Collation: 126; misc. sheets; 15.9 x 21.7 to 30.9 x 20.7; numbered consecutively within groupings but not continuously; 11, 22, 23, 34, 73; fair.

Contents: Complete; frequently revised in pencil; ms. is an early draft of the play, "Oil!"

Dates: Pub. ca. November–December 1929.

359c. Citation: OIL! A PLAY; t. ms.; ribbon, carbon; InU.

Title: OIL! | A Play in Four Acts

Key Words: Soon after the novel, Oil! . . . wave handkerchiefs and cheer). | *CURTAIN*.

Collation: 98; white Sinclair letterhead watermark; 28 x 21.8, 28 x 21.5; 1–98; none; fair, punched for two-ring binder, spindled.

Contents: Complete; infrequently revised in pencil; bears the printer's notations also in pencil; envelope reads: Oil! (A Play) | apparently the printer's copy; has PREFACE.

Dates: Pub. ca. November–December 1929.

360. Citation: O MAN, BE GOOD!; t. ms., a. ms.; ribbon, carbon, pencil; InU.

Title: O Man, Be Good!

Key Words: My soul is sick of . . . Thy knowing to be good.

Collation: 5; white watermarked, white; 20.3 x 12.7, 28 x 21.7; unnumbered; none; good.

Contents: Complete (poem); infrequently revised in blue ink; an original and four carbons.

Dates: Comp. ca. 1954. Pub. ?

361. Citation: ON BEING A JEW; t. ms.; carbon; InU.

Title: ON BEING A JEW

Key Words: I have just been reading . . . interest in this all-important subject.

Collation: 7; brown; 27.8 x 21.5; [1] 2–7; none; good.

Contents: Complete; unrevised; note on page one in pencil: Copy mailed to U.S. 4–6–22; review of L. Lewisohn's *Up Stream*.

Dates: Pub. *Appeal to Reason*, 13 May 1922.

362. Citation: ON BEING TAKEN INTO THE INSTI-TUTE; t. ms.; carbon; InU.

Title: ON BEING TAKEN INTO THE INSTI-TUTE

Key Words: A short while ago I . . . in a pamphlet or book.

Collation: 11; white; 28 x 21.6; 1–11; none, good.

Contents: Complete; infrequently revised in pencil.

Dates: Comp. ca. 1944? Pub. ?

363a. Citation: ONE CLEAR CALL; t. ms.; ribbon; InU.

Title: O SHEPHERD, SPEAK | A Novel

Key Words: Ashore there was a breeze . . . least one square meal." | End.

Collation: 834; misc. sheets; 4.1 x 21.6 to 28 x 21.6; numbered consecutively by chapters but not continuously; 1, 2, 29, 89, 130, 149, 188, 201, 261, 264, 295, 305, 306, 307, 320, 345, 349, 356, 364, 367, 368, 370, 440, 464, 477, 478, 558, 576, 602, 631, 649, 653, 655, 667, 695, 719, 724, 747, 773, 804, 805, 829; good.

Contents: Complete; moderately revised in pencil; box labeled: ONE CLEAR CALL | ORIGINAL DRAFT | CHAPS. 1–25; appears to be a complete draft.

Dates: Pub. ca. July 1948.

363b. Citation: ONE CLEAR CALL; t. ms., a. ms.; ribbon, carbon, pencil, blue ink; InU.

Title: [none]

Key Words: Memorandum over visit to Germany . . . giant cargo for 460,000 rivets.

Collation: 52; misc. sheets; 17 x 11.1 to 35.8 x 22.5; randomly numbered; 33, 35, 52; good.

Contents: Incomplete; infrequently revised in blue, black ink, pencil; only one sheet is in Sinclair's hand; ms. is a collection of notes apparently of European origin for *One Clear Call*.

Dates: Pub. ca. July 1948.

363c. Citation: ONE CLEAR CALL; t. ms.; black, blue ribbon; InU.

Title: ONE CLEAR CALL | [by (c.o.)] | Upton Sinclair

Key Words: The small catboat stopped the . . . they find another like him?

Collation: 856; misc. sheets; 27.9 x 21.5 to 27.9 x 21.8; continuously numbered with variations; none; fair, spindled.

Contents: Complete; infrequently revised in pencil and bears printer's notations in regular, orange, blue, purple, red pencil; ms. is the printer's copy of *One Clear Call*; appears to be a complete copy; one other title crossed out reads: Who Will Go For Us?; box 1 labeled: ONE CLEAR CALL | PRINTER'S COPY | CHAPS. 1–16; box 2 labeled: ONE CLEAR CALL | PRINTER'S COPY | CHAPS. 17–28.

Dates: Pub. ca. July 1948.

364a. Citation: 100%; t. ms., a. ms.; ribbon, carbon, pencil; InU.

Title: 100% | The Story of a Patriot

Key Words: Would you like to go . . . to improve their home, and

Collation: 245; brown; 28 x 21.3; consecutively numbered by groups but not continuously; 64, 78, 104, 112, 115, 125, 127, 134, 135, 136, 142, 146, 147, 169, 188, 189, 192, 199, 200, 201, 202, 229, 235, 238, 241; good.

Contents: Incomplete; frequently revised in pencil; folder labeled: 100% | A draft | p. 7–115.

Dates: Pub. 15 October 1920.

364b. Citation: 100%; t. ms., a. ms.; ribbon, pencil; InU.

Title: [none]

Key Words: Certain, because of this unusual . . . come in on their scheme.

Collation: 45; misc. sheets; 15.6 x 21.4 to 28 x 21.7; randomly numbered; 2, 14, 15, 17, 18, 22, 24, 25, 39, 41; poor.

Contents: Incomplete; frequently revised in pencil; folder labeled: 100% | Miscellaneous | pages | mostly repeats and | not used!

Dates: Pub. 15 October 1920.

364c. Citation: 100%; t. ms.; ribbon; InU.

Title: Appendix [underscored twice in pencil]

Key Words: A little experimenting with the . . . of imitation blood. I quote:

Collation: 11; brown; 28.1 x 21.4; 1–8, [9–11], 10, 9; none; good.

Contents: Incomplete; frequently revised in pencil; appears to be an incomplete Appendix to 100%.

Dates: Pub. 15 October 1920.

365a. Citation: ONE WOMAN'S FIGHT; t. ms.; blue carbon; InU.

Title: *ONE WOMAN'S FIGHT* | A True Story

Key Words: "I can't understand how women . . . by the forcible feeding procedure.

Collation: 12; white; 27.9 x 21.8; [1] 2–12; none; good.

Contents: Complete; unrevised.

Dates: Comp. ca. 1920s. Pub. ?

365b. Citation: ONE WOMAN'S FIGHT; t. ms.; ribbon; InU.

Title: *ONE WOMAN'S FIGHT* | A True Story

Key Words: "I can't understand how women . . . by the forcible feeding procedure.

Collation: 12; white; 27.9 x 21.8; [1] 2–12; none; good.

Contents: Complete; infrequently revised in ink.

Dates: Comp. ca. 1920s? Pub. ?

366. Citation: ON MAKING MONEY; t. ms.; carbon; InU.

Title: ON MAKING MONEY

Key Words: Arthur Brisbane writes a column . . . he believes in making money.

Collation: 4; brown; 27.9 x 21.5; [1] 2–4; none; good.

Contents: Complete; infrequently revised in pencil; someone has written on page one in pencil: Mailed 4/18/22; folder labeled: "Appeal to Reason."

Dates: Pub. *Appeal to Reason*, 20 May 1922.

367. Citation: AN OPEN LETTER TO STALIN; t. ms.; carbon; InU.

Title: AN OPEN LETTER TO MARSHAL STALIN

Key Words: I address you as an . . . prevail in this tormented world.

Collation: 8; white; 28 x 21.7; [1] 2–8; none; good.

Contents: Complete; infrequently revised in pencil.

Dates: Pub. *New Leader*, 30 June 1952 (and widely reprinted).

368. Citation: AN OPEN LETTER TO PRESIDENT ROOSEVELT; t. ms., a. ms.; ribbon, carbon, pencil, ink; InU.

Title: START PLANNING NOW | An Open Letter to President Roosevelt

Key Words: My dear President Roosevelt: This . . . poverty and establish world peace.

Collation: 20; green, white watermarked; 21.2 x 20 to 27.9 x 21.3, 3.5 x 16.4 to 27.9 x 21.6; randomly numbered; none; fair.

Contents: Complete; moderately revised in pencil.

Dates: Pub. *Common Sense*, April 1941.

369. Citation: AN OPEN LETTER TO PRESIDENT ROOSEVELT; t. ms.; ribbon, carbon; InU.

Title: AN OPEN LETTER TO PRESIDENT ROOSEVELT

Key Words: I am aware that I . . . must go forward or perish.

Collation: 38; white watermarked, green; 27.9 x 21.5, 28 x 21.7; [1] 2–14, [1] 2–12, [1] 2–12; 11; good.

Contents: Complete; moderately revised in pencil.

Dates: Pub. *EPIC News*, 9 August 1937.

370. Citation: OPEN LETTER TO WILLIAM ALLEN WHITE; t. ms.; carbon; InU.

Title: OPEN LETTER TO WILLIAM ALLEN WHITE

Key Words: Upon the walls of my . . . cholera and bubonic plague bacilli.

Collation: 10; white watermarked; 28 x 21.6; [1] 2–5, [1] 2–5; good.

Contents: Complete; infrequently revised in pencil.

Dates: Comp. ca. 1935. Pub. ?

371. Citation: ORANGEVALE; t. ms.; ribbon; InU.

Title: ORANGEVALE | A Story by Upton Sinclair

Key Words: Anderson Colby is a writer . . . has to interpret to him.

Collation: 7; yellow; 28 x 21.7; [1] 2–7; none; fair, stained, punched for two-ring binder.

Contents: Complete; infrequently revised in pencil; "Gus Inglis | EX 4074" written in faded blue ink in upper right corner of page 1.

Dates: Comp. ca. 1930s? Pub. ?

372a. Citation: ORDERS FROM AMERICA; t. ms.; ribbon, carbon; InU.

Title: ORDERS FROM AMERICA | Being a Reply to Anna Louise Strong

Key Words: I am replying to an . . . expect Moscow to believe them?

Collation: 9; white watermarked; 28 x 21.6; [1] 2–3, [1] 2–3, [1] 2–3; none; good.

Contents: Complete; infrequently revised in pencil, unidentified hand; original and two carbons.

Dates: Pub. *Pacific Weekly*, 13 April 1936.

372b. Citation: ORDERS FROM AMERICA; t. ms.; carbon; InU.

Title: ORDERS FROM AMERICA | Being a Reply to Anna Louise Strong

Key Words: I am replying to an . . . expect Moscow to believe them?

Collation: 3; white watermarked; 28 x 21.6; [1] 2–3; none; good.

Contents: Complete: unrevised.

Date: Pub. *Pacific Weekly*, 13 April 1936.

373a. Citation: O SHEPHERD, SPEAK!; t. ms.; ribbon; InU.

Title: O, SHEPHERD, SPEAK! A NOVEL

Key Words: Lanny Budd, arriving in Paris . . . Ri, exclaiming: "The Shepherd speaks!"

Collation: 818; white, white watermarked; 28 x 21.7, 6.5 x 21.7 to 21 x 21.7; numbered consecutively by chapters but not continuously; 47, 85, 99, 111, 138, 159, 176, 218, 221, 223, 226, 233, 260, 278, 281, 294, 296, 303, 304, 310, 312, 321, 328, 383, 393, 395, 433, 437, 488, 489, 503, 526, 553, 559, 571, 572, 598, 632, 641, 651, 660, 671, 675, 679, 702, 706, 718, 721, 754, 755, 762, 763, 767, 770, 772, 802; good.

Contents: Complete; frequently revised in pencil; it also bears a few red pen and pencil notations of the printer's or editor's; box labeled: ORIGINAL DRAFT; appears to be a complete draft.

Dates: Pub. ca. July 1949.

373b. Citation: O SHEPHERD, SPEAK!; t. ms.; ribbon; InU.

Title: Contents | Treasures on Earth

Key Words: Lanny Budd, arriving in Paris, . . . as- | sistance before we get through.

Collation: 520; white, white watermarked; 28 x 21.7, 28 x 21.5; continuously numbered with variations; none; fair, smudged, spindled.

Contents: Incomplete; infrequently revised in pencil; there are also infrequent printer's notes in regular, blue, orange pencil; box labeled: O Shepherd, Speak! | Printer's Copy | Chapters 1–21; continued in following box.

Dates: Pub. ca. July 1949.

373c. Citation: O SHEPHERD, SPEAK!; t. ms., print; ribbon, red print; InU.

Title: CHAPTER TWENTY-TWO | The Laborers Are Few

Key Words: The sun of peace had . . . 375, 381, 412; x:83.

Collation: 442; white; 27.9 x 21.6; continuously numbered with variations; none; poor, spindled.

Contents: Incomplete; infrequently revised in red, blue, regular pencil; most of the red and blue notations are printer's notes; box labeled: PRINTER'S COPY | CHAPS. 22–34; completes contents of previous box.

Dates: Pub. ca. July 1949.

373d. Citation: O SHEPHERD, SPEAK!; t. ms.; carbon; InU.

Title: O, SHEPHERD, SPEAK | A NOVEL

Key Words: Lanny Budd, arriving in Paris . . . Rick, exclaiming: | "The Shepherd speaks!"

Collation: 748; white; 27.9 x 21.7; [1]–175, 184–208, 215, 209–214, 216–219, 226–267, 284–478, 485–606, 620–625, 628–731, 716–731, 732–783; 292, 583, 588, 590, 693; good.

Contents: Complete; infrequently revised in red, black, blue, faded ink, orange, regular pencil in a variety of hands; box labeled: PRINTER'S COPY | CARBON; ms. has been grouped by chapters.

Dates: Pub. ca. July 1949.

373e. Citation: O SHEPHERD, SPEAK!; t. ms., a. ms.; ribbon, carbon, pencil, blue ink; InU.

Title: [none]

Key Words: "Fourteen years old, but able . . . LIMITED | PRINTED IN U. S. A. BY.

Collation: 24; misc. sheets; 26.4 x 18.4 to 28.1 x 21.4; numbered consecutively by grouping but not continuously; 1, 4; good.

Contents: Incomplete; infrequently revised in pencil, blue ink; not all in Sinclair's hand; ms. is a collection of misc. sheets of changes and criticism; much of the material is not by Sinclair; there are also some title sheets to the novel.

Dates: Pub. ca. July 1949.

373f. Citation: O SHEPHERD, SPEAK!; t. ms., a. ms.; ribbon, pencil, ink; InU.

Title: [none]

Key Words: H. Hopkins | deep brown eyes . . . Mr. and Mrs. W. B. Tipton.

Collation: 76; misc. sheets, envelopes; 12.1 x 10.5 to 28 x 21.6; unnumbered; 3, 4, 7, 21, 27, 39, 43, 56; fair.

Contents: Incomplete; infrequently revised in pencil, ink by several hands; folder labeled: Lanny Budd vol. 10 | O Shepherd Speak; it contains various notes and sheets of criticism; some of the materials are Sinclair's; the bulk, however, is not.

Dates: Pub. ca. July 1949.

373g. Citation: O SHEPHERD, SPEAK!; t. ms.; ribbon; InU.

Title: OH, SHEPHERD, SPEAK | CHART

Key Words: B. W. Heubsch The Viking . . . Ratiliffe (2nd copy) 26 2/22/49.

Collation: 8; white, white watermarked; 28 x 21.7, 27.8 x 21.6; unnumbered; 4, 5, 6, 7; good.

Contents: Incomplete; infrequently revised in regular, red pencil; ms. is a chart listing the critic to whom various sections of the novel were sent for criticism, his address, and the date sent and returned for each chapter of the novel.

Dates: Pub. ca. July 1949.

374. Citation: OUR CAMPAIGN COMMITTEE; t. ms.; carbon; InU.

Title: Our Campaign Committee

Key Words: Nobody ever ran for a . . . of thanks in the end.

Collation: 3; blue watermarked; 28 x 21.6; [1] 2–3; none; good.

Contents: Complete; infrequently revised in pencil.

Dates: Comp. ca. 7 July 1934. Pub. ?

375a. Citation: OUR LADY; a. ms.; pencil, ink; InU.

Title: [none]

Key Words: Adjuro to serpeus antigue Adjuro . . . [?] lips hang to middle Kerreya [?]

Collation: 12; misc. sheets; 12.8 x 11.8 to 28 x 21.5; unnumbered; 1, 4, 5, 8, 9, 10; fair.

Contents: Complete; moderately revised in pencil, ink; in brown folder labeled: OUR LADY NOTES.

Dates: Pub. ca. June 1938.

375b. Citation: OUR LADY; t. ms., a. ms.; ribbon, pencil; InU.

Title: BOOK __ OUR LADY __ US __

Key Words: "Our Lady" is a novelette . . . been nothing but a dream.

Collation: 117; green, white watermarked; 28 x 21.5, 27.9 x 21.5; consecutively numbered by chapter but not continuously; 11, 17, 36, 42, 57, 72, 82, 91, 108, 109, 110, 114, 117; good.

Contents: Complete; frequently revised in black, blue pencil; page 117 is a manila envelope, canceled stamp to Upton Sinclair from Santa Monica, labeled: "Our Lady" Original Ms.; pages 1–7 appear to be a proposal for the book, have spindle marks in upper right corner.

Dates: Pub. ca. June 1938.

376. Citation: OUR POLITICAL PRISONERS; t. ms., carbon; InU.

Title: OUR POLITICAL PRISONERS

Key Words: There is to be held . . . and intellectual opposition to war.

Collation: 9; brown; 27.9 x 21.5; 1–9; none; good.

Contents: Complete; unrevised.

Dates: Pub. *Appeal to Reason*, 28 January 1922.

377. Citation: OUR SECRET SERVICE CRIMINALS; t. ms.; carbon; InU.

Title: OUR SECRET SERVICE CRIMINALS

Key Words: In the "Nation," New York, . . . on Americans in Great Britain!

Collation: 2; brown; 27.9 x 21.5; [1] 2; none; good.

Contents: Complete; infrequently revised in pencil; someone has written on page 1 in pencil: Mailed to U.S. 4/14/22; folder labeled: "Appeal to Reason."

Dates: Pub. *Appeal to Reason*, 24 June 1922.

378. Citation: OUR SECRET WEAPON; t. ms.; carbon; InU.

Title: AMERICA'S BEST SECRET WEAPON

Key Words: Each morning when I wake . . . 1953 by SPADEA SYNDICATE, INC.

Collation: 6; white watermarked; 33.3 x 21.8; [1] 2–3, [1] 2–3; none; good.

Contents: Complete; unrevised; written for release through the Spadea Syndicate under the heading: FOR THE RECORD; release date: Wednesday, December 16, 1953.

Dates: Pub. *Decatur Herald*, 16 December 1953.

379a. Citation: OUTLINE OF A PROJECT; t. ms.; ribbon; InU.

Title: OUTLINE OF A PROJECT For the Reprinting of [six (c.o. pencil)] Labor Novels

Key Words: In the course of half . . . have to defend and increase.

Collation: 3; white; 27.8 x 21.4; [1] 2–3; 2; good.

Contents: Complete; frequently revised in pencil, blue ink.

Dates: Comp. ca. 1960. Pub. ?

379b. Citation: OUTLINE OF A PROJECT; t. ms.; carbon; InU.

Title: OUTLINE OF A PROJECT | For the Reprinting of Six Labor Novels

Key Words: In the course of half . . . they have to win more.

Collation: 3; white; 27.8 x 21.5; [1] 2–3; none; good.

Contents: Complete; unrevised.

Dates: Comp. ca. 1960. Pub. ?

380. Citation: OUTLINE OF "RED GOLD"; t. ms.; ribbon, carbon; InU.

Title: OUTLINE OF "RED GOLD" | A Projected Novel

Key Words: In a manufacturing city in . . . or some other useful product!

Collation: 29; white, white watermarked; 28 x 21.6; [1] 2–10, [1] 2–10, 2–10; none; good.

Contents: Complete; infrequently revised in pencil.

Dates: Comp. ? Pub. ?

381. Citation: OUTLINE OF SUGGESTED RESEARCH FOR EPIC; t. ms.; carbon; InU.

Title: OUTLINE OF SUGGESTED RESEARCH FOR EPIC

Key Words: What is the total number . . . the co-operative care of children.

Collation: 6; white watermarked; 27.9 x 21.6; [1] 2–6; none; good.

Contents: Complete; infrequently revised in pencil, unidentified hand.

Dates: Comp. ca. 1934. Pub. ?

382. Citation: PAIN SHALL GO!; t. ms.; carbon; InU.

Title: PAIN SHALL GO! | Outline of a Motion Picture Story of | The Discovery of Anesthesia

Key Words: Dr. George Morton is an . . . grim and deeply moving scene.

Collation: 10; white watermarked; 28 x 21.6; [1] 2–5, [1] 2–5; none; good.

Contents: Complete; infrequently revised in pencil.

Dates: Comp. ca. 1938–39. Unpublished.

383a. Citation: THE PAMELA [TWO] PLAY; t. ms., a. ms.; ribbon, pencil; InU.

Title: PAMELA TWO

Key Words: Scene I: Half-set in front of . . . P Two! P i : (sings) (over)

Collation: 107; white; 27.9 x 21.6; [1], 3–30, 30a, 31–32, 1–25, 25a, 26–34, 34a–34f, 35, 1–33; 12, 13, 27, 30, 99 103, 106, 107; good.

Contents: Complete; moderately revised in pencil; first page is a. ms. outline of characters, scene, title.

Dates: Comp. ca. 1949? Pub. See *Another Pamela* (1950).

383b. Citation: THE PAMELA [TWO] PLAY; t. ms.; carbon; InU.

Title: THE PAMELA PLAY [w.i. over c.o. THE PAMELA TWO PLAY] | A DRAMA [w.i. over c.o. PLAY] in Three Acts

Key Words: Scene I: A tar-paper shack on . . . Lord! Good Lord! The Women!

Collation: 109; white; 27.9 x 21.5; [1] 2, 2a, 3–33, 33b, 34, 34, 34a–34f, 35–45, 45a, 46–56, 56a, 57–98; none; fair.

Dates: Comp. ca. 1949? Pub. See *Another Pamela* (1950).

383c. Citation: THE PAMELA [TWO] PLAY; t. ms., a. ms.; ribbon, carbon, pencil; InU.

Title: PAMELA TWO | A Play in Three Acts

Key Words: Scene 1: A tar-paper shack on . . . my arm, I verily think."

Collation: 111; white, green; 27.9 x 21.5, 21.9 x 14.1; randomly numbered; 80; fair, burned.

Contents: Incomplete; infrequently revised in red, black pencil.

Dates: Comp. ca. 1949? Pub. See *Another Pamela* (1950).

384a. Citation: PEACE THAT WILL LAST; t. ms.; carbon; InU.

Title: *Peace That Will Last* | An Appeal to English People.

Key Words: It is easy to understand . . . scrutiny and criticism of mankind.

Collation: 6; white watermarked; 28 x 21.7; [1] 2–6; none; good.

Contents: Complete; infrequently revised in ink.

Dates: Pub. *Western Comrade*, March–April 1918.

384b. Citation: PEACE THAT WILL LAST; t. ms.; carbon; InU.

Title: *Peace That Will Last* | An Appeal to English People.

Key Words: It is easy to understand . . . scrutiny and criticism of mankind.

Collation: 6; white watermarked; 28 x 21.7; [1] 2–6; none; good.

Contents: Complete; infrequently revised in pencil, ink.

Dates: Pub. *Western Comrade*, March–April 1918.

385. Citation: PERKIN'S WIFE; a. ms.; black, blue ink; InU.

Title: Perkin's Wife

Key Words: It is my private opinion . . . trip to Boston." We went.

Collation: 10; white watermarked; 14.5 x 8.7 to 20.3 x 13.3; [1] 1–9; none; good.

Contents: Complete; unrevised; first page is a description of the ms. by Sinclair dated 1957 (ms. is dated by him as written when he was age 16 or 17).

Dates: Comp. ca. 1896–97. Pub. ?

386a. Citation: THE PERMANENT CRISIS; t. ms.; ribbon, carbon; InU.

Title: THE PERMANENT CRISIS

Key Words: I go out on my . . . of the world about progress!

Collation: 23; white; 28 x 22.7; [1] 2–12, [1] 2–11; 10; good.

Contents: Complete; moderately revised in pencil.

Dates: Pub. *The Thinker,* December 1931.

386b. Citation: THE PERMANENT CRISIS; t. ms.; carbon; InU.

Title: THE PERMANENT CRISIS

Key Words: I go out on my . . . of the world about progress!

Collation: 11; white; 28 x 21.6; [1] 2–11; none; good.

Contents: Complete; infrequently revised in pencil.

Dates: Pub. *The Thinker,* December 1931.

387a. Citation: A PERSONAL JESUS; t. ms., a. ms.; ribbon, carbon, pencil; InU.

Title: JESUS LIVES | A Biography

Key Words: There have been learned scholars . . . of seeing it in manuscript.

Collation: 228; misc. sheets; 2.6 x 18.8 to 27.9 x 21.4; numbered consecutively by tape reels but not continuously; 196, 209, 210, 212, 214, 217, 226; good.

Contents: Incomplete; infrequently revised in regular, orange pencil; folder labeled: JESUS LIVES | BIOGRAPHY | FIRST COPY OFF RECORDER | UNRE-

VISED; an incomplete transcription from tapes titled "Jesus Lives"; ms. has been tagged and labeled.

Dates: Pub. November 1952.

387b. Citation: A PERSONAL JESUS; t. ms., a. ms.; ribbon, pencil; InU.

Title: JESUS LIVES [! (w.i. pencil)] | A Biography

Key Words: There are learned scholars who . . . or the line in parenthesis).

Collation: 219; white, misc. sheets; 28 x 21.7, 19.9 x 21.6 to 28.1 x 21.7; continuously numbered with variations; 6, 12, 53, 70, 89, 92, 103, 123, 131, 159, 161, 169, 193; good.

Contents: Incomplete; moderately revised in pencil; ms. labeled: Complete Draft | except for postscript | Earliest version | from which other 4 copies | were taken; ms. numbered 1; folder labeled: [A Personal | (w.i. pencil)] | [JESUS LIVES (c.o.] | COPIES [TO BE (c.o.)] UNIFORMED.

Dates: Pub. November 1952.

387c. Citation: A PERSONAL JESUS; t. ms.; carbon; InU.

Title: *Personal* [(w.i. pencil)] JESUS [LIVES! (c.o.)] | A Biography

Key Words: There are learned men who . . . Comrade back to his own.

Collation: 235; white; 28 x 21.6; continuously numbered with variations; none; good.

Contents: Complete; moderately revised in pencil; some of the revisions are Sinclair's, others are not; ms. labeled: complete draft | Marked | 'Eddy' (George Sherwood

Eddy?) | frequent minor changes | Postscript absent; ms. bound in three green folders using metal binders and labeled: Book I; Book II; Book III; ms. numbered 3.

Dates: Pub. November 1952.

387d. Citation: A PERSONAL JESUS; t. ms.; carbon; InU.

Title: PERSONAL [(w.i. blue ink)] JESUS [LIVES! (c.o.)] [A Biography (c.o.)] A Portrait and a History [(w.i. blue ink)]

Key Words: There are learned men who . . . entirely frank with their congregation.

Collation: 253; white; 28 x 21.7; continuously numbered with variations; 96, 100, 156, 159, 235, 239; fair.

Contents: Complete; moderately revised in pencil; folders labeled: Complete draft | (probably between earliest | and middle drafts of | collection); postscript present; ms. bound in green folders and labeled: Book one; Book two; Book three; the last has come unfastened; ms. numbered 3.

Dates: Pub. November 1952.

387e. Citation: A PERSONAL JESUS; t. ms., a. ms.; ribbon, carbon, pencil; InU.

Title: Contents

Key Words: Greek, German, French, and Italian . . . to use in certain medi-

Collation: 62; misc. sheets; 20.4 x 11.7 to 28 x 21.6; randomly numbered; 15; good.

Contents: Incomplete; infrequently revised in pencil; folder labeled: Personal Jesus | MISC. PARTS OF MSS.; it contains many duplicate pages.

Dates: Pub. November 1952.

387f. Citation: A PERSONAL JESUS; t. ms., print; carbon, brown, gold print; InU.

Title: A Personal Jesus | PORTRAIT AND INTER-PRETATION

Key Words: THIS INSPIRED BOOK DESTROYS THE . . . you to think for your —

Collation: 12; misc. sheets; 21.7 x 21.9 to 27.9 x 21.7; [4], [1] 2–8; none; good.

Contents: Incomplete; infrequently revised in pencil, blue ink; ms. is a misc. collection: an advertising sheet, both carbon and printed final copy, a book cover (boards) and a "POSTSCRIPT," and a loose ms. sheet.

Dates: Pub. November 1952.

387g. Citation: A PERSONAL JESUS; t. ms.; carbon; InU.

Title: I. O. Evans. | Comments on | THE PERSONAL JESUS | By *Upton Sinclair*.

Key Words: This book is a remarkable . . . my comments may be helpful.

Collation: 8; white; 24.2 x 19.2; i–viii; none; good.

Contents: Complete; infrequently revised in blue ink; ms. is a list of revisions by I. O. Evans.

Dates: Pub. November 1952.

387h. Citation: A PERSONAL JESUS; t. ms.; ribbon, carbon; InU.

Title: Personal [(w.i. pencil)] JESUS [LIVES! (c.o.)] | [A Biography (c.o.)] A Portrait and a History.

Key Words: There are learned men who . . . exist to perpetuate ancient myths."

Collation: 263; white watermarked, white; 27.8 x 21.5, 27.9 x 21.6 to 28 x 21.7; numbered continuously with variations; none; good.

Contents: Complete; infrequently revised in pencil, blue ink, not in Sinclair's hand; ms. labeled: complete late draft | probably just prior | to printer's copy. (last page additional | lacking; ms. numbered 4.

Dates: Pub. November 1952.

387i. Citation: A PERSONAL JESUS; t. ms.; ribbon; InU.

Title: PERSONAL [(w.i. pencil)] JESUS [LIVES! (c.o.)] | [A Biography (c.o.)] a Portrait and a History [(w.i. pencil)]

Key Words: There are learned men who . . . cold wars alternating with hot.

Collation: 263; white, white watermarked; 27.9 x 21.6; continuously numbered with variations; none; fair.

Contents: Complete; moderately revised in pencil, blue ink; blue ink markings not in Sinclair's hand; there are also printer's notations in regular, blue pencil; folder is labeled: A Personal Jesus | Printer's Copy.

Dates: Pub. November 1952.

388a. Citation: POET IN A HOGSHEAD; t. ms.; carbon; InU.

Title: POET IN A HOGSHEAD

Key Words: (In November of the year . . . sonnet is about completed. George

Collation: 6; white; 28 x 21.5; [1] 2–6; 4; good.

Contents: Complete; moderately revised in blue ink, pencil; concerns George Sterling.

Dates: Pub. *Westways*, September 1956.

388b. Citation: POET IN A HOGSHEAD; t. ms.; ribbon; InU.

Title: POET IN A HOGSHEAD

Key Words: (In December of the year . . . this page of it! George

Collation: 6; white; 28 x 21.6; [1] 2–6; none; good.

Contents: Complete; infrequently revised in blue ink, pencil, in unidentified hand; concerns George Sterling.

Dates: Pub. *Westways*, September 1956.

388c. Citation: POET IN A HOGSHEAD; t. ms.; carbon; InU.

Title: POET IN A HOGSHEAD

Key Words: (In November of the year . . . sonnet is about completed. George

Collation: 6; white; 28 x 21.6; [1] 2–6; none; good.

Contents: Complete; infrequently revised in blue ink, pencil; concerns George Sterling.

Dates: Pub. *Westways*, September 1956.

388d. Citation: POET IN A HOGSHEAD; t. ms.; carbon; InU.

Title: POET IN A HOGSHEAD

Key Words: (In November of the year . . . sonnet is about completed. George

Collation: 6; white; 28.1 x 21.6; [1] 2–6; none; good.

Contents: Complete; unrevised; concerns George Sterling.

Dates: Pub. *Westways*, September 1956.

389. Citation: POLICE POWER; t. ms.; ribbon; InU.

Title: [POST IMPRESSIONS (c.o.)] Police Power [(w.i. pencil)] | By Simeon Strunsky

Key Words: The Chairman of the Board . . . am professor of Chinese archaeology.

Collation: 5; white watermarked; 27.8 x 21.4; [1] 2–5; none; good.

Contents: Complete; infrequently revised in pencil; style suggests this was written by Sinclair.

Dates: Comp. 1920s? Pub. ?

390. Citation: THE POLITICAL FUTURE IN AMER-ICA; t. ms.; carbon; InU.

Title: [WHY ARE THE INSURGENTS? (c.o.)] *The Political Future in America.* [(w.i. faded ink)]

Key Words: I am writing this immediately . . . reign of free love in

Collation: 21; white watermarked; 25.9 x 20.3 to 32.5 x 20.3; [1] 2, 2a, 2b, 3–4, [1], 6–13, 13a, 14, 16–19; none; good.

Contents: Incomplete; moderately revised in ink.

Dates: Comp. ca. 1909–10. Pub. ?

391. Citation: A POLITICAL PRAYER; t. ms.; carbon; InU.

Title: POLITICAL PRAYER

Key Words: O God my Father, and . . . Guide to Poverty's End. Amen.

Collation: 1; white watermarked; 27.9 x 21.5; unnumbered; none; good.

Contents: Complete; unrevised.

Dates: Pub. *New Republic,* 7 November 1934.

392. Citation: POLITICAL PRAYERS; t. ms., a. ms.; carbon, pencil; InU.

Title: Political Prayers

Key Words: Give me a little pity . . . accounts with me are square.

Collation: 2; white watermarked; 27.9 x 21.5; unnumbered; none; good.

Contents: Complete; infrequently revised in pencil; original and one carbon.

Dates: Comp. ca. 1934. Pub. ?

393a. Citation: THE POT-BOILER; t. ms., a. ms.; blue ribbon, blue, black carbon, pencil; InU.

Title: THE [GREAT AMERICAN PLAY (c.o.)] POT-BOILER [(w.i. faded ink)] | A COMEDY IN FOUR ACTS.

Key Words: Scene: The stage is divided . . . There! There! The Pot-boiler! CURTAIN.

Collation: 213; white watermarked, brown; 27.8 x 21.4 to 28 x 21.7; play consecutively numbered by acts, last copy continuously numbered; 2, 8, 9, 12, 17, 24, 27, 31, 33, 35, 45, 49, 51, 57, 59, 60, 61, 64, 76, 83; good, punched for a two-hole binding.

Contents: Incomplete; frequently revised draft and a carbon infrequently revised, both in pencil, ink; folder labeled Pot-boiler contains two copies of the play; second copy has been bound by two brass studs.

Dates: Comp. 1912–13. Pub. 12 May 1924.

393b. Citation: THE POT-BOILER; t. ms.; carbon; InU.

Title: THE POT-BOILER. | A COMEDY IN FOUR ACTS. BY UPTON SINCLAIR

Key Words: Scene: The stage is divided . . . Hurrah! Charlotte russes [sic] to burn!

Collation: 91; white laid paper, white watermarked; 27.8 x 22, 28.1 x 21.6; numbered by acts but not continuously; none; good.

Contents: Incomplete; infrequently revised in pencil, ink, not all of the ink in Sinclair's hand; appears to be only two acts of *The Pot-Boiler*; bound by two brass studs in a blue wrapper.

Dates: Comp. 1912–13. Pub. 12 May 1924.

393c. Citation: THE POT-BOILER; t. ms.; carbon; InU.

Title: THE ADVENTURER | A Story

Key Words: The scene opens in the . . . story of his own life.

Collation: 16; white watermarked; 28 x 21.7; [1] 1–7, [1] 1–7; none; poor, punched for two-ring binder.

Contents: Incomplete; infrequently revised in blue ink.

Dates: Comp. ca. 1912–13. Pub. 12 May 1924.

393d. Citation: THE POT-BOILER; t. ms.; carbon; InU.

Title: THE POT-BOILER | A COMEDY IN FOUR ACTS [? (c.o.)] BY UPTON SINCLAIR.

Key Words: Scene: The stage is divided . . . what a pot-boiler is! CURTAIN.

Collation: 85; white, white laid; 28.2 x 21.8, 26.7 x 20.4; numbered consecutively by set but not continuously; none; good, punched for three-ring binder.

Contents: Complete; infrequently revised in pencil, ink.

Dates: Comp. 1912–13. Pub. 12 May 1924.

393e. Citation: THE POT-BOILER; t. ms.; carbon; InU.

Title: THE POT-BOILER: | A COMEDY IN FOUR ACTS BY UPTON SINCLAIR.

Key Words: Scene: The stage is divided . . . what a pot-boiler is! *CURTAIN*.

Collation: 86; white, white watermarked; 28.2 x 21.7, 26.6 x 20.2; numbered consecutively by acts but not continuously; none; good.

Contents: Complete; infrequently revised in ink; ms. is complete and bound between gray covers with Selwyn and Company | Author's Representatives on the cover.

Dates: Comp. 1912–13. Pub. 12 May 1924.

393f. Citation: THE POT-BOILER; t. ms.; carbon; InU.

Title: THE GREAT AMERICAN PLAY. | A COMEDY IN FOUR ACTS. BY UPTON SINCLAIR.

Key Words: Scene: The stage is divided . . . The Great American Play. CURTAIN.

Collation: 106; white watermarked; 26.9 x 20.2; numbered consecutively by acts but not continuously; none; good.

Contents: Complete; infrequently revised in pencil, faded ink, not in Sinclair's hand; ms. is bound by two brass studs in a gray SELWYN AND COMPANY wrapper; the titlehead "THE POT-BOILER" on the cover has been crossed out and The Great American Play written in.

Dates: Comp. 1912–13. Pub. 12 May 1924.

393g. Citation: THE POT-BOILER; t. ms.; ribbon, carbon; InU.

Title: FOREWORD

Key Words: In connection with this play . . . light of the precise facts.

Collation: 6; white watermarked; 28 x 21.7; [1]–3, [1]–3; none; fair.

Contents: Complete; unrevised; ms. consists of the original and one carbon of the Foreword to "The POT Boiler."

Dates: Comp. c. 1923. Pub. 12 May 1924.

393h.Citation: THE POT-BOILER; t. ms.; ribbon, carbon; InU.

Title: THE POT-BOILER | A COMEDY IN FOUR ACTS.

Key Words: Scene: A transparent curtain of . . . which play was written first.

Collation: 107; white watermarked; 28 x 21.8; [2], 1–6, 6a, 7–101, [1] 2–3; none; fair, spindled, punched for two-ring binder.

Contents: Complete; moderately revised in pencil, black ink, not all in Sinclair's hand, some are printer's notations; apparently a printer's copy; the last three pages of the ms. are a postscript; the number 589 and copyright date of 1924 indicate that this is the Little Blue Book printer's copy; ms. is in a brown folder labeled: THE POT-BOILER

Dates: Comp. 1912–13. Pub. 12 May 1924.

394a.Citation: PRACTICALLY COUSINS; t. ms.; ribbon, carbon; InU.

Title: PRACTICALLY COUSINS | A Story

Key Words: There are many four-lane highways . . . "Practically cousins," said Sally Lee.

Collation: 22; white, white watermarked; 27.9 x 21.6, 28.1 x 21.7; 1–11, 1–11; 20; good.

Contents: Complete; moderately revised in pencil.

Dates: Comp. ca. 1954? Pub. ?

394b.Citation: PRACTICALLY COUSINS; t. ms.; ribbon; InU.

Title: PRACTICALLY COUSINS | A Story

Key Words: There are many four-lane highways . . . "Practically cousins," said Sally Lee.

Collation: 11; white; 27.9 x 21.6; 1–11; none; good.

Contents: Complete; infrequently revised in blue ink; top of page one: Box 367 Monrovia Calif Buckeye, Ariz. in blue ink.

Dates: Comp. ca. 1954? Pub. ?

395. Citation: THE PRAYER AND THE ANSWER ARE ONE; print; print; InU.

Title: *THE PRAYER AND THE ANSWER ARE ONE*

Key Words: An enemy has dogged my . . . and the answer are one.

Collation: 2; white watermarked; 28 x 21.6; unnumbered; none; good.

Contents: Complete; unrevised.

Dates: Comp. ca. 1938. Pub. ?

396. Citation: PREFACE [TO AUTOBIOGRAPHY OF RICHARD OTTO]; t. ms., print; carbon, green print; InU.

Title: PREFACE

Key Words: I told my friend Dick . . . to share it with posterity.

Collation: 12; white, yellow; 24.3 x 21.4, 28.1 x 21.5; [1] 2–4, [1] 2–4, [1] 2–4; none; good.

Contents: Complete; infrequently revised in pencil, blue ink; for Autobiography of Richard Otto.

Dates: Comp. ca. 1960. Pub. ?

397. Citation: PREFACE [TO AN UPTON SINCLAIR ANTHOLOGY]; a. ms.; pencil; InU.

Title: *Preface*

Key Words: The occasion for this statement . . . gleanings of all my life.

Collation: 4; white; 28 x 21.7; 1–4; none; fair.

Contents: Complete; moderately revised in pencil; verso of all four pages is a newsletter release from Continental Congress of Farmers and Workers.

Dates: Pub. 1933.

398. Citation: PREFACE [TO SIMEON ALLER'S THE RUSSIANS SAID IT FIRST]; t. ms.; ribbon, carbon; InU.

Title: Preface; By Upton Sinclair

Key Words: When my friend Simeon Aller . . . has made us neighbors forever.

Collation: 5; white, white watermarked; 28 x 21.7, 28 x 21.7; [1] 2, [1] 2–3; none; good.

Contents: Complete; moderately revised in pencil.

Dates: Pub. 1963.

399. Citation: PREFACE [TO TONGUE SPEAKING?]; t. ms.; carbon; InU.

Title: Preface

Key Words: This writer of too many . . . work of scholarship and discernment.

Collation: 2; yellow; 28 x 21.6; [1] 2; none; good.

Contents: Complete; infrequently revised in pencil.

Dates: Comp. ca. 1963. Pub. ?

400a. Citation: PREFACE [TO SOUTHERN BELLE]; t. ms.; carbon; InU.

Title: PREFACE TO "SOUTHERN BELLE"

Key Words: This is the story of . . . woman I have ever known.

Collation: 6; white; 27.8 x 21.4; [1] 2–3, [1] 2–3; none; good.

Contents: Complete; infrequently revised in pencil; original and carbon copy.

Dates: Pub. 1957.

400b. Citation: PREFACE [TO SOUTHERN BELLE]; t. ms.; carbon; InU.

Title: PREFACE

Key Words: I approach this task with . . . smiles at her husband's optimism.

Collation: 3; white; 28 x 21.6; [1] 2–3; 3; good.

Contents: Complete, moderately revised in pencil; not used in book.

Dates: Pub. 1957.

401. Citation: PREFACES TO THE JUNGLE; t. ms., a. ms.; ribbon, carbon, pencil; InU.

Title: Preface to the Jungle, 1956.

Key Words: The conditions portrayed in this . . . in fifty years. *Izviestya*, 6/VII/63.

Collation: 56; misc. sheets; 27.8 x 21.5 to 28 x 21.5; numbered consecutively by group but not continuously; none; good.

Contents: Complete; infrequently revised in pencil, brown, blue ink, not all in Sinclair's hand; folder labeled: PREFACE to "The Jungle" contains the prefaces for several editions of *The Jungle* including the Indian and Viking Press Editions of 1946.

Dates: Comp. ca. 1946–63. Pub. 1946–63.

402. Citation: PREPARE FOR THE ENEMIES' ON-SLAUGHTS; t. ms.; carbon; InU.

Title: Prepare for the Enemies' Onslaughts

Key Words: A few days ago some . . . ending of poverty in California.

Collation: 3; blue watermarked; 27.9 x 21.6; [1] 2–3; none; good.

Contents: Complete; infrequently revised in pencil, un-identified hand.

Dates: Comp. ca. 12 March 1935. Pub. ?

403. Citation: PREPARING FOR REVOLUTION; t. ms.; carbon; InU.

Title: Preparing for Revolution

Key Words: I have been collecting a . . . we going to change it?

Collation: 4; blue watermarked; 28 x 21.6; [1] 2–4; none; good.

Contents: Complete; unrevised; dated in pencil in upper right corner of first page: 3/12/35.

Dates: Comp. ca. 12 March 1935. Pub. ?

404a. Citation: PRESIDENTIAL AGENT; t. ms.; ribbon; InU.

Title: [none]

Key Words: TO MARY CRAIG SINCLAIR Without . . . vision of any human mind.

Collation: 1024; misc. sheets; 27.9 x 21.5 to 28.2 x 21.9; consecutively numbered by chapter but not continuously; 23, 30, 45, 58, 77, 91, 119, 128, 144, 165, 166, 171, 172, 201, 208, 218, 219, 226, 236, 237, 239, 263, 280, 302, 326, 330, 349, 361, 400, 401, 452, 474, 522, 523, 528, 534, 550, 568, 591, 592, 609, 640, 657, 683, 689, 708,

728, 735, 783, 798, 810, 825, 826, 829, 840, 855, 878, 886, 889, 905, 931, 957, 1001, 1003, 1009, 1021; good.

Contents: Complete; frequently revised in red, regular pencil; apparently a complete early draft; ms. is kept in two boxes labeled: Earlier Draft I; Earlier Draft II; contains dedication: TO MARY CRAIG SINCLAIR and AUTHOR'S NOTE.

Dates: Pub. 2 June 1944.

404b. Citation: PRESIDENTIAL AGENT; t. ms.; ribbon; InU.

Title: PRESIDENTIAL AGENT

Key Words: Like two ships that rest . . . vision of any human mind.

Collation: 969; white watermarked, white; 28 x 21.8, 27.9 x 21.6; [6], 1a, [1] 2–415, [416], 417–962; none; fair, spindled.

Contents: Complete; moderately revised in pencil; also bears printer's notations in blue, red, regular pencil; ms. is kept in two boxes: Printer's Copy I — books I–IV; Printer's Copy II — books V–VII; contains all additional printer's sheets necessary for copyright, etc.; title page missing.

Dates: Pub. 2 June 1944.

404c. Citation: PRESIDENTIAL AGENT; t. ms., a. ms., p. proof; ribbon, carbon, pencil, print; InU.

Title: [none]

Key Words: Lanny smiled. "You men of . . . invitation to lunch was a

Collation: 41; misc. sheets; 18.3 x 16.8 to 28.1 x 21.8; randomly numbered; 14, 17, 30, 41; fair.

Contents: Incomplete; frequently revised in pencil; some revisions in red, blue pencil not by Sinclair on the page proofs; misc. sheets; many of the sheets have been tagged and labeled.

Dates: Pub. 2 June 1944.

405a. Citation: PRESIDENTIAL MISSION; t. ms., a. ms.; ribbon, carbon, pencil; InU.

Title: [none]

Key Words: he'll have questions to ask . . . the employ of the OSS?"

Collation: 14; white watermarked, white; 28 x 21.7, 28.1 x 21.7; randomly numbered; 12; good.

Contents: Incomplete; infrequently revised in pencil; several misc. sheets both tagged and labeled; ms. appears to be largely an original and a retyped copy plus several carbons.

Dates: Pub. ca. 19 May 1947.

405b. Citation: PRESIDENTIAL MISSION; t. ms., print; ribbon, carbon, print; InU.

Title: PRESIDENTIAL MISSION | A NOVEL

Key Words: Lanny Budd's heart was high . . . places and people in between.

Collation: 826; white watermarked, misc. sheets; 28 x 21.7, 33.9 x 8 to 33.9 x 19; consecutively numbered by chapter but not continuously; 32, 48, 59, 65, 113, 120, 124, 151, 167, 180, 182, 241, 248, 278, 338, 346, 357, 364, 398, 407, 415, 500, 508, 520, 534, 545, 556, 585, 587, 588, 610, 682, 709, 721, 722, 743, 744, 745, 752, 766, 809, 820; good.

Contents: Incomplete; frequently revised in pencil; missing parts are listed on a separate sheet; ms. housed in box labeled: Earlier Draft.

Dates: Pub. ca. 19 May 1947.

405c. Citation: PRESIDENTIAL MISSION; t. ms.; ribbon; InU.

Title: PRESIDENTIAL MISSION [underscored three times]

Key Words: Lanny Budd's heart was high . . . to carry his cross!"

Collation: 846; white watermarked, misc. sheets; 28 x 21.6, 27.9 x 21.5 to 28 x 35; continuously numbered with variations; 817; fair, spindled.

Contents: Complete; moderately revised in pencil; printer's notations in purple, red, regular pencil; ms. is housed in two boxes labeled: Printer's copy I — chaps. I–V, Printer's Copy II — chaps. VI–IX.

Dates: Pub. ca. 12 May 1947.

406. Citation: THE PROBLEM OF FOOD; t. ms.; carbon; InU.

Title: *The Problem of Food*

Key Words: Let us consider the question . . . and an agent of Moscow.

Collation: 9; blue watermarked, white; 28 x 21.6; 14, 16–23; none; good.

Contents: Complete; infrequently revised in pencil.

Dates: Comp. ca. 1934? Pub. ?

407. Citation: THE PROBLEM OF PENSIONS; t. ms.; carbon; InU.

Title: *The Problem of Pensions*

Key Words: The last three planks of . . . Ending of Poverty in California.

Collation: 9; white watermarked; 28 x 21.6; 33–34, 36–42; none; good.

Contents: Incomplete; moderately revised in pencil.

Dates: Comp. ca. 1938. Pub. *Progressive*, 27 August 1938.

408. Citation: A PROCLAMATION TO THE PEOPLE OF CALIFORNIA; t. ms.; ribbon, carbon; InU.

Title: A P R O C L A M A T I O N | To the People of California

Key Words: (The following has been drafted . . . go forward to do it.

Collation: 44; white watermarked; 27.9 x 21.6; [1] 2–8, 2–7, [1] 2–15, [1] 2–8, [1] 2–7; 13, 16; good.

Contents: Complete; moderately revised in pencil; statement released to the press to be made public if Sinclair won gubernatorial seat in California, 1934.

Dates: Comp. ca. November 1934. Unpublished.

409. Citation: A PROCLAMATION TO THE WORLD; t. ms.; ribbon, carbon; InU.

Title: A PROCLAMATION TO THE WORLD | BY FRANKLIN D. ROOSEVELT | Not Written By Him But Respectfully Offered [w.i. over c.o. Suggested] To Him and to you [w.i. over c.o. Others]

Key Words: I, Franklin D. Roosevelt, President of . . . race for all future time.

Collation: 10; white watermarked; 27.9 x 21.6; [1] 2–5, [1] 2–5; 4; good.

Contents: Complete; moderately revised in pencil.

Dates: Comp. ca. 1938. Pub. ?

410. Citation: PRODUCTION FOR USE; t. ms.; carbon; InU.

Title: TEMPLE SHOLOM | Lecture Forum | DE-BATE | UPTON SINCLAIR | vs. | HAMILTON

FISH, JR. | PRODUCTION FOR USE VS. PRO-
DUCTION FOR PROFIT

Key Words: Mr. Fish and I have . . . them to produce
for themselves.

Collation: 20; white, 35 x 21.6; [1], 3–20, [1]; none;
good.

Contents: Complete; unrevised.

Dates: Comp. ca. August 1935. Pub. ?

411. Citation: PRODUCTION FOR USE MUST COME;
t. ms.; carbon; InU.

Title: PRODUCTION FOR USE MUST COME

Key Words: The system under which we . . . instead
of capitalism and war.

Collation: 10; blue watermarked; 27.9 x 21.6; [1] 2–5,
[1] 2–5; none; good.

Contents: Complete; infrequently revised in pencil.

Dates: Pub. *American Guardian*, 31 January 1936.

412a. Citation: THE PROFESSOR AND THE BULL-
THORN; t. ms.; ribbon; InU.

Title: THE PROFESSOR AND THE BULLTHORN

Key Words: Frail little stem, as fine . . . their chloro-
phyll And keeping still.

Collation: 1; white; 27.9 x 21.7; [1]; none; good.

Contents: Complete; infrequently revised in blue ink;
bottom right corner: Buckeye, Arizona.

Dates: Comp. ca. 1955. Pub. ?

412b. Citation: THE PROFESSOR AND THE BULL-
THORN; t. ms.; carbon; InU.

Title: THE PROFESSOR AND THE BULLTHORN

Key Words: Frail little stem, as fine . . . their chloro-
phyll And Keeping still.

Collation: 2; white; 27.9 x 21.7; unnumbered; none; good.

Contents: Complete; infrequently revised in blue ink, two copies.

Dates: Comp. ca. 1955. Pub. ?

413a. Citation: THE PROFITS OF RELIGION; t. ms., a. ms.; ribbon, blue, black carbon, faded, black ink; InU.

Title: [none]

Key Words: Made use of by unheroic . . . our energies in fighting religion!

Collation: 18; brown, white; 27.8 x 21.5, 27.9 x 21.2; randomly numbered; none; fair.

Contents: Incomplete; moderately revised in faded ink, pencil; misc. sheets from Book I.

Dates: Pub. October 1918.

413b. Citation: THE PROFITS OF RELIGION; t. ms., a. ms.; ribbon, purple carbon, faded ink; InU.

Title: *The Rain-makers*

Key Words: The story of the long . . . nation outside Parliament. The Bishop

Collation: 65; brown, white; 27.8 x 21.5, 27.9 x 21.2; randomly numbered; 20, 23, 35, 50, 51, 55, 59; fair.

Contents: Incomplete; frequently revised in faded ink, pencil; misc. sheets from Book II.

Dates: Pub. October 1918.

413c. Citation: THE PROFITS OF RELIGION; t. ms., a. ms., print; ribbon, purple carbon, faded ink, print; InU.

Title: *Charity*

Key Words: Some years ago Mr. Thomas . . . be stopped with a bullet!

Collation: 52; brown, white watermarked; 27.3 x 17.5 to 27.8 x 21.7, 28.1 x 21.7; randomly numbered; 3, 6, 10, 20, 34, 41, 42, 43, 44; fair.

Contents: Incomplete; frequently revised in faded ink, pencil; misc. sheets from Book III; the verso pencil notations in shorthand are not Sinclair's.

Dates: Pub. October 1918.

413d. Citation: THE PROFITS OF RELIGION; t. ms., a. ms., print; ribbon, purple carbon, faded ink, print; InU.

Title: *The [Outlook for Graft* (c.o.)] *Octopus* [(w.i. faded ink)]

Key Words: Dr. Lyman Abbott published this . . . Hand and the Iron Fist!

Collation: 104; brown, misc. sheets; 27.6 x 17.2 to 27.7 x 21.5, 27.8 x 21.8 to 28 x 21.8; randomly numbered; 2, 19, 22, 26, 36, 40, 46, 47, 50, 57, 65, 72, 82, 86, 87, 88, 89; fair.

Contents: Incomplete; frequently revised in faded ink, pencil; misc. sheets from Books IV–V; some of the pencil notations on the verso in shorthand are not Sinclair's.

Dates: Pub. October 1918.

413e. Citation: THE PROFITS OF RELIGION; t. ms., a. ms., print; ribbon, purple carbon, faded ink, print; InU.

Title: [none]

Key Words: I do not wish to . . . a thousand of her disciples.

Collation: 60; brown, white watermarked; 27.8 x 21.6, 21.3 x 21.4 to 27.9 x 21.8; randomly numbered; 9, 16, 34, 46, 60; fair.

Contents: Incomplete; frequently revised in faded ink, pencil; misc. sheets of Book VI; the sheets have been tagged and labeled.

Dates: Pub. October 1918.

413f. Citation: THE PROFITS OF RELIGION; t. ms., a. ms.; ribbon, purple carbon, faded ink; InU.

Title: [none]

Key Words: Conrad Noel again—his excellent . . . and malice and all uncharitableness!

Collation: 41; misc. sheets; 23.2 x 21.7 to 28.1 x 21.7; randomly numbered; 2, 14, 28, 31, 35; fair.

Contents: Incomplete; frequently revised in faded ink, pencil.

Dates: Pub. October 1918.

413g. Citation: THE PROFITS OF RELIGION; t. ms.; carbon; InU.

Title: [none]

Key Words: writes: "No one has ever . . . agents. Upton Sinclair, Pasadena, California.

Collation: 1; brown; 27.9 x 21.6; 2; none; fair.

Contents: Incomplete; infrequently revised in faded ink; page two of a two page circular for *Profits of Religion*; note in pencil by Sinclair remarks: (apparently circular for "Profits of Religion.")

Dates: Pub. October 1918.

414. Citation: PROGRESS FORWARD OR BACKWARD; t. ms.; carbon; InU.

Title: PROGRESS FORWARD OR BACKWARD

Key Words: I am invited to discuss . . . can get it, Tovarish Becher!

Collation: 8; white; 27.9 x 21.6; [1] 2–4, [1] 2–4; none; good.

Contents: Complete; two copies moderately revised in pencil.

Dates: Comp. ca. 1953. Pub. ?

415. Citation: PROGRESSIVE CLUB SPEECH; t. ms.; carbon; InU.

Title: Extracts from Speech of Mr. Upton Sinclair, May 29, 1914, | Progressive Club, Chicago.

Key Words: Dear Friends and Comrades: — The . . . consider all the "Hinky Dinks."

Collation: 7; white; 27.7 x 21.5; [1] 2–7; none; good.

Contents: Complete; infrequently revised in pencil.

Dates: Comp. ca. 29 May 1914. Pub. ?

416a. Citation: PROTECTING OUR LIBERTIES; t. ms.; ribbon; InU.

Title: PROTECTING OUR LIBERTIES.

Key Words: America has a grave question . . . America. Police court Judge Crawford

Collation: 15; brown; 27.8 x 21.6; [1] 2–15; 15; good.

Contents: Complete; moderately revised in pencil.

Dates: Pub. *Nation*, 4 July 1923.

416b. Citation: PROTECTING OUR LIBERTIES; t. ms.; carbon; InU.

Title: PROTECTING OUR LIBERTIES

Key Words: America has a grave question . . . —that was "prolonging the strike!"

Collation: 13; white; 28 x 21.6; [1] 2–13; none; good.

Contents: Complete; unrevised.

Dates: Pub. *Nation*, 4 July 1923.

417. Citation: PUBLISHING FILTH; t. ms.; carbon; InU.

Title: PUBLISHING FILTH

Key Words: Some years ago My friend . . . my writings upon their list.

Collation: 2; brown; 27.9 x 21.5; [1] 2; none; good.

Contents: Complete; unrevised; someone has written on page 1 in pencil: Mailed to U.S. 4/14/22; folder labeled: "Appeal to Reason."

Dates: Pub. *Appeal to Reason*, 8 July 1922.

418. Citation: PUMP-PRIMING AGAIN; t. ms.; carbon; InU.

Title: PUMP-PRIMING AGAIN

Key Words: President Roosevelt has at last decided . . . circle of depressions which from

Collation: 1; white watermarked; 28 x 21.6; [1]; none; fair.

Contents: Incomplete; moderately revised in pencil.

Dates: Pub. *EPIC News*, 25 April 1938.

419a. Citation: THE QUESTION MARK; t. ms.; ribbon; carbon; InU.

Title: THE QUESTION MARK

Key Words: One who, in his youth . . . has never been known before."

Collation: 20; white watermarked; 27.8 x 21.5; 1–11, [1] 2–9; none; fair, water and rust stains, repaired.

Contents: Complete; infrequently revised in blue ink, pencil; first and second draft.

Dates: Comp. ca. 1948? Pub. ?

419b. Citation: THE QUESTION MARK; t. ms.; ribbon; InU.

Title: THE QUESTION MARK

Key Words: One who, in his youth, . . . has never been known before."

Collation: 9; white; 28 x 21.6; [1] 2–9; none; good.

Contents: Complete; infrequently revised in pencil, blue ink.

Dates: Comp. ca. 1948? Pub. ?

419c. Citation: THE QUESTION MARK; t. ms.; carbon; InU.

Title: THE QUESTION MARK

Key Words: One who, in his youth . . . is endlessly curious about it.

Collation: 11; white watermarked; 27.9 x 21.6; 1–11; none; good.

Contents: Complete; unrevised.

Dates: Comp. ca. 1948? Pub. ?

420. Citation: A QUESTIONNAIRE CONCERNING PSYCHIC EXPERIENCES; a. ms.; pencil; InU.

Title: *A Questionnaire Concerning Psychic Experiences.*

Key Words: Two years ago I published . . . your name may be used.

Collation: 1; blue watermarked; 27.8 x 21.6; [1]; none; good.

Contents: Complete; frequently revised in pencil.

Dates: Comp. ca. 1932. Unpublished.

See: MENTAL RADIO

421. Citation: A QUESTIONNAIRE ON MARRIAGE; t. ms.; ribbon; InU.

Title: A Questionnaire On Marriage

Key Words: There is an organization in . . . The address of Dr. Wilson

Collation: 1; blue watermarked; 27.8 x 21.6; [1]; none; good.

Contents: Incomplete; unrevised.

Dates: Comp. ca. 1935. Pub. ?

422. Citation: THE QUESTION OF VIOLENCE [See THE BOOK OF LIFE]; t. ms., a. ms.; ribbon, carbon, pencil; InU.

Title: [CONFISCATION VERSUS PURCHASE (c.o. pencil)] The Question of Violence [w.i. pencil]

Key Words: We now approach the most . . . without abolishing the profit system.

Collation: 134; brown; 14 x 21.6 to 28 x 21.6; randomly numbered; 13, 69, 71, 117; good.

Contents: Incomplete; moderately revised in ink, pencil; contents includes: "The Question of Violence," "Violence and Propaganda," "Working Versus Owning," "The Problem of Propaganda," "The Socialist Party," "The Transition Stage," "The Labor Unions," "The Public Bank," "Freeing the Land," "The Meaning of Graft," "Supplement," and misc. sheets; in manila folder labeled: Unidentified material found with "Book of Life" mss.

Dates: Comp. ca. 1921. Pub. ?

423a. Citation: QUESTION PERIOD FOR CRITICS; t. ms.; ribbon; InU.

Title: Question Period For Critics 27

Key Words: I have just published a . . . as saying that he found

Collation: 12; green; 28 x 21.6; 1–2, 2a, 3–11; 1, 2, 3, 4, 8, 11; good.

Contents: Complete; frequently revised in pencil.

Dates: Comp. ca. 1936. Pub. ?

423b. Citation: QUESTION PERIOD FOR CRITICS; t. ms.; carbon; InU.

Title: QUESTION PERIOD FOR CRITICS

Key Words: I have just published a . . . been continued for twenty-two years.

Collation: 9; white watermarked; 27.8 x 21.6; [1] 2–9; none; good.

Contents: Complete; infrequently revised in pencil.

Dates: Comp. ca. 1936. Pub. ?

423c. Citation: QUESTION PERIOD FOR CRITICS; t. ms.; ribbon; InU.

Title: QUESTION PERIOD FOR CRITICS

Key Words: I have just published a . . . been continued for twenty-two years.

Collation: 9; white watermarked; 27.8 x 21.6; [1] 2–9; none; good.

Contents: Complete; infrequently revised in pencil.

Dates: Comp. ca. 1936. Pub. ?

424. Citation: RADIO KYA; t. ms.; ribbon, carbon; InU.

Title: Radio KYA February 24, 1934 4 p.m. 15 minutes

Key Words: Five or six weeks ago . . . and it will be done.

Collation: 12; white watermarked; 28 x 21.5; [1] 2–6, [1] 2–6; none; good.

Contents: Complete; infrequently revised in pencil in unidentified hand.

Dates: Pub. ?

425. Citation: A RAG-TAG ECONOMY; t. ms.; carbon; InU.

Title: A RAG-TAG ECONOMY

Key Words: In "The Nation" for September . . . me with any Russian idiot.

Collation: 10; blue watermarked; 13.9 x 21.5 to 28 x 21.6; [1] 2, 2a, 3–5, [1], 6–8; none; good.

Contents: Complete; infrequently revised in pencil.

Dates: Pub. *Upton Sinclair's National EPIC News,* 18 November 1935.

426. Citation: THE REACTIONS OF ABRAMS: A RE-PORT; t. ms.; ribbon; InU.

Title: THE REACTIONS OF ABRAMS: A RE-PORT

Key Words: Two years ago the writer . . . so important a possibility requires.

Collation: 14; white; 28 x 21.7; [1] 2–14; none; good.

Contents: Complete; unrevised.

Dates: Pub. *Pearson's Magazine*, September 1922.

See also: THE ABRAMS DISCOVERY and IN DE-
FENSE OF ALBERT ABRAMS.

427a. Citation: THE RED DRAGON; t. ms., a. ms.; ribbon, pencil; InU.

Title: THE RED DRAGON | The Story of Agnes
Smedley in America and China

Key Words: Newspaper dispatches bring us a . . .
Daughters of the American Revolution?

Collation: 13; green, white watermarked; 28 x 21.6,
27.9 x 21.5; [1] 2–7, 6–11; 4; good.

Contents: Complete; moderately revised in pencil.

Dates: Comp. ca. 1950? Pub. ?

427b. Citation: THE RED DRAGON; t. ms.; carbon; InU.

Title: THE RED DRAGON | The Story of Agnes
Smedley in America and China

Key Words: Newspaper dispatches bring us a . . .
Daughters of the American Revolution?

Collation: 10; white watermarked; 27.9 x 21.6; [1]
2–10; none; good.

Contents: Complete; infrequently revised in pencil, unidentified hand.

Dates: Comp. ca. 1950? Pub. ?

428a. Citation: REDS DECEIVED HIM; t. ms.; ribbon;
InU.

Title: Statement by Upton Sinclair.

Key Words: I have been asked by . . . world in the Atlantic Pact.

Collation: 3; white watermarked; 27.8 x 21.6; [1] 2–3; none; good.

Contents: Complete; unrevised; someone has written on signature on page three.

Dates: Pub. *New Leader*, 28 May 1949.

428b. Citation: REDS DECEIVED HIM; t. ms.; carbon; InU.

Title: Statement of Upton Sinclair published in the New Leader in the spring of 1949.

Key Words: I have been asked by . . . world in the Atlantic Pact.

Collation: 6; white watermarked; 27.8 x 21.6; [1] 2–3, [1] 2–3; none; good.

Contents: Complete; two copies infrequently revised in blue ink; signature on pages three and six.

Dates: Pub. *New Leader*, 28 May 1949.

429a. Citation: REDS I HAVE KNOWN; t. ms., a. ms.; ribbon, pencil; InU.

Title: REDS I HAVE KNOWN

Key Words: It is the fashion nowadays . . . before it is too late!

Collation: 101; white; 22.3 x 21.6 to 27.9 x 21.6; [1] 2–11, 11a–11m, [1], 11L, 12–41, [1], 42–43, 43a, 44–70, G1–G4, 71–81; 48, 49, 53, 54, 58, 78, 79, 80, 84, 94, 95; fair.

Contents: Complete; frequently revised in pencil; on page 78 is a clipping from a *Time* magazine, dated by Sinclair as Sept. 25, 1950; in folder labeled: Original ms. Reds I Have Known

Dates: Comp. ca. 1950. Pub. ?

429b.Citation: REDS I HAVE KNOWN; t. ms.; carbon; InU.

Title: REDS I HAVE KNOWN

Key Words: It is the fashion nowadays . . . before it is too late!

Collation: 105; white watermarked; 27.8 x 21.5; [2] 1–50, 50a, 51–82, 82a, 83–101; none; fair, burned and waterstained, spindled.

Contents: Complete; infrequently revised in pencil.

Dates: Comp. ca. 1950. Pub. ?

429c. Citation: REDS I HAVE KNOWN; t. ms.; ribbon; InU.

Title: REDS I HAVE KNOWN

Key Words: It is the fashion nowadays . . . before it is too late!

Collation: 105; white watermarked; 27.9 x 21.6; 1–25, [2], 26–50, 50a, 51–82, 82a, 83–101; none; good.

Contents: Complete; infrequently revised in pencil.

Dates: Comp. ca. 1950. Pub. ?

429d.Citation: REDS I HAVE KNOWN; t. ms.; carbon; InU.

Title: THE REDS I HAVE KNOWN

Key Words: It is the fashion now-a-days . . . country under seal, and the

Collation: 132; white, white watermarked; 27.9 x 21.6, 28 x 21.6; randomly numbered; none; good.

Contents: Incomplete [?]; infrequently revised in regular, red pencil; folder labeled: Machine Transcription "Reds I Have Known"

Dates: Comp. ca. 1950. Pub. ?

430. Citation: RELIEF OF SUFFERING; t. ms.; carbon; InU.

Title: RELIEF OF SUFFERING

Key Words: There is a struggle now . . . our Golden State of California.

Collation: 4; blue watermarked; 27.9 x 21.6; [1] 2–4; none; good.

Contents: Complete; unrevised.

Dates: Comp. ca. 1935. Pub. ?

431a. Citation: REPLY TO MANCHESTER BODDY; t. ms.; ribbon; InU.

Title: Reply to Manchester Boddy 25

Key Words: I am deeply grateful for . . . Boddy; & so will they!

Collation: 4; white watermarked; 28.1 x 21.7; 3–6; none; good.

Contents: Complete; frequently revised in pencil.

Dates: Pub. *Illustrated Daily News*, 19 June 1934.

431b. Citation: REPLY TO MANCHESTER BODDY; t. ms.; carbon; InU.

Title: Reply to Manchester Boddy

Key Words: I am deeply grateful for . . . Boddy; and so will they!

Collation: 10; white watermarked, blue watermarked; 28 x 21.5, 27.9 x 21.6; [1] 2–5, [1] 2–5; fair; good.

Contents: Complete; two copies unrevised; in upper right corner of every page of ms. except 1, 6, is typed: Boddy 6-21-34.

Dates: Pub. *Illustrated Daily News*, 19 June 1934.

432. Citation: REPORT TO THE EPIC CONVENTION;
t. ms.; ribbon; InU.

Title: REPORT TO THE EPIC CONVENTION

Key Words: The Convention of May, 1935, . . . so
throughout the EPIC movement.

Collation: 2; blue watermarked; 27.9 x 21.6; [1] 2;
none; good.

Contents: Complete; infrequently revised in pencil, unidentified hand.

Dates: Pub. *EPIC News*, 2 March 1936.

433. Citation: RESTORE AND KEEP YOUR HEALTH
BY CONTROLLING EMOTIONS; t. ms.; ribbon;
InU.

Title: Restore and Keep your *Health* by Controlling
Emotions.

Key Words: We live in the Golden . . . indulge in
resentment and self-righteousness.

Collation: 7; green, white; 27.9 x 21.5, 27.9 x 21.5;
1–4, 1–3; 5, 7; fair, rust and water stains.

Contents: Complete; infrequently revised in pencil; first
and second draft.

Dates: Comp. 1920s? Pub. ?

434a. Citation: THE RETURN OF LANNY BUDD;
a. ms.; pencil; InU.

Title: [none]

Key Words: When I urged this program . . . [?] re-
copy bottom of 45.

Collation: 2; white, blue watermarked; 14.4 x 21.6,
27.9 x 21.6; 2, insert 45a; none; good.

Contents: Incomplete; infrequently revised in pencil; misc. notes for *Return of Lanny Budd*?

Dates: Pub. April 1953.

434b. Citation: THE RETURN OF LANNY BUDD; t. ms., a. ms.; ribbon, carbon; pencil; InU.

Title: LANNY BUDD FLIES AGAIN

Key Words: A philosopher stood at the . . . our sacred honor.' " THE END

Collation: 839; white; 27.9 x 21.6; continuously numbered with variations; none; good.

Contents: Complete; infrequently revised in pencil; early draft; in two boxes labeled: Early Draft I, Chapters I–XV; Early Draft II, Chapters XVI–XXX.

Dates: Pub. April 1953.

434c. Citation: THE RETURN OF LANNY BUDD; t. ms., mimeo.; ribbon, mimeo.; InU.

Title: "The Return of | Lanny Budd" [w.i. pencil]

Key Words: A philosopher stood at the . . . our sacred honor.' " THE END

Collation: 919; white, white watermarked; 28 x 21.7, 27.9 x 21.6; continuously numbered with variations; 187, 192, 256, 264, 265, 267, 272, 273, 352, 356, 358, 436, 471, 475, 481, 527, 589, 591, 827, 895, 907; fair, punched for three ring binder, spindled.

Contents: Complete; infrequently revised in red, regular pencil, blue ink, not in Sinclair's hand; ms. is mimeograph copy with a few ribbon copy inserts; in two boxes labeled: Printer's Copy I, Printer's Copy II.

Dates: Pub. April 1953.

434d. Citation: RETURN OF LANNY BUDD; t. ms.; ribbon; InU.

Title: THE RETURN OF LANNY BUDD | Outline of proposed dramatization

Key Words: Dear Mr. Sinclair: I am . . . of the play as well.

Collation: 13; white watermarked, white; 25.5 x 20.4, 27.9 x 21.6; [2] 2–12; none; good, water and rust stains.

Contents: Complete; infrequently revised in pencil; page one is letter from Harold Freedman, President, Brandt & Brandt Dramatic Department, Inc., 101 Park Avenue, New York 17, N.Y. to Sinclair in Monrovia, dated 27 May 1953.

Dates: Unpublished.

434e. Citation: THE RETURN OF LANNY BUDD; t. ms., a. ms.; ribbon, carbon, blue ink, pencil; InU.

Title: THE RETURN OF LANNY BUDD | Outline of proposed dramatization.

Key Words: The scenes have been selected . . . B's apartment, L tell all.

Collation: 36; white, misc. sheets; 28 x 21.7, 12.1 x 21.6 to 20.3 x 12.1; [1] 2–11, [1] 2–11, [1] 2–11 [3]; 34, 35, 36; good.

Contents: Complete; unrevised; complete outline plus two carbons; also three notes between Sinclair and his typist; some of the handwriting is that of the typist.

Dates: Unpublished.

435a. Citation: THE RETURN OF UPTON SINCLAIR; t. ms., a. ms.; ribbon, carbon, pencil; InU.

Title: THE RETURN OF UPTON SINCLAIR

Key Words: This is not a ghost . . . The Return of Upton Sinclair.

Collation: 8; white watermarked, white; 27.8 x 21.6, 27.8 x 21.3; [1] 2, [1] 2, [1] 2-4; none; good.

Contents: Complete; moderately revised in blue ink, pencil; original, two copies.

Dates: Comp. ca. 1953? Pub. ?

435b. Citation: THE RETURN OF UPTON SINCLAIR; t. ms.; carbon; InU.

Title: THE RETURN OF UPTON SINCLAIR

Key Words: This is not a ghost . . . The Return of Upton Sinclair.

Collation: 4; white watermarked; 27.9 x 21.5; [3], 2; none; good.

Contents: Complete; infrequently revised in pencil.

Dates: Comp. ca. 1953? Pub. ?

436a. Citation: REVOLUTION IN COLORADO; t. ms.; ribbon; InU.

Title: *REVOLUTION IN COLORADO*

Key Words: Entering one day the headquarters . . . permitted to rob the corpse?

Collation: 11; white; 28 x 21.7; [1] 2-10, 13; none; good.

Contents: Incomplete; infrequently revised in pencil, ink.

Dates: Comp. ca. 1915. Pub. ?

436b. Citation: REVOLUTION IN COLORADO; t. ms.; carbon; InU.

Title: *REVOLUTION IN COLORADO*

Key Words: Entering one day the headquarters . . . similar landmark in our history?

Collation: 13; white; 28 x 21.7; [1] 2–13; none; good.

Contents: Complete; infrequently revised in ink.

Dates: Comp. ca. 1915. Pub. ?

437. Citation: THE REWARD OF LABOR; t. ms.; carbon; InU.

Title: THE REWARD OF LABOR

Key Words: Some months ago you may . . . program for a "servile state?"

Collation: 6; brown; 27.9 x 21.5; [1] 2–6; none; good.

Contents: Complete; unrevised; folder labeled: "Appeal to Reason."

Dates: Pub. *Appeal to Reason*, 8 July 1922.

438. Citation: THE RICE DIET WORKS; t. ms.; carbon; InU.

Title: THE RICE DIET WORKS

Key Words: Most of the contagious diseases . . . tell him to read it!

Collation: 3; white; 27.9 x 21.5; [1] 2–3; none; good.

Contents: Complete; infrequently revised in pencil, blue ink.

Dates: Comp. ca. 1954. Pub. *Harper's Magazine*, December 1963.

439a. Citation: THE RIGHT TO CRITICIZE AND DE-BATE; t. ms.; ribbon, carbon; InU.

Title: THE RIGHT TO CRITICIZE AND DE-BATE

Key Words: By courtesy of a friend . . . free to expand and grow.

Collation: 7; white watermarked; 27.9 x 21.5; [1–2] 2, [1] 2, [1] 2; none; good.

Contents: Complete; infrequently revised in pencil.

Dates: Comp. ca. 1950. Pub. ?

439b. Citation: THE RIGHT TO CRITICIZE AND DEBATE; t. ms.; ribbon, carbon; InU.

Title: THE RIGHT TO CRITICIZE AND DEBATE

Key Words: By courtesy of a friend . . . free to expand and grow.

Collation: 4; white watermarked; 28 x 21.6; unnumbered; none; good.

Contents: Complete; unrevised; page 1 signed in blue ink, page 3 signed in pencil by Sinclair.

Dates: Comp. ca. 1950. Pub. ?

439c. Citation: THE RIGHT TO CRITICIZE AND DEBATE; t. ms.; carbon; InU.

Title: THE RIGHT TO CRITICIZE AND DEBATE

Key Words: By courtesy of a friend . . . 160 Lloyds Road, Royapettah, Madras.)

Collation: 1; white; 27.8 x 21.7; [1]; none; good.

Contents: Complete; unrevised.

Dates: Comp. ca. 1950. Pub. ?

439d. Citation: THE RIGHT TO CRITICIZE AND DEBATE; t. ms.; carbon; InU.

Title: THE RIGHT TO CRITICIZE AND DEBATE

Key Words: By courtesy of a friend . . . free to expand and grow.

Collation: 2; white; 27.9 x 21.5; [1] 2; none; good.

Contents: Complete; unrevised.

Dates: Comp. ca. 1950. Pub. ?

440. Citation: THE ROMAN CATHOLIC WAR ON SOCIALISM IN NEW YORK CITY; t. ms.; blue carbon; InU.

Title: The Roman Catholic War on | Socialism in New York City

Key Words: I told in the Appeal . . . Commissioner of New York city.

Collation: 8; white watermarked; 28 x 21.5; [1] 2–8; none; good.

Contents: Complete; infrequently revised in ink; page 7 has pinned to it a newspaper clipping from the *New York Times* concerning Dr. Robbins Gilman's resignation as head worker of University Settlement at Eldridge and Rivington Streets, New York.

Dates: Comp. ca. 1914. Pub. ?

441a. Citation: ROMAN HOLIDAY; t. ms.; ribbon; InU.

Title: ROMAN HOLIDAY

Key Words: From the case records of . . . about himself all the time.

Collation: 265; green, white watermarked; 28 x 21.6, 28.2 x 21.9; numbered consecutively by chapter but not continuously; 96, 116, 131, 138, 147, 232, 240, 241, 256; good.

Contents: Incomplete; frequently revised in pencil; a relatively complete early draft.

Dates: Pub. ca. 3 January 1931.

441b. Citation: ROMAN HOLIDAY; t. ms.; carbon; InU.

Title: Roman Holiday [(w.i. pencil)] [ROMAN HOLI-DAY interlude, (c.o.)].

Key Words: From the case records of . . . all the time. THE END

Collation: 269; white; 28 x 21.7 to 28.1 x 21.9; continuously numbered with variations; none; good.

Contents: Complete; infrequently revised in pencil not in Sinclair's hand; a ms. of the English edition; both parts have been bound by two brass studs in brown covers: "not for setting" has been written on the cover; folder labeled: Roman Interlude, *Part First*; Roman Interlude, *Part Second*.

Dates: Pub. ca. 3 January 1931.

441c. Citation: ROMAN HOLIDAY; t. ms.; ribbon; InU.

Title: ROMAN INTERLUDE [(w.i. pencil)] [HOLI-DAY (c.o.)]

Key Words: From the case records of . . . all the time. *The End.*

Collation: 248; white; 28 x 21.6; [1] 2–248; none; good.

Contents: Complete; infrequently revised in pencil; not for setting: marked on the cover; ms. has been bound by two brass studs in brown covers; folder 1 labeled: Roman Interlude, Part I; folder 2: Roman Interlude, Part II.

Dates: Pub. ca. 3 January 1931.

441d. Citation: ROMAN HOLIDAY [ROMAN INTER-LUDE]; t. ms., print; carbon, print; InU.

Title: ROMAN [Interlude (w.i. pencil)] [HOLIDAY (c.o.)].

Key Words: From the case records of . . . all the time.
THE END

Collation: 274; white; 25.5 x 20.3 to 28 x 21.8; [1]
I–IV, [1] 2–131, [1], [1], 132–270 [1]; none; good,
punched for two-ring binder.

Contents: Complete; infrequently revised in pencil, ink,
not in Sinclair's hand; a complete printer's copy of the
manuscript of the English edition of ROMAN HOLI-
DAY in a brown cover; also included are four of
Werner Laurie's mock-up sheets for their edition; folders
labeled: Roman Interlude Part I; Roman Interlude
Part II.

Dates: Pub. ca. 3 January 1931.

442. Citation: THE RUDEST MAN IN THE WORLD;
t. ms.; ribbon, carbon; InU.

Title: THE RUDEST MAN IN THE WORLD

Key Words: One of our leading lady . . . lines of it
were published.

Collation: 12; white watermarked; 28 x 21.6; 1–6, 1–6;
none; good.

Contents: Complete; infrequently revised in pencil.

Dates: Comp. ca. 1933. Pub. ?

443. Citation: THE SACRED SWORD; t. ms.; carbon;
InU.

Title: THE SACRED SWORD

Key Words: At the side of every . . . boys in all the
world

Collation: 3; white watermarked; 27.8 x 21.7; [1] 2–3;
none; good.

Contents: Complete; unrevised.

Dates: Comp. ? Pub. ?

444. Citation: A SAFE WORLD: HOW TO MAKE IT;
t. ms.; carbon; InU.

Title: A SAFE WORLD: HOW TO MAKE IT

Key Words: What sort of world are . . . Internation
of the immediate future.

Collation: 6; white watermarked; 28 x 21.6; [1] 2–3,
[1] 2–3; none; good.

Contents: Complete; unrevised.

Dates: Pub. *Writers' War Board*, December 1944.

445a. Citation: SALESLADY; t. ms.; carbon; InU.

Title: SALESLADY | A Little Play for the White
Collar Folks | In Three Acts

Key Words: Scene 1: Lingerie department of the . . .
the union makes us strong.

Collation: 121; white watermarked; 28 x 21.6; [2] 2–102,
102a, 103–119; none; good, spindled.

Contents: Complete; infrequently revised in pencil.

Dates: Comp. ca. 1925? Unpublished.

445b. Citation: SALESLADY; t. ms.; carbon; InU.

Title: SALESLADY | A Little Play for the White
Collar Folks | In Three Acts

Key Words: Scene I: Lingerie department of the . . .
of several cousins of hers.

Collation: 124; brown, white watermarked; 12.2 x 21.4,
28 x 21.6; [3] 2–102, 102a, 103–119, 115; none; good.

Contents: Complete; infrequently revised in pencil;
page one is a cardboard with "Saleslady | Original MS."
in blue pencil, in unidentified hand.

Dates: Comp. ca. 1925? Unpublished.

445c. Citation: SALESLADY; t. m.; ribbon, carbon; InU.

Title: SALESLADY | A Little Play for the White Collar[s (c.o.)] Folks [(w.i. pencil)] | In Three Acts [(w.i. pencil)]

Key Words: Scene I: Lingerie department of the . . . the union makes us strong.

Collation: 118; white watermarked, green; 28 x 21.6, 28.2 x 21.6; consecutively numbered by acts but not continuously; 4, 5, 7, 59, 80, 84; good.

Contents: Complete; frequently revised in pencil; first three pages are misc. sheets.

Dates: Comp. ca. 1925? Unpublished.

446a. Citation: SAMUEL THE SEEKER; t. ms.; carbon; InU.

Title: SAMUEL THE SEEKER | (Chapter XXXII)

Key Words: When Samuel opened his eyes . . . teach his fellows about it.

Collation: 22; white; 27.9 x 21.5; 1–11, 1–11; none; good.

Contents: Incomplete; unrevised; label with ms. reads: 2 copies of Chapt | XXXII revised | Chapt deleted

Dates: Pub. 21 March 1910.

446b. Citation: SAMUEL THE SEEKER; t. ms.; carbon; InU.

Title: Samuel the Seeker | (Chapter XXXII)

Key Words: When Samuel opened his eyes . . . teach his fellows about it.

Collation: 12; white watermarked; 28 x 21.6; [1] 2–12; none; good.

Contents: Incomplete; moderately revised in pencil; label with ms. reads: Chapt. XXXII revised | deleted

Dates: Pub. 21 March 1910.

446c. Citation: SAMUEL THE SEEKER; t. ms.; carbon; InU.

Title: Samuel the Seeker | (Chapter XXXII)

Key Words: When Samuel opened his eyes . . . teach his fellows about it.

Collation: 11; white watermarked; 28 x 21.6; [1] 2–6, 8–12; none; good.

Contents: Incomplete; unrevised; label with ms. reads: Chapt XXXII | complete | deleted | Book has 31 chapts.

Dates: Pub. 21 March 1910.

447. Citation: A SCHOOL FOR SCANDAL; t. ms.; carbon; InU.

Title: A SCHOOL FOR SCANDAL

Key Words: This is a great big . . . waste of space: | (no clipping)

Collation: 1; brown; 27.9 x 21.5; unnumbered; none; good.

Contents: Complete; unrevised; someone has written "Sent 4/18/22" and "(no clipping)," on page 1 in pencil; folder labeled: "Appeal to Reason."

Dates: Pub. *Appeal to Reason*, 6 May 1922.

448. Citation: THE SEAMY SIDE OF SOCIAL DRINKING; t. ms.; carbon; InU.

Title: THE SEAMY SIDE OF SOCIAL DRINKING

Key Words: It is a fancy he . . . and quote them at your

Collation: 1; white; 27.8 x 21.5; [1]; 1; good.

Contents: Complete; unrevised.

Dates: Pub. *Rhythm* (Calcutta), January 1956.

449. Citation: THE SECOND STORY MAN; t. ms.; carbon; InU.

Title: THE SECOND STORY MAN

Key Words: The following synopsis for a . . . to you, you punish him."

Collation: 6; brown; 28 x 21.6; [1] 2, [1] 2, [1] 2; none; fair.

Contents: Complete; unrevised.

Dates: Pub. 1912, 1925.

450. Citation: SENSATIONAL CHARGES BY SINCLAIR; t. ms.; carbon; InU.

Title: THE EISENSTEIN PICTURE: | A statement from the other side of the case.

Key Words: I have read the articles . . . they have placed in us.

Collation: 3; white watermarked; 28 x 21.8; [1] 2-3; none; good.

Contents: Complete; infrequently revised in pencil, not in Sinclair's hand.

Dates: Pub. *The New Leader* (London), 13 April 1934.

451. Citation: THE SHEPHERD IS DEAD; t. ms.; ribbon, black, blue carbon; InU.

Title: THE SHEPHERD IS DEAD

Key Words: The shepherd is dead and . . . shepherd, speak from the grave!

Collation: 3; white, white watermarked; 28 x 21.5, 28 x 21.6; unnumbered; none; good.

Contents: Complete; infrequently revised in pencil; one original and two carbons; note beneath title mentions that the body of F. D. Roosevelt is not yet in the grave.

Dates: Pub. *Rob Wagner's Script*, 12 May 1945.

452a. Citation: THE SINCLAIR FOUNDATION; t. ms.; ribbon; InU.

Title: *THE SINCLAIR FOUNDATION* | Upton Sinclair makes the most important announcement of his life

Key Words: For twenty-five years I have . . . "The Goslings", paper, for $1.50.

Collation: 6; white; 28 x 21.7; 1–6; none; good.

Contents: Complete; infrequently revised in pencil, ink.

Dates: Pub. 2 September 1931 (pamphlet).

452b. Citation: THE SINCLAIR FOUNDATION; t. ms.; carbon; InU.

Title: THE SINCLAIR FOUNDATION | A statement to the Readers and Friends of Upton Sinclair

Key Words: For the past thirty years . . . Trustees and all other data.

Collation: 2; white; 28 x 21.6; [1] 2; none; good.

Contents: Complete; unrevised.

Dates: Pub. 2 September 1931 (pamphlet).

453. Citation: SINGING JAILBIRDS; t. ms., a. ms.; ribbon, pencil; InU.

Title: [CALIFORNIA (c.o.)] SINGING JAILBIRDS [(w.i. pencil)] | A Drama in Four Acts

Key Words: D.A. Well, this might be . . . all wrong —it's an outrage."

Collation: 325; white lined, misc. sheets; 16.9 x 10.5 to 21.9 x 12, 21.6 x 13.7 to 28 x 21.6; randomly numbered; 1, 3, 4, 7, 9, 10–28, 44, 46, 76–161, 230; fair, spindled.

Contents: Complete; revised frequently in pencil by Sinclair and unidentified hand; includes three notebooks and 16 misc. sheets of notes and one 163-page printer's copy of the complete play; dated on card attached on page 162 as 1924.

Dates: Pub. 1 June 1924.

454. Citation: SIT-DOWN STRIKE; t. ms.; carbon; InU.

Title: SIT-DOWN STRIKE | Outline of Story

Key Words: Opening scenes at the outbreak . . . of the workers' organization movement.

Collation: 8; white watermarked; 27.9 x 21.6; [1] 2–4, [1] 2–4; none; good.

Contents: Complete; two copies unrevised.

Dates: Comp. ca. 1930s. Unpublished, but see *EPIC News*, 5 April 1937.

455. Citation: THE SLAVERY OF "FREE LOVE"; t. ms.; carbon; InU.

Title: THE SLAVERY OF "FREE LOVE."

Key Words: There have always been a . . . ban tried in the world.

Collation: 13; white; 26.7 x 20.6; [1] 2–9, 9b, 9a, 10, 11; none; good.

Contents: Complete; infrequently revised in pencil.

Dates: Comp. ca. 1910–12. Unpublished, but see *Current Opinion*, May 1920.

456a. Citation: SMOKED OUT! A REPLY TO THE CRITIC OF THE BRASS CHECK; t. ms.; carbon; InU.

Title: SMOKED OUT! | A REPLY TO THE CRITIC OF "THE BRASS CHECK"

Key Words: "The Brass Check," a study . . . known as the Associated Press!"

Collation: 31; white; 28 x 21.6; randomly numbered or unnumbered; none; good.

Contents: Complete [?]; unrevised; in folder labeled: "Brass Check."

Dates: Comp. ca. July 1921. Pub. See *Appeal to Reason*, esp. Spring and Summer, 1921.

456b. Citation: SMOKED OUT! A REPLY TO THE CRITICS OF THE BRASS CHECK; t. ms., print; ribbon, print; InU.

Title: SMOKED OUT! | A REPLY TO THE CRITICS [S (w.i. pencil)] | OF "THE BRASS CHECK" [Second single-bar in pencil on ms.]

Key Words: "The Brass Check: a study . . . departments are of the worst."

Collation: 60; brown, white; 27.9 x 21.7, 19.1 x 12 to 25.9 x 16.9; randomly numbered; 3, 4, 14, 17, 19, 21, 23–37, 41–44, 46, 47, 51, 54, 55; fair.

Contents: Complete; infrequently revised in pencil; includes tear sheets from pamphlets, books, newspapers.

Dates: Comp. ca. 1920–21. Pub. See *Appeal to Reason,* esp. Spring and Summer, 1921.

457. Citation: SOCIAL ART; t. ms.; carbon; InU.

Title: SOCIAL ART.

Key Words: There comes to my desk . . . which is safe from corruption.

Collation: 6; brown; 27.9 x 20.3; [1] 2–3, [1] 2–3; none; good.

Contents: Complete; infrequently revised in pencil.

Dates: Pub. *Modern Quarterly,* March 1923.

458. Citation: SOCIALISM AND CULTURE; t. ms.; carbon; InU.

Title: SOCIALISM AND CULTURE

Key Words: What will be the effect . . . and thought in the world."

Collation: 24; white; 28.1 x 21.8; [1] 2–24; none; good.

Contents: Complete; infrequently revised in pencil.

Dates: Pub. *American Freeman,* 6–13 June; June 1931 (pamphlet).

459. Citation: SOCIALISM AND ME; t. ms.; ribbon; InU.

Title: SOCIALISM AND ME

Key Words: The editor of "The Call" . . . and Raymond Moley didn't know.

Collation: 9; white; 27.9 x 21.5; [1] 2–8, 8; none; good.

Contents: Complete; infrequently revised in pencil.

Dates: Comp. ca. 1955. Pub. ?

460. Citation: SOCIALISM AND WAR; t. ms., a. ms.; black, blue ribbon, ink; InU.

Title: SOCIALISM AND THE WAR.

Key Words: To help, even in the . . . from Socialist papers are appended.)

Collation: 15; white, misc. sheets; 27.9 x 21.5, 27.7 x 25.7 to 28 x 21.7; 1, 1–14; none; fair

Contents: Complete; moderately revised in ink.

Dates: Pub. *Upton Sinclair's*, April 1918.

461. Citation: SOCIALISM IN AMERICA; t. ms.; carbon; InU.

Title: SOCIALISM IN AMERICA

Key Words: The average American, if you . . . ridicule, obloquy, and sometimes martyrdom.

Collation: 16; white watermarked; 27.8 x 21.5; 1–8, 1–8; none; good.

Contents: Complete; two copies infrequently revised in pencil.

Dates: Comp. ca. 1943. Pub. ?

462. Citation: SOCIALISM, RED OR WHITE [A REVIEW]; t. ms.; carbon; InU.

Title: SOCIALISM, RED OR WHITE | Bolshevism at a Deadlock, by Karl Kautsky, | Rand School Press, Price $1.75

Key Words: The present writer approaches this . . . Marxian Theoretician of our Times."

Collation: 3; white; 28 x 21.6; [1] 2–3; none; good.

Contents: Complete; infrequently revised in pencil.

Dates: Pub. *Nation*, 9 September 1931.

463. Citation: A SOCIALIST MOVING PICTURE CIR-
CUIT; t. ms.; ribbon; InU.

Title: A SOCIALIST MOVING PICTURE CIR-
CUIT

Key Words: It is generally agreed among . . . and get
action on it.

Collation: 4; white; 28 x 21.6; [1] 2–4; none; good.

Contents: Complete; infrequently revised in ink.

Dates: Comp. ca. 1915? Pub. ?

464. Citation: A SOCIALIST PEACE; t. ms.; ribbon; InU.

Title: *A SOCIALIST PEACE*

Key Words: For fifteen years I have . . . about a
Peace for Democracy.

Collation: 17; white; 27.7 x 21.5; [1] 2–17; none; good.

Contents: Complete; infrequently revised in ink.

Dates: Pub. *Pearson's Magazine*, August 1917.

465. Citation: SOCIALIST URAEMIA; t. ms.; carbon;
InU.

Title: *Socialist Uraemia*

Key Words: The late Doctor Salisbury used . . . in
the American Socialist Party.

Collation: 4; white watermarked; 28 x 21.7; [1] 2–4;
none; good.

Contents: Complete; infrequently revised in ink, unidentified hand.

Dates: Comp. ca. 1917. Pub. ?

466. Citation: SOCIAL JUSTICE WITHOUT VIOLENCE; t. ms.; ribbon; InU.

Title: *Social Justice Without Violence*

Key Words: Note: A month or two . . . is being rapidly left behind.

Collation: 20; brown; 28 x 21.5; [2] 3–20; none; good.

Contents: Complete; moderately revised in pencil.

Dates: Comp. ca. 1923. Pub. ?

467. Citation: SOCIOLOGY FOR AMERICA; t. ms.; carbon; InU.

Title: SOCIOLOGY FOR AMERICA

Key Words: The people of our country . . . Thorstein Veblen and Lester F. Ward.

Collation: 3; white watermarked; 28 x 21.7; [1] 2–3; none; good.

Contents: Complete; infrequently revised in pencil; book review of *Lester F. Ward, The American Aristotle: A Summary and Interpretation of His Sociology*, by Samuel Shugerman (Duke University Press); in upper right corner of page one, written in pencil; Sept. 12–39.

Dates: Comp. ca. 12 September 1939. Pub. ?

468. Citation: THE SONG OF THE ID; t. ms.; ribbon, carbon; InU.

Title: THE SONG [G (w.i. pencil)] OF THE ID

Key Words: This is the song of . . . Copyright 1948 by Upton Sinclair.

Collation: 2; white watermarked; 27.9 x 21.7; unnumbered; good.

Contents: Complete; infrequently revised in pencil; one original and carbon.

Dates: Comp. ca. 1948. Pub. ?

469a. Citation: SONGS NEARING SIXTY; a. ms.; pencil; InU.

Title: Songs Nearing Sixty

Key Words: God said: The time has . . . you too had this disease!

Collation: 12; miscellaneous sheets; 4 x 21.6 to 27.5 x 21.2; 1–7, 7a, 7b, 8–10; 1; fair.

Contents: Complete [?]; infrequently revised in pencil; collection of eleven poems titled: Calling, War News, Broadcasting, For Children, The Poet, Challenge, Special Providence, Occasional Verse, Apology, Real Estate Note, Envoi; note on page one: 2/28/36 Pasadena, Calif.

Dates: Comp. ca. 1936. Pub ?

469b. Citation: SONGS NEARING SIXTY; t. ms.; ribbon, carbon; InU.

Title: Songs Nearing Sixty

Key Words: God said: The time has . . . you too have heart disease!

Collation: 12; white watermarked; 28 x 21.6; 1–4, 1–4, 1–4; none; good.

Contents: Complete; infrequently revised in pencil; note attached: Rejected by *Redbook Magazine* See letter of Jan. 27, 1937 also 5/11/1936.

Dates: Comp. ca. 1936. Pub. ?

470a. Citation: SONGS OF A SOIL SLAVE; t. ms., print; blue, black ribbon, carbon, print; InU.

Title: SONGS OF A SOIL SLAVE | By | GERALD LIVELY | With an Introduction by | UPTON SIN-CLAIR

Key Words: A Socialist author seems to . . . That's waiting in the grave.

Collation: 78; white watermarked, brown; 21.7 x 20.4 to 28 x 21.4, 27.7 x 21.6; [2] 2–77; 3; fair.

Contents: Complete; infrequently revised in ink, pencil.

Dates: Comp. ca. 1918. Pub. ?

470b. Citation: SONGS OF A SOIL SLAVE; t. ms.; carbon; InU.

Title: Songs of a Soil Slave | Gerald Lively

Key Words: A socialist author seems to . . . price of the children's play."?

Collation: 80; brown, white; 28.1 x 21.5, 27.6 x 21.7; [1] 1–51, 53–80; none; good, two brass studs.

Contents: Complete; infrequently revised in pencil; un-identified collection of poetry by Gerald Lively, intro-duction by Sinclair.

Dates: Comp. ca. 1918. Pub. ?

471. Citation: SPEECH BY UPTON SINCLAIR; t. ms.; ribbon, carbon; InU.

Title: SPEECH BY UPTON SINCLAIR | AT | OLYMPIC AUDITORIUM, LOS ANGELES, CALIF. | March 28th, 1935.

Key Words: Friends of EPIC, and Friends . . . and the pursuit of happiness.

Collation: 22; white watermarked; 27.9 x 21.6; [1] 2–11, [1] 2–11; none; good.

Contents: Complete; moderately revised in pencil.

Dates: Pub. *Upton Sinclair's EPIC News*, 1 April 1935.

472. Citation: SPEECH GIVEN BY MR. UPTON SIN-
CLAIR; t. ms.; ribbon, carbon; InU.

Title: SPEECH GIVEN BY MR. UPTON SIN-
CLAIR. | at Lawndale, March 24, at 7:30 P.M.

Key Words: Mr. Chairman, ladies, and gentlemen:
. . . will not hurt my feelings.

Collation: 10; white; 28 x 21.7; 1–8, 8, 9; none; good.

Contents: Complete; infrequently revised in pencil, unidentified hand; speech taken and transcribed by Miss
Karalyn Pickett, 1202 Walnut Ave. Long Beach.

Dates: Comp. ca. March 1934. Pub. ?

473. Citation: SPEECH OF UPTON SINCLAIR; t. ms.;
carbon; InU.

Title: SPEECH OF UPTON SINCLAIR | before the
| MASS MEETING HELD AT THE STATE CAP-
ITOL | Denver, Colorado, May 15, 1914.

Key Words: I shall be able to . . . permitted to rob
the corpse?

Collation: 7; white; 32.1 x 21.5; 1, 4, 1–2, [1], 4–5;
none; fair.

Contents: Complete; infrequently revised in blue ink,
pencil.

Dates: Pub. *Appeal to Reason*, 30 May 1914.

474. Citation: SPEECH OF UPTON SINCLAIR; t. ms.;
carbon; InU.

Title: SPEECH OF UPTON SINCLAIR | AT MASS
MEETING IN CELEBRATION OF RUSSIAN REV-

OLUTION | LOS ANGELES CALIF. MARCH 10, 1918.

Key Words: Friends and Comrades: I come . . . right here in Los Angeles.

Collation: 18; brown; 28.1 x 21.6; 1–9, 1–9; none; good.

Contents: Complete; infrequently revised in ink, pencil.

Dates: Pub. ?

475a. Citation: SPIDER LORE; t. ms., a. ms.; carbon, pencil; InU.

Title: SPIDER LORE

Key Words: Beautiful spider, round as a . . . cheat 'em, I eat 'em!

Collation: 3; white; 20 x 12.7 to 27.9 x 21.7; unnumbered; none; good.

Contents: Complete (poem); infrequently revised in pencil; verso page three is cover for Hytone Bond Writing Tablet.

Dates: Comp. ? Pub. ?

475b. Citation: SPIDER LORE; t. ms.; ribbon; InU.

Title: SPIDER LORE

Key Words: Beautiful spider, round as a . . . cheat 'em, I eat 'em!

Collation: 1; white; 27.9 x 21.7; [1]; none; good.

Contents: Complete (poem); unrevised.

Dates: Comp. ? Pub. ?

476a. Citation: SPIRITS, OR MIND-READING?; t. ms., a. ms.; ribbon, pencil; InU.

Title: SPIRITS, OR MIND-READING? | A Second Seance With Arthur Ford

Key Words: The factor which makes psychic . . . that you have "gone spooky"!

Collation: 20; green; 27.9 x 21.5; [1] 2–3, 3a, 4–19; 15; good.

Contents: Complete; frequently revised in pencil.

Dates: Pub. *Occult Review*, July 1931.

476b. Citation: SPIRITS, OR MIND-READING?; t. ms.; ribbon; InU.

Title: SPIRITS, OR MIND-READING? | A Second Seance With Arthur Ford

Key Words: The factor which makes psychic . . . that you have "gone spooky!"

Collation: 17; white; 28.1 x 21.7; [1] 2–12, 16–20; 1; good.

Contents: Incomplete; frequently revised in pencil.

Dates: Pub. *Occult Review*, July 1931.

476c. Citation: SPIRITS, OR MIND-READING?; t. ms.; ribbon; InU.

Title: SPIRTS, OR MIND-READING? | A Second Seance with Arthur Ford

Key Words: The factor which makes psychic . . . that you have "gone spooky!"

Collation: 20; white; 6.3 x 10.3 to 28.1 x 21.7; [2] 2–10, [11–12], 13–20; [1]; good, torn corner.

Contents: Complete; infrequently revised in pencil; first page is a note by Sinclair: Final top copy 8/4/30.

Dates: Pub. *Occult Review*, July 1931.

477. Citation: SPLITTING THE LIBERALS; t. ms.; ribbon; InU.

Title: SPLITTING THE LIBERALS

Key Words: A while ago I wrote . . . most varied set of pensions.)

Collation: 6; white watermarked; 28 x 21.7; [1] 2–6; 2; good.

Contents: Complete; frequently revised in pencil.

Dates: Comp. ca. 1935. Pub. ?

478a. Citation: THE SPOKESMAN'S SECRETARY; t. ms., a. ms.; ribbon, pencil; InU.

Title: THE SPOKESMAN'S SECRETARY | Being the Letters of Mame to Mom

Key Words: Letter I In which I join . . . and let the fun begin!

Collation: 146; green, yellow, white; 27.8 x 21.6, 28.1 x 21.6, 28.1 x 21.7; consecutively numbered by chapter but not continuously; 17, 121; good.

Contents: Complete; moderately revised in regular, red pencil.

Dates: Pub. ca. Aug. 1926.

478b. Citation: THE SPOKESMAN'S SECRETARY; t. ms.; ribbon; InU.

Title: THE SPOKESMAN'S SECRETARY | Being the Letters of Mame to Mom

Key Words: Letter I in which I join . . . of Your high-up daughter Mame.

Collation: 128; white; 28 x 21.6; [1] 2–61, 61–84, 86–114, 114a, 115–127; 36, 67, 108; fair.

Contents: Complete; moderately revised in pencil not all in Sinclair's hand; printer's copy.

Dates: Pub. ca. August 1926.

479. Citation: SPONTANEOUS COMBUSTION; t. ms.; carbon; InU.

Title: SPONTANEOUS COMBUSTION

Key Words: I am living on the . . . inside one old black skull.

Collation: 2; white watermarked; 27.9 x 21.6; [1] 2; none; good.

Contents: Complete; infrequently revised in pencil.

Dates: Comp. ca. 1915. Pub. ?

480. Citation: STAND FIRM, NORWEGIANS!; t. ms.; carbon; InU.

Title: STAND FIRM, NORWEGIANS! | Radio Broadcast by Upton Sinclair

Key Words: I have been asked to . . . thee a crown of life."

Collation: 10; white watermarked; 27.9 x 21.5; [1] 2–5, [1] 2–5; none; good.

Contents: Complete; two copies infrequently revised in pencil.

Dates: Pub. *News of Norway*, 13 March 1941.

481. Citation: STARTING EPIC IN NEW YORK; t. ms.; carbon; InU.

Title: STARTING EPIC IN NEW YORK

Key Words: I am writing this brief . . . read End Poverty in Civilization.

Collation: 5; white; 28.2 x 21.5; [1] 2–5; none; good.

Contents: Complete; unrevised.

Dates: Comp. ca. 1934. Pub. ?

482. Citation: STATEMENT BY UPTON SINCLAIR; t. ms.; carbon; InU.

Title: STATEMENT by Upton Sinclair

Key Words: Mr. William J. Perlman of . . . is putting on its boots."

Collation: 6; white watermarked; 28 x 21.6; [1] 2–3, [1] 2–3; none; good.

Contents: Complete; unrevised.

Dates: Comp. ca. 1934. Pub. ?

482a. Citation: STATEMENT BY UPTON SINCLAIR; t. ms.; carbon; InU.

Title: STATEMENT BY UPTON SINCLAIR

Key Words: The EPIC movement to end . . . are asked to work elsewhere.

Collation: 4; white watermarked; 27.8 x 21.5; [1] 2–4; none; good.

Contents: Complete; infrequently revised in pencil.

Dates: Pub. *Upton Sinclair's National EPIC News*, 26 August 1935.

483a. Citation: A STATEMENT BY UPTON SINCLAIR; t. ms.; carbon; InU.

Title: A STATEMENT BY UPTON SINCLAIR | May 1, 1950

Key Words: I have read a copy . . . am now doing it again.

Collation: 2; white; 27.8 x 21.5; [1] 2; none; good.

Contents: Complete; infrequently revised in blue ink; signature on page two.

Dates: Comp. ca. 1 May 1950. Pub. ?

483b. Citation: A STATEMENT BY UPTON SINCLAIR;
t. ms.; carbon; InU.

Title: A STATEMENT BY UPTON SINCLAIR |
May 1, 1950

Key Words: I have read a copy . . . am now doing it
again.

Collation: 3; white watermarked; 27.8 x 21.6; [1] 2–3;
none; good.

Contents: Complete; infrequently revised in blue ink;
signature on page three.

Dates: Comp. ca. 1 May 1950. Pub. ?

483c. Citation: A STATEMENT BY UPTON SINCLAIR;
t. ms.; carbon; InU.

Title: A STATEMENT BY UPTON SINCLAIR |
May 1, 1950

Key Words: I have read a copy . . . am now doing it
again.

Collation: 2; white watermarked; 27.9 x 21.6; [1] 2;
none; good.

Contents: Complete; infrequently revised in green, blue
ink; signature on page two.

Dates: Comp. ca. 1 May 1950. Pub ?

483d. Citation: A STATEMENT BY UPTON SINCLAIR;
t. ms.; carbon; InU.

Title: A STATEMENT BY UPTON SINCLAIR |
May 1, 1950

Key Words: I have read a copy . . . am now doing it
again.

Collation: 2; white watermarked; 27.9 x 21.6; [1] 2;
none; good.

Contents: Complete; unrevised.

Dates: Comp. ca. 1 May 1950. Pub. ?

484. Citation: STATEMENT FOR JIM TULLY; t. ms.; carbon; InU.

Title: STATEMENT FOR JIM TULLY

Key Words: I don't think the NRA . . . job he will do it.

Collation: 3; white; 28 x 21.8; [1] 2–3; none; good.

Contents: Complete; unrevised.

Dates: Comp. ca. 1934. Pub. ?

485. Citation: A STATEMENT FROM UPTON SIN-CLAIR; t. ms.; carbon; InU.

Title: A STATEMENT FROM UPTON SINCLAIR

Key Words: Some eighteen months ago I . . . item. Address: Box 266, Monrovia, California.

Collation: 4; white; 28 x 21.6; [1] 2, [1] 2; none; good.

Contents: Complete; infrequently revised in pencil.

Dates: Comp. ca. 1956. Pub. ?

486. Citation: [STATEMENT OF UPTON SINCLAIR]; t. ms.; ribbon; InU.

Title: [none]

Key Words: The present tale was begun . . . she could or would help.

Collation: 5; brown; 28 x 21.6; 2a, 2–4, 2b; none; fair.

Contents: Incomplete; moderately revised in pencil, ink.

Dates: Comp. ca. April 1913. Pub. ?

487. Citation: STATEMENT TO EPIC NEWS; t. ms., a. ms.; ribbon, pencil; InU.

Title: STATEMENT TO EPIC NEWS

Key Words: It appears that Barclay W. Bradley . . . were handling other people's money.

Collation: 2; white watermarked; 28 x 21.6; [1] 1; none; good.

Contents: Complete; frequently revised in pencil.

Dates: Comp. ca. 1936. Pub. ?

488a. Citation: A STATEMENT TO THE EPICS; t. ms.; ribbon; InU.

Title: A STATEMENT TO THE EPICS

Key Words: Our EPIC movement is now . . . future. It's up to you!

Collation: 12; white watermarked, misc. sheets; 13.7 x 21.6 to 28 x 21.6, 24.2 x 15.3 to 27.9 x 21.6; randomly numbered; none; good.

Contents: Complete; frequently revised in pencil.

Dates: Pub. *Upton Sinclair's National EPIC News*, 13 January 1936.

488b. Citation: A STATEMENT TO THE EPICS; t. ms.; carbon; InU.

Title: A STATEMENT TO THE EPICS

Key Words: Our EPIC movement is now . . . future. It's up to you!

Collation: 8; blue watermarked; 27.9 x 21.6; [1] 2–8; none; good.

Contents: Complete; infrequently revised in pencil.

Dates: Pub. *Upton Sinclair's National EPIC News*, 13 January 1936.

489a. Citation: STATES RIGHTS SOCIALISM; t. ms.; carbon; InU.

Title: "States Rights Socialism"

Key Words: Creeping Socialism is a terrible . . . blue," and for Dixie, too.

Collation: 2; white; 28.1 x 21.7; [1] 2; none; good.

Contents: Complete; infrequently revised in pencil.

Dates: Comp. ca. 1952. Pub. ?

489b. Citation: STATES RIGHTS SOCIALISM; t. ms.; carbon; InU.

Title: "States Rights Socialism"

Key Words: Creeping Socialism is a terrible . . . blue," and for Dixie, too.

Collation: 2; white; 28.1 x 21.7; [1] 2; none; good.

Contents: Complete; unrevised.

Dates: Pub. ca. 1952. Comp. ?

489c. Citation: STATES RIGHTS SOCIALISM; t. ms.; ribbon; InU.

Title: "States Rights Socialism"

Key Words: Creeping Socialism is a terrible . . . blue," and for Dixie, too.

Collation: 2; white watermarked; 27.9 x 21.6; [1] 2; none; good.

Contents: Complete; unrevised.

Dates: Pub. ca. 1952. Comp. ?

490. Citation: STEALING ONE ANOTHER'S WASH-
ING; t. ms.; carbon; InU.

Title: STEALING ONE ANOTHER'S WASHING

Key Words: You have perhaps heard the . . . into
one another's laundry tubs.

Collation: 5; blue; 27.8 x 21.5; [2] 3–5; none; good.

Contents: Complete; unrevised.

Dates: Pub. *EPIC News,* 27 September 1937.

491. Citation: THE STEPMOTHER; t. ms.; carbon; InU.

Title: THE STEPMOTHER

Key Words: The door of the studio . . . impossible to
be a stepmother!' "

Collation: 2; white watermarked; 27.8 x 21.4; [1] 2;
none; good.

Contents: Complete; infrequently revised in ink, unidentified hand; apparently written in Gulfport, Miss.

Dates: Comp. ca. 1915. Pub. ?

492. Citation: THE STOCKYARDS; t. ms.; carbon; InU.

Title: THE STOCKYARDS

Key Words: Forty-six years ago there was . . . enslave-
ment, in darkness, unto death.

Collation: 7; white; 27.9 x 21.6; 1–5, [1], 6; 6; good.

Contents: Complete; infrequently revised in pencil.

Dates: Comp. ca. 1950. Pub. ?

493. Citation: THE STORY OF ADELAIDE BRANCH
[see THE BRASS CHECK]; t. ms.; carbon; InU.

Title: *THE STORY OF ADELAIDE BRANCH.*

Key Words: I remember once hearing in . . . it when I see it!"

Collation: 8; white watermarked; 33.4 x 21.7; 1–8; none; good, spindled.

Contents: Complete; infrequently revised in pencil.

Dates: Comp. ca. 1919. Pub. See Chap. XXIII, *The Brass Check*.

494. Citation: THE STORY OF A BOOK; t. ms.; carbon; InU.

Title: THE STORY OF A BOOK

Key Words: For close to three-quarters of . . . see, I speak from knowledge.

Collation: 6; white; 28 x 21.5; [1] 2–3, [1] 2–3; none; good.

Contents: Complete; unrevised.

Dates: Comp. ca. 1956. Pub. ?

495a. Citation: THE STORY OF CRAIG [MARY CRAIG SINCLAIR]; t. ms., a. ms.; ribbon, carbon, pencil, blue ink; InU.

Title: THE STORY OF CRAIG

Key Words: This is a story of . . . to end new para | p 5)

Collation: 430; white, green; 21.5 x 13.9 to 27.8 x 21.5, 21.5 x 13.7; randomly numbered; 1, 2, 4–6, 8, 17–20, 25–27, 33, 35–39, 41, 42, 45, 47, 50, 56, 59, 61, 62, 64, 66–69, 71, 73, 76, 77, 80, 81, 84, 87, 115, 146, 158, 161, 179, 181, 186, 199, 201, 221, 227, 242, 273, 283, 327, 330, 340, 345, 349, 351, 356, 357, 363, 364, 371, 373, 379, 384, 385, 388, 399, 411, 421; good, rust stains.

Contents: Complete; frequently revised in red, black pencil; early draft of ms.; arranged in two folders in one box labeled: The Story of Craig Early Draft; page

394 is a postal card addressed to Mrs. C. W. Richards, Box S-180-F, Elsinore, Calif., postmarked June 18, 1949. Dates: Comp. ca. 1949. Unpublished.

495b. Citation: THE STORY OF CRAIG [MARY CRAIG SINCLAIR]; t. ms., a. ms.; ribbon, pencil; InU.

Title: THE STORY OF CRAIG

Key Words: This is a story of . . . is but a poet's dream.

Collation: 487; white; 13.3 x 10.9 to 27.9 x 21.5; randomly numbered; 4, 177, 111, 111, 224, 225; fair, rust and water stains.

Contents: Complete; moderately revised in pencil; later draft of ms.; arranged in five folders in one box, folders labeled: Folder #1 Chps. I–VI, Folder #2 Chps. VII–IX, Folder #3 Chps. X–XII, Folder #4 Chps. XIII–XV, Folder #5 Chps. XVI–XVIII.

Dates: Comp. ca. 1949. Unpublished.

496a. Citation: THE STORY OF SUSIE; t. ms.; ribbon, carbon; InU.

Title: THE STORY OF ["MUFFINS" (c.o.)] SUSIE [(w.i. pencil)] | A Backward Child Comes Forward.

Key Words: Susie is a girl, fourteen . . . this method had been known.

Collation: 20; white; 14 x 5.4 to 27.9 x 21.6; [1], 1–6, [1] 2–4, [1] 2–9; none; good.

Contents: Complete; infrequently revised in pencil.

Dates: Comp. ca. 1954? Pub. ?

496b. Citation: THE STORY OF SUSIE; t. ms.; ribbon; InU.

Title: THE STORY OF SUSIE | A Backward Child Comes Forward

Key Words: Susie is a girl, fourteen . . . this method had been known.

Collation: 9; white; 27.9 x 21.5; [1] 2–9; none; good.

Contents: Complete; infrequently revised in blue ink, pencil; upper right corner page one: Buckeye, Arizona.

Dates: Comp. ca. 1954. Pub. ?

496c. Citation: THE STORY OF SUSIE; t. ms.; carbon; InU.

Title: THE STORY OF SUSIE | A BACKWARD CHILD COMES FORWARD

Key Words: Susie is a girl, fourteen . . . this method had been known.

Collation: 9; white; 27.9 x 21.5; [1] 2–9; none; good.

Contents: Complete; infrequently revised in pencil.

Dates: Comp. ca. 1954. Pub. ?

496d. Citation: THE STORY OF SUSIE; t. ms.; carbon; InU.

Title: THE STORY OF SUSIE | A BACKWARD CHILD COMES FORWARD

Key Words: Susie is a girl, fourteen . . . this method had been known.

Collation: 9; white; 27.9 x 21.5; [1] 2–9; none; good.

Contents: Complete; infrequently revised in pencil, unidentified hand.

Dates: Comp. ca. 1954? Pub. ?

497. Citation: THE STRANGE CASE OF CAREY MC-WILLIAMS; t. ms.; carbon; InU.

Title: THE STRANGE CASE OF CAREY MC-WILLIAMS

Key Words: Mr. Carey McWilliams writes quite . . .
their own opinion about it.

Collation: 10; white watermarked, blue watermarked;
27.9 x 21.5, 27.8 x 21.6; [1] 2–5, [1] 2–5; none; good.

Contents: Complete; infrequently revised in pencil.

Dates: Pub. *Pacific Weekly*, 24 February 1936.

498. Citation: SUFFRAGETTELAND; t. ms.; carbon; InU.

Title: SUFFRAGETTELAND

Key Words: The essence of this comedy . . . as to the
manless infants.

Collation: 2; white watermarked; 28 x 21.6; [1] 2; none;
good.

Contents: Complete; unrevised.

Dates: Comp. 1915? Pub. ?

499. Citation: SUPPORT FOR SPANISH DEMOCRACY;
t. ms.; carbon; InU.

Title: SUPPORT FOR SPANISH DEMOCRACY

Key Words: I am supporting this struggle . . . arms
for its own defense.

Collation: 2; white watermarked, blue; 28 x 21.6, 28 x
21.5; unnumbered; none; good.

Contents: Complete; infrequently revised in pencil, unidentified hand.

Dates: Comp. ca. 1936–37. Pub. ?

500. Citation: THE SUPREME COURT SPEAKS; t. ms.;
carbon; InU.

Title: THE SUPREME COURT SPEAKS

Key Words: I see "be the papers," . . . United States
would declare unconstitutional.

Collation: 4; blue watermarked; 27.9 x 21.6; [1] 2–4; none; good.

Contents: Complete; unrevised.

Dates: Pub. *Upton Sinclair's National EPIC News*, 13 January 1936.

501a. Citation: SYLVIA'S MARRIAGE; t. ms.; ribbon, blue carbon; InU.

Title: SYLVIA'S MARRIAGE, | A Novel

Key Words: When I set out to . . . were items in the papers.

Collation: 36; white, white lined; 26.1 x 20.3, 25.4 x 20.1; randomly numbered; none; fair.

Contents: Incomplete; frequently revised in ink, pencil.

Dates: Pub. ca. 26 September 1914.

501b. Citation: SYLVIA'S MARRIAGE; t. ms.; black, blue carbon; InU.

Title: SYLVIA'S MARRIAGE | A Novel

Key Words: When I set out to . . . by the chariot of fire!

Collation: 94; white watermarked; 25.7 x 20.2 to 27.8 x 21.3; [2] 2–13, 15–36, 36a, 37–45, 45a, 46–92; none; fair, spindled.

Contents: Incomplete; infrequently revised in ink, pencil.

Dates: Pub. ca. 26 September 1914.

501c. Citation: SYLVIA'S MARRIAGE; t. ms., a. ms.; black, blue carbon, pencil; InU.

Title: [none]

Key Words: "Sylvia" was a story of . . . 13 up 3 lines 14.

Collation: 12; white watermarked; 20.5 x 12.6 to 33 x 20.3; randomly numbered; none; good.

Contents: Complete; infrequently revised in pencil, unidentified; signed in ink on page nine by Russell H. Ramsey.

Dates: Pub. ca. 26 September 1914.

502. Citation: SYNOPSIS OF METROPOLIS-MONEY-CHANGERS-MACHINE; t. ms.; blue carbon; InU.

Title: SYNOPSIS | OF | METROPOLIS-MONEY-CHANGERS-MACHINE.

Key Words: The following synopsis, it must . . . Tenn. Coal & Iron Co.

Collation: 1; white watermarked; 28.7 x 21.6; [1]; none; good.

Contents: Complete; unrevised.

Dates: Comp. ca. 1912. Unpublished (but see each work).

503. Citation: TALK UNITED STATES!; t. ms.; carbon; InU.

Title: Talk United States!

Key Words: I have been laid up . . . my guess unless I will.

Collation: 8; blue watermarked; 27.9 x 21.6; [1] 2–4, [1] 2–4; none; good.

Contents: Complete; two copies infrequently revised in pencil; in upper right corner: 4-16-35.

Dates: Pub. *Upton Sinclair's EPIC News*, 12 April 1935.

504. Citation: THE TALLEST-MEN TOWN; t. ms.; carbon; InU.

Title: THE TALLEST-MEN TOWN | An idea for a magazine feature

Key Words: Traveling the highways of Southern . . . whatever seems fair to you.

Collation: 2; white; 28 x 21.7; [1] 2; none; good.

Contents: Complete; unrevised.

Dates: Comp. ca. 1955? Pub. ?

505. Citation: TAPE RECORDING BY UPTON SINCLAIR; t. ms.; ribbon; InU.

Title: Tape-Recording by Upton Sinclair [underscored twice] | (Oct. 15, 1958)

Key Words: My fellow Alumni of the . . . paternal greetings to you all.

Collation: 4; white; 27.9 x 21.6; [1] 2–4; none; good.

Contents: Complete; frequently revised in pencil.

Dates: Comp. 15 October 1958. Pub. ?

506. Citation: TARRYTOWN SPEECH; t. ms.; ribbon; InU.

Title: Upton Sinclair spoke in Tarrytown as follows:

Key Words: Ladies and Gentlemen: We all . . . similar landmark in our history?

Collation: 15; white; 28 x 21.6; [1] 2–11, 11, 12, 12, 13; none; good.

Contents: Complete; infrequently revised in ink; note attached: Headline for NYT 14th June 14, 1914 June 13 Mrs. G. offered Tarrytown estate for meeting.

Dates: Comp. ca. 14 June 1914. Pub. ?

507. Citation: TAXING STOCK TRANSFERS; t. ms.; ribbon, carbon; InU.

Title: TAXING STOCK TRANSFERS

Key Words: In the last issue of . . . an ample margin for error."

Collation: 6; white, green; 27.9 x 21.6, 27.9 x 21.6; [1] 2, [1] 2, [1] 2; none; good.

Contents: Complete; three copies infrequently revised in pencil, unidentified hand.

Dates: Pub. *Upton Sinclair's Paper End Poverty*, April 1934.

508. Citation: TECHNICIANS AWAKE; t. ms.; ribbon; InU.

Title: [THE (c.o.)] TECHNICIANS [REBEL (c.o.)] AWAKE [(w.i. pencil)]

Key Words: I remember that in some . . . Rodale Press, Emaus, Pa., 1938.

Collation: 6; white watermarked; 28 x 21.5; [1] 2–6; 6; good.

Contents: Complete; moderately revised in pencil.

Dates: Pub. *New English Weekly*, 15 December 1938.

509a. Citation: TELLING THE WORLD; t. ms., a. ms., print; ribbon, carbon, pencil, print; InU.

Title: ADDRESSING THE WORLD | 1901–1931

Key Words: The first time I was . . . letters received asking for books.

Collation: 197; white, misc. sheets; 28 x 21.6, 12.5 x 21.5 to 28.9 x 21.5; continuously numbered with variations; 11, 18, 20; good.

Contents: Incomplete; infrequently revised in pencil; folder labeled: "Addressing the world."

Dates: Pub. 1939 (only English edition).

509b. Citation: TELLING THE WORLD; t. ms.; ribbon, carbon; InU.

Title: ADDRESSING THE WORLD | 1901–1931

Key Words: The first time the present . . . make you gasp. | *Come along!*

Collation: 143; white, misc. sheets; 28.2 x 21.5, 28 x 21.7; numbered consecutively by item but not continuously; none; good.

Contents: Complete; unrevised; folder labeled: "Addressing the World".

Dates: Pub. 1939 (only English edition).

510. Citation: THEIRS BE THE GUILT; t. ms., a. ms.; ribbon, carbon, pencil, ink; InU.

Title: THEIRS BE THE GUILT | A Novel of the War Between the States

Key Words: Here is one of Upton . . . freeman | To ransom the slave!

Collation: 343; white, white watermarked; 28 x 21.6, 20.2 x 12.6 to 27.9 x 21.6; randomly numbered; 44, 91, 111, 136, 148, 217; good.

Contents: Complete; moderately revised in blue, black ink, pencil, some by MCS; contained in two folders labeled: n.d. . . . Theirs Be The Guilt. Books I–II, Books III–V; apparently as described in two carbons included in box 1; this is the revision reprinted in 1959; revision of *Manassas*.

Dates: Pub. February 1959.

511a. Citation: THEY CALL ME CARPENTER; t. ms., print; ribbon, print; InU.

Title: Mobland: a Nightmare

Key Words: The beginning of this strange . . . the Austrian critic about it.

Collation: 234; brown; 27.9 x 21.5; randomly numbered; 5, 13, 38, 65, 85, 87, 96, 97, 99, 124, 132, 133, 152, 167, 175, 180, 185, 192, 193, 196, 201, 218, 227, 228, 230; good.

Contents: Complete; moderately revised in pencil; page 18 is torn from the *Nation*, 23 November 1921, p. 593.

Dates: Pub. 15 September 1922.

511b. Citation: THEY CALL ME CARPENTER; t. ms., print; carbon, print; InU.

Title: THEY CALL ME CARPENTER | A Play in Four Acts | From the | BOOK | THEY CALL ME CARPENTER

Key Words: The scene: St. Bartholomew's Church . . . Curtain END OF THE PLAY

Collation: 118; green, misc. sheets; 20.1 x 14 to 27.9 x 21.6; [5], [1] 2–24, [25] 26–51, [52] 53–77, [78] 79–112, [1]; 81, 99; good.

Contents: Complete; infrequently revised in blue, black ink, pencil, not all in Sinclair's hand; this adaptation by Muriel Culp Berry contains a play bill dated 9 May 1935 inserted inside the front cover and an inscription dated 1/7/35 by Miss Berry to Sinclair on the inside title page; the play is bound at the top with a green front and brown back wrapper.

Dates: Pub. 15 September 1922 (as novel).

512a. Citation: THIRTY DOLLARS EVERY THURSDAY; t. ms.; carbon; InU.

Title: THIRTY DOLLARS EVERY THURSDAY

Key Words: What a musical sound this . . . our money-masters on a griddle.

Collation: 14; white; 27.9 x 21.5; [1] 1–13; none; good, staple marks.

Contents: Complete; moderately revised in black, blue pencil.

Dates: Comp. ca. 9 September 1938. Pub. ?

512b. Citation: THIRTY DOLLARS EVERY THURSDAY; t. ms.; ribbon, carbon; InU.

Title: *"Thirty Dollars Every Thursday!"*

Key Words: What a musical sound this . . . two plus seven equals two.

Collation: 36; green, white watermarked; 28 x 21.6, 27.9 x 21.7; 1–14, [1] 2–5, 5a–b, 6–9, [1] 2–5, 5a–b, 6–9; 5, 7; good.

Contents: Complete; infrequently revised in pencil.

Dates: Comp. ca. 9 September 1938. Pub. ?

513a. Citation: THIS BRAVE NEW PARTY; t. ms.; ribbon, carbon; InU.

Title: This [Brand (c.o.)] Brave [(w.i. pencil)] New Party

Key Words: For the second time in . . . party of any progress whatever.

Collation: 4, white watermarked; 27.9 x 21.6; randomly numbered; none; good.

Contents: Incomplete; moderately revised in pencil.

Dates: Pub. *Progressive*, 16 July 1938.

513b. Citation: THIS BRAVE NEW PARTY; t. ms.; ribbon; InU.

Title: This Brave New Party

Key Words: For the second time in . . . ahead is a terrific one.

Collation: 4; white watermarked; 28 x 21.6; [1] 2–4; none; Good.

Contents: Incomplete; infrequently revised in pencil, unidentified hand.

Dates: Pub. *Progressive*, 16 July 1938.

513c. Citation: THIS BRAVE NEW PARTY; t. ms.; carbon; InU.

Title: THIS BRAVE NEW PARTY

Key Words: For the second time in . . . every state should now get

Collation: 5; white watermarked; 28 x 21.6; [1] 2–5; none; good.

Contents: Incomplete; unrevised.

Dates: Pub. *Progressive*, 16 July 1938.

513d. Citation: THIS BRAVE NEW PARTY; t. ms.; carbon; InU.

Title: This Brave New Party

Key Words: For the second time in . . . Progressive party under experienced leadership.

Collation: 6; white watermarked; 27.9 x 21.6; [1] 2–6; none; good.

Contents: Complete; infrequently revised in blue, regular pencil; dates in upper right corner 1936.

Dates: Pub. *Progressive*, 16 July 1938.

513e. Citation: THIS BRAVE NEW PARTY; t. ms.; ribbon; InU.

Title: THIS BRAVE NEW PARTY

Key Words: For the second time in . . . Progressive Party under experienced leadership.

Collation: 6; white watermarked; 28 x 21.6; [1] 2–6; none; good.

Contents: Complete; unrevised; dated in upper right corner 1936.

Dates: Pub. *Progressive*, 16 July 1938.

513f. Citation: THIS BRAVE NEW PARTY; t. ms.; carbon; InU.

Title: THIS BRAVE NEW PARTY

Key Words: For the second time in . . . Progressive Party under experienced leadership.

Collation: 6; white watermarked; 28 x 21.6; [1] 2–6; none; good.

Contents: Complete; unrevised; in upper right corner of page one: Pasadena, California 1936.

Dates: Pub. *Progressive*, 16 July 1938.

514a. Citation: THIS I BELIEVE; t. ms., a. ms.; carbon, pencil; InU.

Title: C.B.S., COLUMBIA SQUARE, HOLLY-WOOD

Key Words: A strange thing has happened . . . hope this is not egotistical.)

Collation: 42; white watermarked; 14 x 21.6 to 28 x 21.6; randomly numbered; 11, 12, 18; good.

Contents: Complete; infrequently revised in blue ink, pencil; original a. ms., several revised copies.

Dates: Comp. ca. 1952. Pub. Tape available at the Lilly Library.

514b. Citation: THIS I BELIEVE; t. ms., a. ms.; carbon, pencil; InU.

Title: C.B.S. COLUMBIA SQUARE, HOLLYWOOD

Key Words: (Note 1 for p. 5 . . . but to Upton Sinclair's novels."

Collation: 26; white; 20.3 x 12.2 to 27.9 x 21.6; consecutively numbered but not continuously; 3, 4; fair.

Contents: Complete; moderately revised in pencil, blue ink; contains notes and two drafts, one earlier than the other, of the speech.

Dates: Comp. ca. 1952. Pub. Tape available at the Lilly Library.

514c. Citation: THIS I BELIEVE; t. ms.; carbon; InU.

Title: THIS I BELIEVE

Key Words: I was brought up as . . . life helped to change it.

Collation: 6; white, white watermarked; 28 x 21.7, 28 x 21.6; [1] 2–3, [1] 2–3; 2; good.

Contents: Complete; moderately revised in blue ink, pencil.

Dates: Comp. ca. 1952? Pub. Tape available at the Lilly Library.

514d. Citation: THIS I BELIEVE; t. ms.; ribbon; InU.

Title: THIS I BELIEVE | SCRIPT #

Key Words: I hesitate to talk about . . . life helped to change it.

Collation: 2; white watermarked; 27.6 x 21.4; [1] 2; none; good.

Contents: Complete; infrequently revised in pencil; note on page one: for Murrow over CBS.

Dates: Comp. ca. 1952? Pub. Tape available at the Lilly Library.

514e. Citation: THIS I BELIEVE; a. ms.; pencil; InU.

Title: This I Believe

Key Words: I have been asked to . . . may account for my tenacity.

Collation: 6; white; 20.3 x 25.4; [3] 2–4; none; good.

Contents: Complete; infrequently revised in pencil.

Dates: Comp. 1952? Pub. Tape available at the Lilly Library.

514f. Citation: THIS I BELIEVE; t. ms.; ribbon, carbon; InU.

Title: THIS I BELIEVE

Key Words: I was brought up as . . . own minds. This I believe.

Collation: 9; white, yellow; 28 x 21.7, 28 x 21.6; [1] 2–3, [1] 2–3, [1] 2–3; none; good.

Contents: Complete; infrequently revised in pencil.

Dates: Comp. ca. 1952? Pub. Tape available at the Lilly Library.

514g. Citation: THIS I BELIEVE; t. ms.; carbon; InU.

Title: THIS I BELIEVE | SCRIPT #

Key Words: I hesitate to talk about . . . life helped to change it.

Collation: 3; white watermarked; 27.9 x 21.5; [1] 2–3; none; good.

Contents: Complete; infrequently revised in blue ink; note on page one: This was used in CBS.

Dates: Comp. ca. 1952? Pub. Tape available at the Lilly Library.

514h. Citation: THIS I BELIEVE; t. ms.; carbon; InU.

Title: THIS I BELIEVE | SCRIPT #

Key Words: I actually hesitate to talk . . . life helped to change it.

Collation: 3; white; 28.1 x 21.5; [1] 2–3; none; good.

Contents: Complete; infrequently revised in ink, pencil.

Dates: Comp. ca. 1952? Pub. Tape available at the Lilly Library.

514i. Citation: THIS I BELIEVE; t. ms.; ribbon, carbon; InU.

Title: THIS I BELIEVE | SCRIPT #

Key Words: I hesitate to talk about . . . in papers around the world.

Collation: 6; white watermarked, white; 28 x 21.7, 24.2 x 20.3; [1] 2–3, [1] 2, [1]; none; good.

Contents: Complete; infrequently revised in black, blue ink; original, carbon of script for CBS radio; page six is a statistical description of the broadcast.

Dates: Comp. ca. 1952? Pub. Tape available at the Lilly Library.

515. Citation: THIS IS HOW IT WAS; t. ms.; ribbon; InU.

Title: THIS IS HOW IT WAS | The Adventures of Upton Sinclair | Preface

Key Words: In recent years several publishers . . . of this century in America.

Collation: 3; white; 27.9 x 21.6; [1] 2–3; none; good.

Contents: Complete; infrequently revised in pencil; preface to autobiography. Not printed as Preface to *Autobiography*. . . .

Dates: Comp. ca. 1960?

516a. Citation: THIS IS ROB!; t. ms.; ribbon; InU.

Title: THIS IS ROB! | An Anthology for Script-sized Heads | Collected, with an Introduction.

Key Words: He called himself Rob Rex; . . . Rex. Long live the King!

Collation: 7; white; 27.9 x 21.5; 1–7; none; good.

Contents: Complete; infrequently revised in blue ink, pencil; about publisher of *Rob Wagner's Script*.

Dates: Comp. ca. 27 December 1951. Unpublished.

516b. Citation: THIS IS ROB!; t. ms.; ribbon, carbon; InU.

Title: THIS IS ROB! | An Anthology for Script-sized Heads | Collected, with an Introduction

Key Words: He called himself Rob Rex; . . . wait for the sun!" (over)

Collation: 16; white; 27.9 x 21.5; 1–8, 1–8; 9, 14, 16; good.

Contents: Complete; moderately revised in pencil; about publisher of *Rob Wagner's Script*.

Dates: Comp. ca. 27 December 1951. Unpublished.

516c. Citation: THIS IS ROB!; t. ms.; carbon; InU.

Title: THIS IS ROB! | An Anthology for Script-[sized (c.o.)] shaped [(w.i. in pencil)] Heads | Collected, with an Introduction

Key Words: He called himself "Rob Rex"; . . . Rex. Long live the Kings!

Collation: 26; white; 27.9 x 21.5; 1–7, 1–7, [1] 2–6, [1] 2–6; 1, 2, 4; good.

Contents: Complete; moderately revised in pencil; about publisher of *Rob Wagner's Script*.

Dates: Comp. ca. 27 December 1951. Unpublished.

516d. Citation: THIS IS ROB!; t. ms., a. ms., print; ribbon, pencil, blue ink, print; InU.

Title: THIS IS ROB! An Anthology for Script-shaped Heads Collected, with an Introduction

Key Words: Dear Mr. Lewis: With the . . . a vulgar ex- | ROB WAGNER'S Script

Collation: 109; white, misc. sheets; 14 x 21.6 to 28 x 21.6, 14 x 10.8 to 27.9 x 21.6; randomly numbered; 12, 14–18, 21–22, 24–26, 29–30, 36–37, 40–42, 44, 49, 51, 55, 56–60, 63–69, 71–109; fair.

Contents: Complete; moderately revised in blue ink, pencil; cover letter to publisher Lewis, pages 3–8 are t. ms. ribbon introduction, following pages are torn from *Rob Wagner's Script* from Sept. 28, 1929 to Aug. 1, 1942; in manila envelope with Railway Express Agency sticker, addressed to F. Lewis, 707 S. Bdway, Los Angeles, dated Dec. 27, 1951, labeled: THIS IS ROB MANUSCRIPT

Dates: Comp. ca. 27 December 1951. Unpublished.

517a. Citation: [THIS IS UPTON SINCLAIR SPEAKING]; t. ms.; carbon; InU.

Title: [none]

Key Words: This is UPTON SINCLAIR speaking . . . put it, "it contains everything."

Collation: 5; white watermarked; 27.9 x 21.6; [1] 2–4, 7; none; good.

Contents: Incomplete; frequently revised in blue ink, pencil; it is a speech.

Dates: Comp. 26 April 1960. Unpublished.

517b. Citation: THIS IS UPTON SINCLAIR SPEAKING; t. ms.; ribbon, carbon; InU.

Title: [none]

Key Words: This is Upton Sinclair speaking . . . put it, "it contains everything."

Collation: 11; white watermarked; 27.9 x 21.6; 1–4, 7, 1–6; none; good.

Contents: Complete; infrequently revised in blue, black ink.

Dates: Comp. 26 April 1960. Unpublished.

518a. Citation: [THUNDER OVER MEXICO]; t. ms., a. ms., mimeo; ribbon, carbon, pencil, blue ink; mimeo; InU.

Title: [none]

Key Words: Born in Riga 1898. Studied . . . in fierce and rigid relief.

Collation: 183; misc. sheets; 14 x 21.6 to 33.2 x 21.6; randomly numbered; 10, 17, 19, 73, 74, 75, 76, 77, 78, 84; fair.

Contents: Incomplete; moderately revised in pencil; not all of the items are Sinclair's; misc. items about Eisenstein and the Thunder Over Mexico project; folder contains various biographies of Eisenstein, promotional literature for the picture, an article by Edmund Wilson plus interviews, most with carbons.

Dates: Comp. ca. 1930–33. Pub. Mostly unpublished.

518b. Citation: [THUNDER OVER MEXICO]; t. ms., a. ms.; ribbon, black, purple, blue carbons, pencil, ink; InU.

Title: [none]

Key Words: 11. The Cabin 12. thru . . . resultado de la Revolución. FIN.

Collation: 91; misc. sheets; 22 x 12 to 31.7 to 20.4; randomly numbered; 2, 13, 15, 20, 23, 25, 76; fair.

Contents: Incomplete; moderately revised in orange, regular pencil; only part of the material is Sinclair's; misc. material on the Scenario.

Dates: Comp. ca. 1931. Unpublished.

518c. Citation: [THUNDER OVER MEXICO]; t. ms., a. ms.; ribbon, carbon, pencil, ink; InU.

Title: [none]

Key Words: Account rendered 11 Kimbrough Mex . . . 220.00 Petty Cash—1,656.70 ($30,009.55

Collation: 138; misc. sheets; 11.1 x 5.7 to 28 x 21.9; unnumbered; 5, 6, 7, 9, 10, 18, 42, 43, 44, 45, 51, 56, 57, 59, 68, 70, 71, 72, 73, 74, 75, 76, 77, 78, 79, 80, 81, 82, 83, 84, 85, 86, 87, 94, 96, 97; fair.

Contents: Incomplete; infrequently revised in pencil, not in Sinclair's hand; most of the material is by Hunter Kimbrough; misc. sheets covering finances and supplies.

Dates: Comp. ca. 1931–33. Unpublished.

518d. Citation: [THUNDER OVER MEXICO]; t. ms., a. ms., print; ribbon, carbon, pencil, blue ink, print; InU.

Title: [none]

Key Words: To the Editor of the . . . which all that mass of

Collation: 50; misc. sheets, envelope; 13.3 x 11.1 to 28 x 21.7; randomly numbered; 23, 26, 27, 37, 38, 48, 49, 50; fair.

Contents: Incomplete; infrequently revised in pencil; some of the material is not Sinclair's; ms. is a collection of correspondence.

Dates: Comp. ca. 1931–33. Unpublished.

518e. Citation: [THUNDER OVER MEXICO]; t. ms., a. ms.; ribbon, carbon, pencil; InU.

Title: [none]

Key Words: Coming Sergei Eisenstein's Mexican Masterpiece . . . believed that he could work

Collation: 5; misc. sheets; 17.9 x 12.4 to 28 x 21.6; un-numbered; 2; good.

Contents: Incomplete; infrequently revised in pencil; misc. sheets about Eisenstein and the film.

Dates: Comp. ca. 1933. Unpublished.

518f. Citation: [THUNDER OVER MEXICO]; t. ms., a. ms., print; ribbon, carbon, pencil, ink, print; InU.

Title: [none]

Collation: 76; misc. sheets; 5 x 7.3 to 28 x 21.6; un-numbered; 2, 3, 7, 8, 10, 11, 12, 13, 14, 17, 18, 19, 20, 21, 22, 23, 24, 53, 57, 73; fair.

Contents: Incomplete; infrequently revised in pencil; some of the material is not Sinclair's; various lists of names and business cards used either as testimonials or as a guest list for the opening of the picture.

Dates: Comp. ca. 1933. Unpublished.

518g. Citation: [THUNDER OVER MEXICO]; t. ms.; ribbon, carbon; InU.

Title: Introduction to "Hacienda."

Key Words: The man who directed this . . . greatest out-door photography ever made.

Collation: 95; misc. sheets; 7.9 x 21.7 to 35.7 x 21.7; randomly numbered; 13, 19, 87, 88; fair.

Contents: Incomplete; moderately revised in pencil, not all in Sinclair's hand; a series of mss. by Sinclair and Hunter Kimbrough on the Eisenstein episode with carbons; enclosed in folder labeled: Thunder Over Mexico, Introduction & Story.

Dates: Comp. ca. 1933. Pub. 1933 (in part as Prologue to film).

518h.Citation: [THUNDER OVER MEXICO]; t. ms., print; ribbon, carbon, ink, print; InU.

Title: [none]

Key Words: 1. Sinclair pays from the . . . and year first above written.

Collation: 13; white, white watermarked; 28 x 21.3, 27.8 x 21.4 to 28 x 21.7; randomly numbered; 6, 7; fair.

Contents: Incomplete; infrequently revised in pencil, not in Sinclair's hand; folder contains legal material.

Dates: Comp. ca. 1933. Unpublished.

518i. Citation: [THUNDER OVER MEXICO]; t. ms., print; ribbon, carbon, print; InU.

Title: [none]

Key Words: "Eisenstein's 'Thunder Over Mexico' is . . . bandits, guitar players or waiters.

Collation: 53; misc. sheets; 27.9 x 21.6 to 35.6 x 21.7; randomly numbered; 21; good.

Contents: Incomplete; infrequently revised in pencil, ink, not all in Sinclair's hand; misc. items of criticism and publicity; many testimonials for the film plus reviews.

Dates: Comp. ca. 1933. Unpublished.

519. Citation: TO THE BUSINESS MEN OF AMERICA; t. ms.; ribbon; InU.

Title: TO THE "BUSINESS MEN OF AMERICA."

Key Words: This book offers a solution . . . possible anarchy at the outcome.

Collation: 5; white; 28 x 21.7; [1] 2–5; none; good.

Contents: Complete; infrequently revised in pencil; an introduction.

Dates: Comp. ca. 1924. Pub. ?

520. Citation: TO THE CONGRESS FOR CULTURAL FREEDOM; t. ms.; carbon; InU.

Title: To the Congress for Cultural Freedom

Key Words: Friends and Colleagues: I address . . . another chance to save freedom!

Collation: 6; white; 27.9 x 21.6; unnumbered; none; fair.

Contents: Complete; unrevised; two copies of one speech; two of a second, altered version.

Dates: Comp. ca. 1953–54. Pub. See tape at Lilly Library: "Message from Upton Sinclair to the Cultural Congress in Paris," 1954.

521. Citation: TO GEORGE BERNARD SHAW: AN OPEN LETTER; t. ms.; ribbon, carbon; InU.

Title: TO GEORGE BERNARD SHAW: AN OPEN LETTER

Key Words: My dear Shaw: You have . . . not visit them too often.

Collation: 8; white watermarked; 28.1 x 21.6; [1] 2–8; none; good.

Contents: Complete; infrequently revised in pencil.

Dates: Pub. *Liberty*, 22 April 1932.

522. Citation: TOMMY JUNIOR THE SECOND; t. ms.; carbon; InU.

Title: TOMMY JUNIOR THE SECOND

Key Words: Yes, there could be no . . . dat bird! 'Deed I is!"

Collation: 22; white; 27.9 x 21.6; [1] 2–22; none; good.

Contents: Complete; infrequently revised in pencil; note on page one: "Argosy" July 1895.

Dates: Pub. *Argosy*, July 1895.

523a. Citation: TOMORROW MAY BE BEAUTIFUL;
t. ms.; carbon; InU.

Title: TOMORROW MAY BE BEAUTIFUL

Key Words: In these fast moving days . . . she tells it
too freely.

Collation: 3; white; 28 x 21.6; [1] 2–3; none; good.

Contents: Complete; infrequently revised in red pencil,
unidentified hand; dated on page one: 8/16/51.

Dates: Comp. ca. 16 August 1951. Pub. ?

532b. Citation: TOMORROW MAY BE BEAUTIFUL;
t. ms.; carbon; InU.

Title: TOMORROW MAY BE BEAUTIFUL

Key Words: In these fast-moving days of . . . the City
College of N.Y.

Collation: 6; white; 27.9 x 21.7; [1] 2–3, [1] 2–3; none;
good.

Contents: Complete; infrequently revised in blue ink.

Dates: Comp. ca. 16 August 1951. Pub. ?

524a. Citation: TO MY FELLOW DEMOCRATS; t. ms.;
ribbon; InU.

Title: TO MY FELLOW DEMOCRATS

Key Words: This statement is planned for . . . both
of hand and brain.

Collation: 6; white watermarked; 28 x 21.6; [1] 2–6;
none; good.

Contents: Complete; infrequently revised in pencil.

Dates: Comp. ca. 1934. Pub. ?

524b. Citation: TO MY FELLOW DEMOCRATS; t. ms.;
carbon; InU.

Title: TO MY FELLOW DEMOCRATS

Key Words: This statement is planned for . . . both of hand and brain.

Collation: 6; blue watermarked; 28 x 21.6; [1] 2–6; none; good.

Contents: Complete; infrequently revised in pencil.

Dates: Comp. ca. 1934. Pub. ?

525a. Citation: TO MY FRENCH READERS; t. ms.; carbon; InU.

Title: To My French Readers

Key Words: Pillows, cases & sheets & . . . Secretary of State Dean Acheson.

Collation: 13; white watermarked; 13.8 x 6.7 to 27.8 x 21.7; [2] 2–6, [1] 2–6; none; good.

Contents: Complete; two copies infrequently revised in pencil.

Dates: Comp. ca. 10 May 1951. Pub. ?

525b. Citation: TO MY FRENCH READERS; t. ms.; ribbon; InU.

Title: TO MY FRENCH READERS

Key Words: I have been invited by . . . Secretary of State Dean Acheson.

Collation: 6; white watermarked; 27.9 x 21.6; [1] 2–6; none; good.

Contents: Complete; unrevised.

Dates: Comp. ca. 10 May 1951. Pub. ?

525c. Citation: TO MY FRENCH READERS; t. ms.; carbon; InU.

Title: To My French Readers

Key Words: I have been invited by . . . Secretary of State Dean Acheson.

Collation: 12; white watermarked; 27.8 x 21.7; [1] 2–6, [1] 2–6; none; good.

Contents: Complete; infrequently revised in blue ink; signature on page six.

Dates: Comp. ca. 10 May 1951. Pub. ?

525d. Citation: TO MY FRENCH READERS; t. ms., a. ms.; ribbon, pencil; InU.

Title: TO MY FRENCH READERS

Key Words: Doubtless my French readers know . . . here) (Note b goes here)

Collation: 11; white watermarked, white; 27.9 x 21.6, 27.9 x 21.6; [2] 3–8, [2] 2; 8; good.

Contents: Complete; frequently revised in pencil.

Dates: Comp. ca. 10 May 1951. Pub. ?

525e. Citation: TO MY FRENCH READERS; t. ms.; carbon; InU.

Title: TO MY FRENCH READERS

Key Words: Doubtless my French readers know . . . by force or by fraud.

Collation: 7; white watermarked; 27.9 x 21.6; [1] 2–7; none; good.

Contents: Complete; unrevised.

Dates: Comp. ca. 10 May 1951. Pub. ?

526. Citation: TO PRESIDENT ROOSEVELT; t. ms.; carbon; InU.

Title: TO PRESIDENT ROOSEVELT

Key Words: By the time these words . . . and not for private profit!

Collation: 3; blue watermarked; 27.8 x 21.6; [1] 2–3; none; good.

Contents: Complete; infrequently revised in pencil.

Dates: Pub. *Upton Sinclair's National EPIC News*, 30 September 1935.

527. Citation: TO THE READERS OF MY BOOKS IN YUGOSLAVIA; t. ms.; ribbon, carbon; InU.

Title: *TO THE READERS OF MY BOOKS IN YUGOSLAVIA*

Key Words: The men in the Kremlin . . . intellectual, to her own people.

Collation: 4; white watermarked; 27.9 x 21.7; unnumbered; none; good.

Contents: Complete; unrevised.

Dates: Comp. ca. 1953. Pub. ?

528. Citation: TO A WOULD BE DEBATER; t. ms.; carbon; InU.

Title: TO A WOULD BE DEBATER

Key Words: A couple of months ago . . . him direct. My letter follows:

Collation: 2; brown; 27.8 x 21.7; [1] 2; none; good.

Contents: Incomplete; unrevised.

Dates: Comp. ca. 1922. Pub. ?

529. Citation: THE TOY AND THE MAN; t. ms.; carbon; InU.

Title: THE TOY AND THE MAN

Key Words: This discussion of a rather . . . of their life's irrevocable symphony!

Collation: 11; white; 28 x 21.6; 1–11; none; good.

Contents: Complete; unrevised; beneath title on page one: (Written at the age of 22, and published in Wilshire's Magazine)

Dates: Pub. *Wilshire's Magazine*, December 1903.

530. Citation: TRANSCRIPT OF TAPE RECORDING; t. ms.; ribbon, carbon; InU.

Title: TRANSCRIPT OF TAPE RECORDING MADE BY | UPTON SINCLAIR AT THE REQUEST OF THE | REPRESENTATIVES OF THE YUGOSLAVE | GOVERNMENT AT THE UNITED NATIONS FOR | BROADCAST TO THE PEOPLE OF YUGOSLAVIA | ON NEW YEAR'S DAY, 1960.

Key Words: I have been asked to . . . Yugoslavia. This is Upton Sinclair.

Collation: 13; white; 27.9 x 21.6; [1] 1–5, [1] 1–5; none; good.

Contents: Complete; infrequently revised in blue, black ink, unidentified hand.

Dates: Comp. 15 December 1959.

531. Citation: TRUTH; t. ms.; carbon; InU.

Title: TRUTH | An address delivered by UPTON SINCLAIR at a dinner of the Southern California | Women's Press Club, Tuesday evening, October 24th, 1916.

Key Words: Ladies of the Press Club, . . . him to consider the program!

Collation: 14; white watermarked; 28 x 21.5; [1] 2–6, [1] 2–8; none; good.

Contents: Complete; infrequently revised in ink, pencil, in unidentified hand.

Dates: Pub. *New Age,* 7 December 1916.

532. Citation: TULLY VERSUS SINCLAIR; t. ms.; carbon; InU.

Title: TULLY VERSUS SINCLAIR

Key Words: One of the problems of . . . the word "granted" or "refused")

Collation: 18; white; 28 x 21.7 to 34 x 21.7; randomly numbered; none; good.

Contents: Complete; moderately revised in pencil.

Dates: Comp. ca. 1930? Pub. ?

533. Citation: THE TWO-FOOT SHELF; t. ms.; carbon; InU.

Title: THE TWO-FOOT SHELF [underscored three times] | *of Upton Sinclair*

Key Words: To readers of my books, . . . down a program of action.

Collation: 3; white; 27.9 x 21.5; [1] 2–3; none; fair.

Contents: Complete; infrequently revised in pencil.

Dates: Comp. ca. July 1925. Pub. ?

534. Citation: TWO SOCIALIST POETS; t. ms.; carbon; InU.

Title: TWO SOCIALIST POETS

Key Words: I have sometimes thought that . . . more than we could bear!"

Collation: 8; white watermarked; 28 x 21.6; [1] 2–8; none; good.

Contents: Complete; unrevised.

Dates: Pub. *Pearson's Magazine*, January 1918.

535. Citation: TWO UNUSUAL BOOKS; t. ms.; carbon; InU.

Title: [none]

Key Words: From an article entitled "Two . . . a novel, buy this one!

Collation: 2; white; 27.9 x 21.6; unnumbered; none; good.

Contents: Complete; unrevised.

Dates: Pub. *Appeal to Reason*, 1 April 1922.

536. Citation: TWO VIEWS OF RUSSIA; t. ms.; carbon; InU.

Title: TWO VIEWS OF RUSSIA

Key Words: A friend of mine played . . . of a prophet I am!

Collation: 10; white; 28 x 21.6; [1] 2–5, [1] 2–5; none; good.

Contents: Complete; unrevised.

Dates: Comp. ca. 1938. Pub. See *Terror in Russia* (with Eugene Lyons), 1938.

537a. Citation: UNFAIR HARVARD; t. ms.; carbon; InU.

Title: UNFAIR HARVARD

Key Words: For those who have never . . . off to some other planet!"

Collation: 16; white watermarked; 28 x 21.6; [1] 2–8, [1] 2–8; none; good.

Contents: Complete; infrequently revised in pencil.

Dates: Pub. *EPIC News*, 24 February 1936.

537b. Citation: UNFAIR HARVARD; t. ms.; ribbon; InU.

Title: UNFAIR HARVARD

Key Words: For those who have never . . . off to some other planet!"

Collation: 8; white watermarked; 27.9 x 21.6; [1] 2–8; none; good.

Contents: Complete; moderately revised in pencil.

Dates: Pub. *EPIC News*, 24 February 1936.

538. Citation: UNKNOWN UNIVERSE; t. ms., a. ms.; ribbon, carbon, pencil; InU.

Title: The Unknown Universe | Experiments in Psychic Research

Key Words: All my thinking life I . . . which way we phrase it.

Collation: 65; white, white watermarked; 16.5 x 21.6, 28 x 21.6; [2] 2–32, [1] 2–32; 1; good.

Contents: Complete; infrequently revised in pencil; pages [1] 2–32 of the carbon bound by two brass studs.

Dates: Comp. ca. 1932–33. Pub. ?

539. Citation: AN UNMARRIED MOTHER; t. ms.; carbon; InU.

Title: AN UNMARRIED MOTHER

Key Words: I was waiting for Harriet . . . Centre with my 'little Jonathan'!"

Collation: 40; white watermarked; 27.8 x 21.5; [2] 2–19, [1] 2–19; none; good.

Contents: Complete; infrequently revised in ink, pencil.

Dates: Comp. ca. 1915. Pub. ?

540. Citation: UPTON SINCLAIR; mimeo; mimeo; InU.

Title: *UPTON SINCLAIR*

Key Words: Good evening and welcome to . . . reports on the living arts.

Collation: 6; white; 27.9 x 21.6; [1] 2–6; none; good.

Contents: Complete; no revisions; appears to be a radio script headed: Central Program Services Division. Talks and Features Branch, CRITIC'S CHOICE #46, Don Agger, September 19, 1958.

Dates: Comp. ca. 19 September 1958. Pub. ?

541. Citation: UPTON SINCLAIR; t. ms., a. ms.; ribbon, pencil; InU.

Title: UPTON SINCLAIR | Monrovia, California

Key Words: I have recently completed a . . . at Monrovia, California. (facsimile signature)

Collation: 4; yellow; 27.9 x 21.6; [1] 2–4; 4; good.

Contents: Complete; moderately revised in blue ink, pencil.

Dates: Comp. 1959–60. Unpublished.

542. Citation: UPTON SINCLAIR ADDRESS; t. ms.; ribbon; InU.

Title: UPTON SINCLAIR ADDRESS | WEAF, New York City | Saturday, Sept. 8, 1934 | "My Meeting with the President"

Key Words: Friends of the Air: In . . . thank you for your courtesy.

Collation: 4; white; 28 x 21.6; unnumbered; none; good.

Contents: Complete; unrevised.

Dates: Comp. ca. 8 September 1934. Unpublished.

543. Citation: UPTON SINCLAIR ENDORSED FOR NOBEL PRIZE; a. ms.; pencil; InU.

Title: Upton Sinclair [named (c.o.)] endorsed [(w.i. pencil)] for Nobel Prize

Key Words: Farrar and Rinehart, publishers of . . . Sinclair committee explains that no

Collation: 5; green; 27.9 x 21.5; 1–5; none; good.

Contents: Complete; moderately revised in pencil.

Dates: Comp. ca. December 1931. Pub. See *The Candidacy of Upton Sinclair for the Nobel Prize for Literature* (1932).

544. Citation: UPTON SINCLAIR HAS A DREAM; t. ms.; ribbon, carbon; InU.

Title: UPTON SINCLAIR HAS A [BIG IDEA (c.o.)] DREAM [(w.i. pencil)]

Key Words: Thirty-seven years have passed since . . . one may be less so.

Collation: 8; green, white watermarked; 27.9 x 21.4, 28 x 21.6; 1–4, [1] 2–4; none; good.

Contents: Complete; moderately revised in pencil.

Dates: Pub. *Nation*, 9 December 1939.

545. Citation: UPTON SINCLAIR, OVER KHJ; t. ms.; carbon; InU.

Title: UPTON SINCLAIR, over K H J, Monday, October 28, 1934

Key Words: Fellow citizens of California: Eight . . . "It is up to you."

Collation: 6; white watermarked; 27.9 x 21.6; [1] 2–6; none; good.

Contents: Complete; unrevised.

Dates: Comp. ca. 28 October 1934. Pub. ?

546a. Citation: UPTON SINCLAIR PRESENTS WILLIAM FOX; t. ms.; carbon; InU.

Title: UPTON SINCLAIR | PRESENTS | WILLIAM FOX

Key Words: A FEATURE PICTURE OF WALL . . . others look out for themselves.

Collation: 6; white; 28 x 21.7; 1–6; none; good.

Contents: Complete; infrequently revised in pencil.

Dates: Pub. ca. February 1933.

546b. Citation: UPTON SINCLAIR PRESENTS WILLIAM FOX; t. ms.; carbon; InU.

Title: REEL TEN | The Octopus

Key Words: There is one more of . . . lives across your property. More

Collation: 1; white; 28.3 x 21.7; unnumbered; none; good.

Contents: Incomplete; moderately revised in pencil; misc. sheets.

Dates: Pub. ca. February 1933.

546c. Citation: UPTON SINCLAIR PRESENTS WILLIAM FOX; t. ms.; ribbon; InU.

Title: [none]

Key Words: I have written six novels . . . of people are homeless and

Collation: 3; misc. sheets; 27.9 x 21.6 to 28.1 x 21.9; randomly numbered; none; fair.

Contents: Incomplete; frequently revised in pencil; misc. sheets.

Dates: Pub. ca. February 1933.

546d. Citation: UPTON SINCLAIR PRESENTS WILLIAM FOX; t. ms., a. ms.; ribbon, carbon, pencil; InU.

Title: [none]

Key Words: I do not know what . . . and furnishings to dress the

Collation: 13; white envelope, white watermarked; 24.2 x 10.2, 28 x 21.7; [1], 379, 287, 383–387, 383–387; none; good, punched for two-ring binder.

Contents: Incomplete; moderately revised in pencil; misc. sheets; original plus carbon and misc. other sheets.

Dates: Pub. ca. February 1933.

546e. Citation: UPTON SINCLAIR PRESENTS WILLIAM FOX; t. ms., a. ms.; ribbon, pencil; InU.

Title: UPTON SINCLAIR | PRESENTS | WILLIAM FOX [underscored twice] | A Feature Picture [(w.i. pencil)] of Wall Street and [Romance (c.o.)] Finance [(w.i. pencil)] | In Twenty Reels / (w.i. pencil)] with Prologue and Epilogue

Key Words: A Melodrama of Fortune, Conflict . . . telling his story for money.

Collation: 38; misc. sheets; 21.6 x 14.1 to 28 x 21.6; [3], 1–16, 5, [1] 2–4, 6a, 7, [8–11], 12–21, 16a; 2; fair.

Contents: Incomplete; moderately revised in pencil; folder contains the title page and prologue in various states.

Dates: Pub. ca. February 1933.

546f. Citation: UPTON SINCLAIR PRESENTS WILLIAM FOX; t. ms., a. ms.; ribbon, carbon, pencil; InU.

Title: [none]

Key Words: Climb out on top, to . . . the bench states as follows:

Collation: 50; misc. sheets; 13.8 x 21.6 to 28.2 x 21.6; randomly numbered; 35, 36; good.

Contents: Incomplete; frequently revised in pencil; misc. sheets.

Dates: Pub. ca. February 1933.

546g. Citation: UPTON SINCLAIR PRESENTS WILLIAM FOX; t. ms., a. ms.; ribbon, carbon, pencil; InU.

Title: REEL ONE | CLOSE-UP [of the Fox (c.o.)]

Key Words: I began by "presenting" to . . . you, the people, will decide.

Collation: 390; misc. sheets; 21.5 x 21.6 to 30.3 x 21.6; numbered by grouping consecutively but not continuously; 17, 126, 321, 327, 356, 371, 372, 383; good.

Contents: Complete; frequently revised in pencil; complete early draft; early version from which other three typescripts were taken; folder labeled: Reel 1 – Epilogue.

Dates: Pub. ca. February 1933.

546h. Citation: UPTON SINCLAIR PRESENTS WILLIAM FOX; t. ms.; ribbon; InU.

Title: [none]

Key Words: My earliest recollection would take . . . you so. Your own Mona."

Collation: 755; white, white watermarked; 28 x 21.7; 1–118, 120–466, 468–541, 545–758, [2]; none; good.

Contents: Incomplete; moderately revised in pencil, not all in Sinclair's hand; ms. bound in brown covers by two brass studs; folders labeled: 1–99, 100–199, 200–299, 300–399, 400–499, 500–599, 600–758.

Dates: Pub. ca. February 1933.

546i. Citation: UPTON SINCLAIR PRESENTS WILLIAM FOX; t. ms.; ribbon, carbon; InU.

Title: UPTON SINCLAIR | PRESENTS | WILLIAM FOX | A Feature Picture of Wall Street and High Finance | In Twenty Nine [(w.i. pencil)] Reels with Prologue and Epilogue

Key Words: A Melodrama of Fortune, Conflict . . . be less pleasant for you.

Collation: 643; white watermarked; 28 x 21.6; continuously numbered with variations; none; good.

Contents: Complete; moderately revised in pencil, not all in Sinclair's hand; ms. is approximately same condition as "Farrar" draft; this draft bound in brown wrappers, each section numbered and labeled: 1– pages 1 to 121, 2– pages 121a to 260, 3– pages 261 to 331, 4– pages 322 to 463, 5– pages 464 to 597.

Dates: Pub. ca. February 1933.

546j. Citation: UPTON SINCLAIR PRESENTS WIL-LIAM FOX; t. ms.; carbon; InU.

Title: UPTON SINCLAIR | PRESENTS | WIL-LIAM FOX | A Feature Picture of Wall Street and High Finance | In Twenty Nine [(w.i. pencil)] Reels with Prologue and Epilogue

Key Words: A Melodrama of Fortune, Conflict . . . initiative, enterprise, foresight, daring, industry

Collation: 563; white watermarked; 27.9 x 21.6; continuously numbered with variations; none; good, punched for two-ring binder.

Contents: Incomplete; moderately revised in pencil, not all in Sinclair's hand; ms. bound in brown wrappers with two brass studs; folders numbered and labeled: 1– pages 1 to 129, 2– pages 130 to 272, 3– pages 273 to 437, p 438–539.

Dates: Pub. ca. February 1933.

546k. Citation: UPTON SINCLAIR PRESENTS WIL-LIAM FOX; t. ms.; ribbon, carbon; InU.

Title: PROLOGUE

Key Words: For thirty years I have . . . be less pleasant for you.

Collation: 644; white watermarked; 28.1 x 21.7; continuously numbered with variations; none; good.

Contents: Incomplete; infrequently revised in pencil, not all in Sinclair's hand; ms. bound in each brown wraper with two brass studs; numbered and labeled; 1–

pages 1 to 121, 2– pages 122 to 260, 3– 261 to 331, 4–
333 to 463, 5– pages 464–597.

Dates: Pub. ca. February 1933.

546l. Citation: UPTON SINCLAIR PRESENTS WIL-
LIAM FOX; t. ms.; ribbon, carbon; InU.

Title: *INDEX TO WILLIAM FOX RECORD*

Key Words: "A" | Accident 146, 179, Aldrich . . .
against Hon. Frank L. Coleman.

Collation: 25; white watermarked; 28 x 21.7; unnumbered; none; good.

Contents: Complete; infrequently revised in pencil;
index; ms. bound in brown folder by two brass studs.

Dates: Pub. ca. February 1933.

546m.Citation: UPTON SINCLAIR PRESENTS WIL-
LIAM FOX; t. ms.; ribbon; InU.

Title: THE MAN WHO OWNED THE MOTION
PICTURE INDUSTRY

Key Words: The rags to riches to . . . busy as you
may be.

Collation: 2; white watermarked; 28 x 21.7; unnumbered; none; good.

Contents: Complete; unrevised; a proposal outlining the
contents of the book: *Upton Sinclair Presents William
Fox;* apparently *not* by Sinclair.

Dates: Pub. ca. February 1933.

547. Citation: UPTON SINCLAIR RADIO TALK; t. ms.;
carbon; InU.

Title: UPTON SINCLAIR RADIO TALK

Key Words: Fellow Citizens of California: We . . .
"It is up to you!"

Collation: 11; white; 27.8 x 21.5; [1] 2–6, [1] 2–5; none; good.

Contents: Complete; infrequently revised in ink, pencil; note in upper right corner of page one: Return to Gus Inglis K–N–X 8–6–34.

Dates: Comp. ca. 6 August 1934. Pub. ?

548a. Citation: UTOPIA ON THE TREK; t. ms.; ribbon, carbon; InU.

Title: UTOPIA ON THE TREK | Being the Adventures of a Co-operative Caravan | By Michael Williams and Upton Sinclair.

Key Words: Introduction: The talking out of . . . in England, France, and Italy.

Collation: 6; white watermarked; 26.7 x 20.2; unnumbered; none; good.

Contents: Complete; two copies unrevised.

Dates: Comp. ca. November 1907. Unpublished; see *The Autobiography of Upton Sinclair*, p. 141.

548b. Citation: UTOPIA ON THE TREK; t. ms.; carbon; InU.

Title: UTOPIA ON THE TREK: | Being the Adventures of a Co-operative Caravan. | By Michael Williams and Upton Sinclair

Key Words: Introduction: The talking out of . . . in England, France and Italy.

Collation: 3; white; 27.8 x 21.3; [1] 2–3; none; fair.

Contents: Complete; unrevised.

Dates: Comp. ca. November 1907. Unpublished; see *The Autobiography of Upton Sinclair*, p. 141.

549. Citation: A VISIT TO BOSTON; t. ms.; carbon; InU.

Title: A VISIT TO BOSTON

Key Words: Two or three years ago . . . upon the rest of America!

Collation: 7; white; 28 x 21.6; 1–7; none; good.

Contents: Complete; infrequently revised in pencil.

Dates: Comp. ca. August 1927. Pub. ?

550a. Citation: THE VOICE IS THE VOICE OF EVIL: t. ms., a. ms.; carbon, pencil; InU.

Title: The Party Line Surveyed; The Burned Bramble by | Manes Sperber. Published by Doubleday & Company. | Reviewed by Upton Sinclair

Key Words: This is indeed a timely . . . Italian, German, or Russian forms.

Collation: 7; white; 28 x 21.7; 1–7; none; good.

Contents: Complete; infrequently revised in pencil.

Dates: Pub. *New York Times Book Review*, 18 March 1951.

550b. Citation: THE VOICE IS THE VOICE OF EVIL: t. ms., a. ms.; carbon, pencil; InU.

Title: The Party Line Surveyed; The Burned Bramble by | Manes Sperber. Published by Doubleday & Company. | Reviewed by Upton Sinclair.

Key Words: This is indeed a timely . . . "Et LE Buissian Devint Cendre"–

Collation: 8; white; 21.7 x 14.2 to 28 x 21.7; 1–7 [1]; 8; good.

Contents: Complete; infrequently revised, unidentified hand.

Dates: Pub. *New York Times Book Review*, 18 March 1951.

551. Citation: VOICE OF AMERICA; t. ms., a. ms.; ribbon, pencil; InU.

Title: Voice of America & | other such

Key Words: My friends: I address you . . . another chance to save freedom.

Collation: 3; white; 21.5 x 17.1 to 27.8 x 21.5; unnumbered; none; good.

Contents: Complete; unrevised speech with penciled note describing title.

Dates: Recorded 1950; tape available in Lilly Library.

552a. Citation: WALL STREET AND FIFTH AVENUE; t. ms.; carbon; InU.

Title: WALL STREET AND FIFTH AVENUE.

Key Words: Exactly two years ago I . . . can—if I am prevented.

Collation: 3; white watermarked; 27.9 x 21.7; [2] 3; none; good.

Contents: Complete; infrequently revised in ink, in unidentified hand.

Dates: Comp. ca. 1907–8. Unpublished.

552b. Citation: WALL STREET AND FIFTH AVENUE; t. ms.; blue carbon; InU.

Title: WALL STREET AND FIFTH AVENUE

Key Words: Exactly two years ago I . . . can—if I am prevented.

Collation: 3; white watermarked; 27.9 x 21.7; [2] 3; none; good.

Contents: Complete, unrevised.

Dates: Comp. ca. 1907–8. Unpublished.

553a. Citation: WALLY FOR QUEEN!; t. ms., a. ms.,; ribbon, carbon, pencil; InU.

Title: WALLY FOR QUEEN! | The Private Life of Royalty

Key Words: I wrote this little sketch . . . enter, and stare in horror.

Collation: 18; yellow, misc. sheets; 8.8 x 21.6, 28 x 21.6; [3] 1–15; 8; good.

Contents: Complete; moderately revised in pencil.

Dates: Pub. 1936.

See: MY COUSIN MRS. SIMPSON

553b. Citation: WALLY FOR QUEEN!; t. ms., a. ms.; ribbon, pencil; InU.

Title: BALTIMORE GIRL | A Sketch in One Act

Key Words: would you have seen if . . . up our minds about this.

Collation: 20; yellow (letterhead), misc. sheets; 21.4 x 13.9, 28 x 21.6; 1–3, 1–16, [1]; 1, 2, 5, 8, 9, 13, 14, 16, 17; good.

Contents: Complete; frequently revised in pencil by Sinclair and MCS (?); first three leaves are notes, final one is later stage of composition.

Dates: Pub. 1936.

See: MY COUSIN MRS. SIMPSON

554. Citation: WALTER LIPPMANN CLARIFIES HIS MIND; t. ms.; carbon; InU.

Title: WALTER LIPPMANN CLARIFIES HIS MIND

Key Words: I think it was twenty-six . . . has been in the past.

Collation: 11; blue watermarked; 27.9 x 21.6; [1] 2–11; none; good.

Contents: Complete; infrequently revised in pencil.

Dates: Pub. *EPIC News*, 23 November 1936.

555. Citation: WANTED: AN EPIC DRAMA; t. ms.; carbon; InU.

Title: WANTED: AN EPIC DRAMA LEAGUE

Key Words: A few days ago I . . . and map out a program.

Collation: 3; blue watermarked; 27.9 x 21.6; [1] 2–3; none; good.

Contents: Complete; unrevised.

Dates: Pub. *Upton Sinclair's EPIC News*, 25 February 1935.

556. Citation: WANTED—A MARTYR; t. ms.; carbon; InU.

Title: WANTED—A MARTYR

Key Words: Are you looking for a . . . up his job of martyrdom.

Collation: 8; white; 28 x 21.7; [1] 2–4, [1] 2–4; none; fair.

Contents: Complete; infrequently revised in pencil.

Dates: Comp. ? Pub. ?

557. Citation: WANTED: A NATIONAL ORGAN; t. ms.; carbon; InU.

Title: WANTED: A NATIONAL ORGAN!

Key Words: It is the morning after . . . as their "fair-haired farmer boy."

Collation: 5; white; 27.9 x 21.6; 1–5; none; fair.

Contents: Complete; infrequently revised in pencil.

Dates: Pub. See Circular Letter, 4 November 1924.

558a. Citation: THE WAR LETTERS OF CAPTAIN CRANE GARTZ; a. ms.; pencil; InU.

Title: The War Letters of | Captain Crane Gartz

Key Words: Captain Gartz returned to California . . . the French, reads as follows:

Collation: 3; green; 27.8 x 21.6; unnumbered; none; good.

Contents: Complete; infrequently revised in pencil.

Dates: Comp. ca. 1920s. Pub. ?

558b. Citation: THE WAR LETTERS OF CAPTAIN CRANE GARTZ; t. ms.; carbon; InU.

Title: The War Letters of | Captain Crane Gartz

Key Words: The following letters were written . . . deals with this later period.

Collation: 4; white watermarked; 28 x 21.5; [1] 1–3; none; good.

Contents: Complete; unrevised.

Dates: Comp. ca. 1920s. Pub. ?

559a. Citation: THE WAY OUT; a. ms.; pencil; InU.

Title: The Way Out

Key Words: Note: This booklet, first published . . . of "boom and butt" after

Collation: 8; white; 21.6 x 14; 1, [1], 2, [1], 3, [1], 4, [1]; 2, 3, 4, 6, 8; good.

Contents: Complete; infrequently revised in pencil.

Dates: Pub. 1933; Preface 1947.

559b. Citation: THE WAY OUT; t. ms.; carbon; InU.

Title: THE WAY OUT: | WHAT LIES AHEAD FOR AMERICA | Preface

Key Words: When the Spanish novelist, Blasco . . . bullet into his own forehead.

Collation: 5; white; 28 x 21.7; 1–5; none; good.

Contents: Complete; infrequently revised in pencil.

Dates: Pub. 1933; Preface 1947.

560a. Citation: WE, PEOPLE OF AMERICA AND HOW WE ENDED POVERTY; t. ms., a. ms.; ribbon, pencil; InU.

Title: WE, PEOPLE OF AMERICA | And How We Ended Poverty

Key Words: The beginning of the EPIC . . . the products of modern machinery.

Collation: 25; white watermarked, misc. sheets; 7.8 x 21.7 to 28 x 21.6, 13.2 x 21.6 to 27.9 x 21.6; randomly numbered; 6, 18, 21, 25; fair.

Contents: Incomplete; moderately revised in pencil.

Dates: Pub. 1934.

560b. Citation: WE, PEOPLE OF AMERICA AND HOW WE ENDED POVERTY; t. ms., a. ms.; ribbon, pencil; InU.

Title: WE, PEOPLE OF AMERICA | And How We Ended Poverty

Key Words: The beginning of the EPIC . . . We People of America 1935

Collation: 114; brown, misc. sheets; 26.7 x 20.3, 28 x 21.6 to 32.5 x 21.7; randomly numbered; 28, 30, 57, 60, 61, 81, 114; good.

Contents: Complete; moderately revised in pencil; page 114 is a manila envelope.

Dates: Pub. 1934.

561a. Citation: WE SPEAK FOR OURSELVES; t. ms.; carbon; InU.

Title: WE SPEAK FOR OURSELVES: An anthology of American autobiography, | edited by Irving Stone with Richard Kennedy. Doubleday & Com-|pany, New York. $5. | Reviewed by Upton Sinclair.

Key Words: An unpleasant experience which befalls . . . and are glad to read.

Collation: 5; white; 28 x 21.7; [1] 2–5; none; good.

Contents: Complete; infrequently revised in pencil.

Dates: Pub. 1950.

561b. Citation: WE SPEAK FOR OURSELVES; t. ms.; carbon; InU.

Title: WE SPEAK FOR OURSELVES: An anthology of American autobiography, | edited by Irving Stone with Richard Kennedy. Doubleday & Com-|pany, New York. $5. | Reviewed by Upton Sinclair.

Key Words: An unpleasant experience which befalls . . . and are glad to read.

Collation: 5; white; 28 x 21.7; [1] 2–5; none; good.

Contents: Complete; unrevised.

Dates: Pub. 1950 (book).

562a. Citation: THE WET PARADE; t. ms., a. ms.; ribbon, carbon, pencil; InU.

Title: [none]

Key Words: One imaginative host had his . . . anything in the world's history."

Collation: 152; misc. sheets; 13.1 x 21.5 to 30.4 x 21.6; randomly numbered; 12, 14, 25, 28, 30, 33, 64, 71, 73, 76, 84, 105, 108, 117, 123, 125, 126, 131, 132, 133, 134, 135; fair.

Contents: Incomplete; frequently revised in pencil.

Dates: Pub. 12 September 1931.

562b. Citation: THE WET PARADE; t. ms.; carbon; InU.

Title: [none]

Key Words: "Fellow citizens, the proudest boast . . . his tail between his legs.

Collation: 38; white; 28 x 21.7; 90–93, 94–126; 4, 14, 19, 22, 23, 24, 25, 26, 28; fair, punched for two-ring binder.

Contents: Incomplete; moderately revised in pencil, not in Sinclair's hand; has been tagged and labeled: early draft of chapt. IV.

Dates: Pub. 12 September 1931.

562c. Citation: THE WET PARADE; t. ms., a. ms.; ribbon, pencil; InU.

Title: THE EIGHTEENTH AMENDMENT [(w.i. pencil)] [PROHIBITION (c.o.)] | A Novel

Key Words: The visiting lady from the . . . NOT BEEN TRIED! TRY IT!

Collation: 635; green, misc. sheets; 27.9 x 21.6, 28 x 21.5 to 28.1 x 21.8; numbered consecutively by chapter but not continuously; 12, 15, 17, 29, 39, 72, 114, 143, 166, 210, 276, 308, 380, 391, 404, 477, 478, 514, 518, 529, 538, 539, 559, 573, 602, 608; good.

Contents: Incomplete; frequently revised in pencil; three folders labeled: Chapts. 1–7; Chapts. 8–12; Chapts. 13–18; a nearly complete earlier draft.

Dates: Pub. 12 September 1931.

562d. Citation: THE WET PARADE; t. ms., a. ms.; ribbon, carbon, pencil; InU.

Title: The Wet Parade [⟨w.i. pencil⟩] [EIGHTEENTH AMENDMENT (c.o.)] | A Novel

Key Words: The visitor from the north . . . NOT BEEN TRIED! TRY IT!

Collation: 625; white, green; 28.2 x 21.8, 21.6 x 14.6; continuously numbered with variations; 4, 49, 70, 84, 86, 90, 126, 147, 224, 414, 457, 475; good, punched for two-ring binder.

Contents: Complete; moderately revised in pencil; a complete final draft; ms. has been bound into a series of brown covers with two brass studs except for the final three chapters, which have apparently been unbound; folders labeled: Chapters I, II, and III; Chapters IV, V, VI; Chapters VII, VIII, IX; Chapters X, XI, XII; Chapters XIII, XIV, XV; Chapters XVI–XVIII.

Dates: Pub. 12 September 1931.

563. Citation: WHAT COLUMBUS STARTED: RICHARD ARMOUR FINDS HISTORY HILARIOUS; t. ms.; carbon; InU.

Title: IT ALL STARTED WITH COLUMBUS | Reviewed by Upton Sinclair

Key Words: This morning the mail came, . . . as well as your own.

Collation: 6; white; 27.8 x 21.5; [1] 2–3, [1] 2–3; none; good.

Contents: Complete; infrequently revised in pencil.

Dates: Pub. *Pasadena Star-News*, 17 May 1953.

564. Citation: WHAT DIDYMUS DID
See: IT HAPPENED TO DIDYMUS

565. Citation: WHAT DOES DEMOCRACY MEAN; t. ms.; carbon; InU.

Title: WHAT DOES DEMOCRACY MEAN | Essay Submitted in Town Hall Competition

Key Words: King Louis of France said: . . . democracy is democracy in politics.

Collation: 8; white watermarked; 27.9 x 21.6; [1] 2–4, [1] 2–4; none; good.

Contents: Complete; infrequently revised in pencil.

Dates: Comp. ca. 1930s. Pub. ?

566a. Citation: WHAT GOD MEANS TO ME; t. ms., a. ms.; ribbon, pencil, InU.

Title: ME AND GOD | Some Guesses at a Working Religion

Key Words: Not so long ago I . . . hold sway upon earth. (over)

Collation: 120; misc. sheets; 27.9 x 21.6 to 28 x 21.5; numbered consecutively by chapter but not continuously; 42, 63, 66, 98, 108, 119; good.

Contents: Incomplete; frequently revised in pencil; original draft.

Dates: Pub. 1935, 1936.

566b. Citation: WHAT GOD MEANS TO ME; t. ms., a. ms., print; ribbon, carbon, print; InU.

Title: [none]

Key Words: With other men's thoughts; I . . . you are still making Me."

Collation: 222; misc. sheets; 7.5 x 10.1 to 27.9 x 21.6; numbered consecutively in groups but not continuously; 130, 132; good.

Contents: Incomplete; moderately revised in pencil, not all in Sinclair's hand; misc. sheets.

Dates: Pub. 1935, 1936.

566c. Citation: WHAT GOD MEANS TO ME; t. ms.; carbon; InU.

Title: WHAT GOD MEANS TO ME | Some Guesses at a Working Religion

Key Words: Not so long ago I . . . is an essay in God-making.

Collation: 148; white watermarked; 28 x 21.6; continuously numbered with variations; none; good.

Contents: Incomplete; infrequently revised in pencil, not all in Sinclair's hand; a later draft; ms. bound in manila folder by two brass studs; it has been tagged and labeled; note on cover: Office Copy — | Completely revised 9-18-35 | Copy A

Dates: Pub. 1935, 1936.

566d. Citation: WHAT GOD MEANS TO ME; t. ms.; ribbon, carbon; InU.

Title: WHAT GOD MEANS TO ME | An Attempt [(w.i. pencil)] [Some Guesses (c.o.)] at a Working Religion

Key Words: Not so long ago I . . . wish that body, and to

Collation: 13; white watermarked, blue watermarked; 28 x 21.7, 27.9 x 21.6; randomly numbered; none; fair, smudged.

Contents: Incomplete; infrequently revised in pencil; misc. sheets and the title page, copyright, and preface; title page, etc. part of printer's copy.

Dates: Pub. 1935, 1936.

566e. Citation: WHAT GOD MEANS TO ME; t. ms.; ribbon, carbon; InU.

Title: WHAT GOD MEANS TO ME

Key Words: When I was a little . . . is an essay in God-making.

Collation: 150; white watermarked, misc. sheets; 28.1 x 21.5, 25.4 x 20.3 to 29.8 x 21.4; continuously numbered with variations; none; good, smudged, punched for two-ring binder, spindled.

Contents: Complete; moderately revised in pencil, not all in Sinclair's hand; both blue, regular pencil notations by the printer; complete printer's copy.

Dates: Pub. 1935, 1936.

566f. Citation: WHAT GOD MEANS TO ME; t. ms.; carbon; InU.

Title: GOD AS SUGGESTION

Key Words: We have seen that the . . . day! God save the people!

Collation: 31; white; 28 x 21.6; 1–31; none; good.

Contents: Complete; infrequently revised in pencil.

Dates: Pub. 1935, 1936.

567. Citation: WHAT LIFE MEANS TO ME; t. ms.; carbon; InU.

Title: WHAT LIFE MEANS TO ME.

Key Words: I was born in what . . . out the way of deliverance!

Collation: 22; white; 27.8 x 20.5; [1] 2–11, [1] 2–11; none; fair.

Contents: Complete; unrevised.

Dates: Pub. *Open Forum*, 29 December 1928–5 January 1929.

568. Citation: WHAT NEXT?; t. ms.; ribbon, carbon; InU.

Title: WHAT NEXT?

Key Words: One week after the outbreak . . . when the war is over!

Collation: 23; white watermarked, blue; 28 x 21.6; [1] 2–4, 7, 7, 8, [1] 2–8, [1] 2–8; none; good.

Contents: Complete; infrequently revised in pencil; top of page 16: Sept. 11, 1939.

Dates: Comp. ca. 11 September 1939. Pub. ?

569. Citation: WHAT PRICE HOLIDAYS?; t. ms.; carbon; InU.

Title: WHAT PRICE HOLIDAYS?

Key Words: These words are scheduled to . . . have liquor upon your breath.

Collation: 4; white; 27.9 x 21.6; 1–4; none; good.

Contents: Complete; infrequently revised in pencil, unidentified hand.

Dates: Comp. ca. 1954? Pub. ?

570. Citation: WHAT RIGHTS HAS AN AUTHOR?; t. ms.; carbon; InU.

Title: WHAT RIGHTS HAS AN AUTHOR?

Key Words: I am submitting herewith to . . . rejecting what they have ordered.

Collation: 16; white watermarked; 27.9 x 21.6; 1–8, 1–8; none; good.

Contents: Complete; infrequently revised in pencil.

Dates: Pub. *Writer's Digest Year Book*, 1934.

571a. Citation: WHAT SHALL BE DONE WITH HITLER?; t. ms.; ribbon; InU.

Title: WHAT SHALL BE DONE WITH HITLER?

Key Words: The time of Germany's collapse . . . and sent to join them.

Collation: 7; white watermarked; 28.2 x 21.2; [1] 2–7; none; good.

Contents: Complete; infrequently revised in pencil; top of page one: Oct Sep. 49

Dates: Pub. *Free World*, February 1944.

571b. Citation: WHAT SHALL BE DONE WITH HITLER?; t. ms.; carbon; InU.

Title: WHAT SHALL BE DONE WITH HITLER?

Key Words: The time of Germany's collapse . . . of humane or religious ideals.

Collation: 14; white; 27.9 x 21.6; [1] 2–7, [1] 2–7; none; good.

Contents: Complete; two copies infrequently revised in pencil; top of page one: Free World Feb. 44

Dates: Pub. *Free World*, February 1944.

572. Citation: WHEN DOES THE SHOOTING BEGIN? t. ms.; carbon; InU.

Title: WHEN DOES THE SHOOTING BEGIN?

Key Words: So runs the question in . . . with enemies from the sky.

Collation: 13; white watermarked; 27.9 x 21.6; [1], 3, 5, 1–5, [1] 2–5; 1, 2, 3; good.

Contents: Complete; infrequently revised in pencil.

Dates: Comp. ca. 1940. Pub. ?

573. Citation: WHEN IS A COMMUNIST?; t. ms.; carbon; InU.

Title: WHEN IS A COMMUNIST?

Key Words: As I write this, we . . . is truly a complicated situation!

Collation: 3; white watermarked; 28 x 21.7; [1] 2–3; none; good.

Contents: Complete; infrequently revised in pencil.

Dates: Comp. ca. 20 May 1954. Pub. ?

574. Citation: WHEN I WAS A TEENER; t. ms.; carbon; InU.

Title: WHEN I WAS A TEENER

Key Words: (Author and playwright. Active in . . . writing jokes for comic papers.

Collation: 1; white watermarked; 27.9 x 21.6; unnumbered; none; good.

Contents: Complete; unrevised.

Dates: Comp. ca. 1945? Pub. ?

575a. Citation: WHEN THERE IS NO PEACE; t. ms.; carbon; InU.

Title: WHEN THERE IS NO PEACE

Key Words: These thoughts are set down . . . tasting fruits and deadly poisonous.

Collation: 4; white; 27.9 x 21.7; [1] 2–4; none; good.

Contents: Complete; infrequently revised in blue ink.

Dates: Comp. ca. 1954? Pub. ?

575b. Citation: WHEN THERE IS NO PEACE; t. ms.; carbon; InU.

Title: WHEN THERE IS NO PEACE

Key Words: These thoughts are set down . . . tasting fruits and deadly poisonous.

Collation: 3; white; 28 x 21.6; [1], 3, 4; 1; good.

Contents: Complete; unrevised.

Dates: Comp. ca. 1954? Pub. ?

576. Citation: WHO DEFIES THE POWER OF ALMIGHTY GOD?; t. ms.; carbon; InU.

Title: Who Defies the Power of Almighty GOD?

Key Words: The predictions concerning this campaign . . . of mass poverty in California.

Collation: 4; blue watermarked; 27.9 x 21.6; [1] 2–4; none; good.

Contents: Complete; infrequently revised in pencil; on page two: 7-1-34

Dates: Comp. ca. 7 January 1934. Pub. ?

577. Citation: WHY ARE THE INSURGENTS?; t. ms.; ribbon; InU.

Title: WHY ARE THE INSURGENTS?

Key Words: I am writing this immediately . . . of free love in America!

Collation: 13; white watermarked; 27.8 x 21.5; [1] 2–13; 13; fair.

Contents: Complete; infrequently revised in ink, pencil.

Dates: Comp. ca. 1910? Pub. ?

578. Citation: WHY WE CAN WIN; t. ms., a. ms.; carbon, blue ink; InU.

Title: Why We Can Win

Key Words: Each morning when I wake . . . we can buy Japanese tuna.

Collation: 6; white; 19.9 x 21.5 to 27.8 x 21.5; 1–3, 1–3; none; good.

Contents: Complete; frequently revised in blue ink; a frequently revised first carbon and infrequently revised carbon of revision.

Dates: Comp. ca. 1946. Pub. ?

579a. Citation: WIDE IS THE GATE; t. ms., a. ms.; ribbon, carbon, pencil; InU.

Title: Chapter One | Dust to Dust

Key Words: Freddi himself wouldn't have wanted . . . time to be born in.

Collation: 1034; green, white watermarked; 27.7 x 21.5, 27.9 x 21.6; numbered consecutively by chapters but not continuously; 5, 20, 81, 83, 98, 135, 141, 142, 159, 165, 178, 199, 211, 212, 217, 221, 223, 337, 349, 353, 362, 363, 391, 395, 428, 445, 450, 452, 474, 476, 493, 508, 554, 587, 590, 601, 616, 632, 645, 649, 699, 700, 705, 706, 712, 722, 786, 787, 805, 811, 815, 816, 820, 838, 893, 897, 939, 946, 953, 954, 1014; good.

Contents: Incomplete; frequently revised in pencil; original draft; in two library boxes labeled: Chaps. 1–21, Chaps. 22–32.

Dates: Pub. 4 January 1943.

579b. Citation: WIDE IS THE GATE; t. ms., a. ms., print; ribbon, carbon, pencil, blue, black ink, print; InU.

Title: [none]

Key Words: You understand, I am assuming . . . ones, the politicians making promises?

Collation: 133; misc. sheets; 7.4 x 12.6 to 31.6 x 20.2; either unnumbered or randomly numbered; 5, 7, 8, 11, 13, 15, 16, 18, 20, 22, 23, 25, 26, 28, 31, 48, 64, 85, 86, 87, 89, 93, 94, 95, 97, 100, 101, 109, 110, 120, 121, 130, 132; fair.

Contents: Incomplete; infrequently revised in pencil, black, blue ink; most of the material does not appear to be Sinclair's; notes and corrections.

Dates: Pub. 4 January, 1943.

579c. Citation: WIDE IS THE GATE; t. ms., a. ms.; ribbon, pencil; InU.

Title: [none]

Key Words: This was in October of . . . of it," said L. sadly.

Collation: 24; green, white watermarked; 28.2 x 21.8, 27.9 x 21.6; randomly numbered; 21, 24; good.

Contents: Incomplete; frequently revised in pencil; misc. sheets.

Dates: Pub. 4 January 1943.

579d. Citation: WIDE IS THE GATE; t. ms., a. ms.; ribbon, pencil; InU.

Title: [none]

Key Words: L, for his part, thought: . . . questions as to what he

Collation: 17; misc. sheets; 10.4 x 13.4 to 27.8 x 21.6; randomly numbered; 1, 2, 3, 6, 10, 15; good.

Contents: Incomplete; moderately revised in pencil; misc. sheets.

Dates: Pub. 4 January 1943.

579e. Citation: WIDE IS THE GATE; t. ms.; ribbon; InU.

Title: [CHAPTER ONE (c.o.)] Dust to Dust

Key Words: Freddi himself wouldn't have wanted . . . bad time to be born.

Collation: 1030; white watermarked, green; 28 x 21.6, 28.1 x 21.8; continuously numbered with variations; none; fair, spindled.

Contents: Complete; moderately revised in pencil; printer's notations in orange, blue, regular pencil; printer's copy; boxes labeled: PRINTER'S COPY | CHAPS. 1–16, PRINTER'S COPY | CHAPS. 17–32.

Dates: Pub. 4 January 1943.

580. Citation: WILL AMERICANS WORK?; t. ms.; carbon; InU.

Title: WILL AMERICANS WORK?

Key Words: I was discussing the EPIC . . . in working on the land.

Collation: 1; blue; 27.9 x 21.6; unnumbered; none; fair.

Contents: Complete; unrevised.

Dates: Comp. ca. 1934. Pub. ?

581. Citation: WILL THE GOBBEL-UNS GIT YOU?; t. ms., a. ms.; ribbon, carbon, pencil; InU.

Title: WILL THE GOBBEL-[-(w.i. pencil)]UNS GIT YOU?

Key Words: The child's verses by James . . . what we lose is America.

Collation: 10; white; 28 x 21.6; [1] 2–8, 8a, 9; none; good.

Contents: Complete; moderately revised in blue ink, pencil.

Dates: Comp. ca. 1953; Pub. ?

582. Citation: WINNING; t. ms.; carbon; InU.

Title: WINNING

Key Words: The people of California have . . . carry out our campaign promises.

Collation: 1; blue watermarked; 28 x 21.7; unnumbered; none; good.

Contents: Complete; infrequently revised in pencil.

Dates: Comp. ca. October 1934. Pub. ?

583a. Citation: THE WISE CHICKENS; t. ms., a. ms.; carbon, pencil; InU.

Title: THE WISE CHICKENS

Key Words: An old-time story put into . . . dem chickins warn't even hatched!"

Collation: 2; white; 19.4 x 14 to 27.9 x 21.7; unnumbered; none; good.

Contents: Complete; infrequently revised in pencil; original and carbon.

Dates: Comp. ? Pub. ?

583b. Citation: THE WISE CHICKENS; t. ms.; carbon; InU.

Title: THE WISE CHICKEN

Key Words: An old-time story put into . . . dem chickins warn't even hatched!"

Collation: 1; white; 27.9 x 21.7; unnumbered; none; good.

Contents: Complete; unrevised poem.

Dates: Comp. ? Pub. ?

584. Citation: WORK FOR ALL CANDIDATES; t. ms.; carbon; InU.

Title: Work For All Candidates

Key Words: The time for filing candidates . . . and follower of my ideas.

Collation: 3; blue watermarked; 27.9 x 21.6; [1] 2–3; none; good.

Contents: Complete; unrevised.

Dates: Comp. ca. August 1934. Pub. ?

585. Citation: WORLDS APART; t. ms.; brown carbon; InU.

Title: WORLDS APART

Key Words: The story of a Jewish . . . great applause of the audience.

Collation: 6; white watermarked; 27.9 x 21.5; 1–6; none; good, punched for two-ring binder.

Contents: Complete; unrevised.

Dates: Comp. ca. 1930s. Pub. ?

586a. Citation: THE WORLD'S CRISIS; t. ms.; ribbon; InU.

Title: THE WORLD'S CRISIS

Key Words: Distinguished guests and friends of . . . has not overlooked to use

Collation: 7; white watermarked; 28 x 21.6; [1] 2–7; none; good.

Contents: Incomplete; infrequently revised in pencil.

Dates: Comp. ca. 24 March 1938. Pub. ?

586b. Citation: THE WORLD'S CRISIS; t. ms.; carbon; InU.

Title: THE WORLD'S CRISIS

Key Words: Comrades and friends of the . . . the work of their hands."

Collation: 11; white watermarked; 27.9 x 21.7; [1] 2–11; none; good.

Contents: Complete; infrequently revised in pencil.

Dates: Comp. ca. 24 March 1938. Pub. ?

587a. Citation: WORLD'S END; t. ms., a. ms.; carbon, pencil; InU.

Title: WORLD'S END—corrections, June 17, 1939

Key Words: page 321, middle of page . . . & mail Airmail to Freedman

Collation: 7; misc. sheets; 15.2 x 19.5 to 28.3 x 21.6; unnumbered; none; fair.

Contents: Incomplete; unrevised; misc. correction sheets.

Dates: Pub. 21 June 1940.

587b. Citation: WORLD'S END; t. ms., a. ms.; ribbon, carbon, pencil; InU.

Title: [none]

Key Words: The American boy's name was . . . nations to keep everything straight!"

Collation: 67; misc. sheets; 7.5 x 10.4 to 27.9 x 21.7;
randomly numbered; 34, 43, 62, 67; good.

Contents: Incomplete; frequently revised in blue, regular pencil; misc. sheets.

Dates: Pub. 21 June 1940.

587c. Citation: WORLD'S END; t. ms., a. ms.; ribbon, carbon, pencil; InU.

Title: WORLD'S END | A Novel

Key Words: Orpheus, the singer, had descended . . .
would come to an end!"

Collation: 1060; green, misc. sheets; 28.2 x 21.6, 27.9 x
21.6 to 28.1 x 21.6; numbered consecutively by chapters
but not continuously; 10, 19, 25, 50, 61, 63, 121, 141,
172, 187, 194, 203, 219, 223, 266, 269, 287, 289 290,
293, 296, 305, 321, 348, 376, 380, 395, 415, 421, 429,
441, 443, 444, 445, 461, 463, 473, 516, 553, 557, 564,
566, 573, 600, 601, 618, 641, 747, 806, 894, 901, 912,
925, 930, 931, 937, 946, 947, 953, 964, 986, 1003, 1010,
1015, 1016, 1036; good.

Contents: Incomplete; frequently revised in pencil;
earlier draft; in two boxes labeled: Earlier copy I [Bks
I–III] and copy II [Bks IV–VI]

Dates: Pub. 21 June 1940.

587d. Citation: WORLD'S END; t. ms.; ribbon, carbon; InU.

Title: WORLD'S END | A Novel

Key Words: In the course of this . . . world come to
an end!"

Collation: 1025; white watermarked; 28 x 21.7; continuously numbered with variations; none; good, punched
for two-ring binder.

Contents: Incomplete; moderately revised in purple, red,
blue, regular pencil, not all in Sinclair's hand; a nearly

complete draft; housed in two boxes labeled: LATER COPY I [Bks I–III], LATER COPY [Bks IV–VI].

Dates: Pub. 21 June 1940.

587e. Citation: WORLD'S END; t. ms.; ribbon; InU.

Title: BOOK ONE | God's In His Heaven

Key Words: The American boy's name was . . . world come to an end!"

Collation: 1022; white watermarked; 28 x 21.6; continuously numbered with variations; none; good, spindled, smudged.

Contents: Complete printer's copy; moderately revised in blue, red, regular pencil; printer's notations in red, blue, regular pencil.

Dates: Pub. 21 June 1940.

588. Citation: WORLD'S END IMPENDING; t. ms.; carbon; InU.

Title: WORLD'S END IMPENDING

Key Words: When the first volume of . . . serious error in these books.

Collation: 6; white; 28 x 21.6; 1–6; none; good.

Contents: Complete; infrequently revised in pencil.

Dates: Pub. *Wings*, July 1940.

589a. Citation: A WORLD TO WIN; t. ms., a. ms.; ribbon, pencil; InU.

Title: PRESIDENTIAL ERRAND

Key Words: Lanny kept thinking: "This must . . . grant that he means it!"

Collation: 935; white watermarked, green; 21.8 x 13.9 to 27.9 x 21.7, 21.6 x 13.7 to 28.2 x 21.8; numbered consecutively by chapters but not continuously; 8, 23, 76, 91, 97, 116, 175, 179, 193, 223, 227, 237, 275, 286, 311, 342, 377, 388, 402, 410, 417, 422, 429, 436, 467, 474, 481, 548, 559, 561, 578, 592, 593, 599, 623, 676, 686, 695, 696, 737, 741, 746, 754, 758, 759, 761, 794, 818, 825, 851, 869, 873, 928, 929, 931; good.

Contents: Complete; frequently revised in pencil; later draft; ms. in two boxes labeled: chaps 1–14, chaps 15–28; on CONTENTS pages: A WORLD TO [GAIN (c.o.)] WIN [(w.i. pencil)].

Dates: Pub. ca. 25 May 1946.

589b. Citation: A WORLD TO WIN; t. ms.; ribbon, carbon; InU.

Title: A World to Win

Key Words: Lanny kept thinking: This must . . . grant that he means it!"

Collation: 803; white watermarked; 27.9 x 21.6 to 27.9 x 21.9; continuously numbered with variations; none; good, spindled.

Contents: Complete; moderately revised in blue, regular pencil; printer's notations in orange, blue, regular pencil; printer's copy; boxes labeled: PRINTER'S COPY, CHAPS. 1–14, PRINTER'S COPY, CHAPS. 15–28.

Dates: Pub. ca. 25 May 1946.

589c. Citation: A WORLD TO WIN; a. ms.; blue, regular pencil, faded ink; InU.

Title: [none]

Key Words: World to win Holmes? Villard? . . . Evans Brit Library Herbert Morrison

Collation: 1; brown cardboard; 20.4 x 16.1; unnumbered; 1; fair.

Contents: Incomplete; infrequently revised in pencil, faded ink; list of names.

Dates: Pub. ca. 25 May 1946.

589d. Citation: A WORLD TO WIN; t. ms., a. ms.; ribbon, carbon, pencil; InU.

Title: [none]

Key Words: You cold [sic] mention the luxurious . . . anyone except their native drivers.

Collation: 23; misc. sheets; 13.2 x 9.9 to 28 x 21.7; unnumbered; 9; good.

Contents: Incomplete; infrequently revised in black ink, pencil; none of the material appears to be Sinclair's; notes on the ms.

Dates: Pub. ca. 25 May 1946.

590. Citation: YOUNG LANNY BUDD; t. ms.; carbon; InU.

Title: YOUNG LANNY BUDD

Key Words: The opening scene is an . . . to an end!" *THE END*

Collation: 142; white; 27.9 x 21.5; 1–74, 74a, 75–92, 92a, 93–140; none; fair, water-stained.

Contents: Complete; unrevised outline for a Lanny Budd book.

Dates: Comp. ca. 1940. Unpublished.

591a. Citation: YOUR MILLION DOLLARS; t. ms.; carbon; InU.

Title: YOUR MILLION DOLLARS

Key Words: My dear Joe: | Thirty-four . . . thought to what I say.

Collation: 3; white; 28 x 21.6; 1–3; none; good.

Contents: Complete; infrequently revised in pencil.

Dates: Pub. 1938–39, 1939 (pamphlet).

591b. Citation: YOUR MILLION DOLLARS; t. ms.; ribbon, carbon; InU.

Title: THE PAMPHLET WHICH IS GOING TO BE THE TEXT BOOK OF | THE AMERICAN PEOPLE IN THEIR STRUGGLE FOR ECONOMIC PEACE AND | SECURITY | Y O U R M I L L I O N D O L L A R S

Key Words: For years Upton Sinclair's mail . . . my foes, call it God.

Collation: 88; white watermarked, green; 27.9 x 21.6, 28 x 21.6; randomly numbered; 30, 47, 76, 80, 82, 85; good.

Contents: Complete; frequently revised in pencil; page 24, note attached: middle draft, complete | ending expanded in later drafts; page note attached: revised ending lacks last 2–3 pages.

Dates: Pub. 1938–39, 1939 (pamphlet).

592. Citation: ZILLIONS OF DOLLARS; t. ms.; ribbon; InU.

Title: ZILLIONS OF [MONEY (c.o.)] [Dollars (w.i. pencil)] A Truth Story

Key Words: Dear Diary: I must have . . . far, and that's the story.

Collation: 173; white watermarked, white; 28 x 21.7, 27.9 x 21.6; [1] 1–33, 33a, 34–53, 53a, 53a–e, 54–69, 69a–c, 70–114, 114a–d, 115–129; 4, 35, 40, 124; good.

Contents: Complete; frequently revised in pencil; in manila envelope addressed to: Mr. Upton Sinclair, Box #367, Monrovia, Calif. From: Brier MuHi-Copy Service, 1347 1/2 N. Highland Ave., Hollywood 28, Calif., labeled in blue ink on verso: Zillions of Dollars.

Dates: Comp. ca. 1953. Pub. ?

B.

A GUIDE TO THE LETTERS OF UPTON SINCLAIR

Upton Sinclair wrote literally tens of thousands of letters to thousands of persons, and it would obviously be futile to attempt to list and describe each of them as has been done in calendars of other less prolific writers. Indeed, it is just as obviously impossible to provide a fully reliable guide even to major private and institutional collections of these letters. What we have done instead is to offer two lists that provide trails into territory that must still be explored in fresh directions by each investigator, each of whom will discover a good many caches that exist in private hands. But we have decided not to try to list such collections; there are too many, and they are too limited in permanence and availability to researchers.

Sinclair Letters in the Lilly Library

The largest bulk of Sinclair's letters—or copies of them—may be found in the Sinclair Archive at the Lilly Library. What follows is a handlist of the letters to Sinclair from persons judged by Mary Craig Sinclair to be celebrities. This list was prepared under the direction of Miss Doris Reed, retired curator of manuscripts, and her successor, Elfrieda Lang. The list reflects the group of some 10,000 letters that were at one time filed separately at the Lilly. Now all letters to and from Sinclair are arranged in one continuous chronological file, but only those by the individuals listed below have been entered in the general manuscript index to collections in the Lilly.

As a guide to Upton Sinclair's letters, this list must, of course, be used inferentially. That is, if some two hundred of H. L. Mencken's letters are preserved in the Sinclair Archive, one can be reasonably sure that a roughly corresponding number of carbon copies of Sinclair's letters to Mencken are to be found in the same file. Of course, the originals of Sinclair's half of the correspondence may have been preserved in another place and, therefore, turn up on List B (which reports on institutional holdings other than the Lilly's). A name followed by a question mark means that we were unable to provide reliable dates.

Abbott, Leonard Dalton, 1878–1953

Abercrombie, Lascelles, 1881–1938

Abernathy, Milton Aubrey, 1892–1955

Abrams, Albert, 1863–1924

Acheson, Dean Gooderham, 1893–1971

Adamic, Louis, 1899–1951

Adams, Franklin Pierce, 1881–1960

Adams, Frederick Upham, 1859–1921

Adams, James Truslow, 1878–1949

Adams, Samuel Hopkins, 1871–1958

Addams, Jane, 1860–1935

Adlard, Henry J., ?

Aldrich, Richard, 1863–1947

Allen, Devere, 1891–1955

Allen, Hervey, 1889–1949

Allen, James Lane, 1849–1925

Allport, Gordon Willard, 1897–1967

Alsop, Stewart Johonnot Oliver, 1914–

Anderson, Mrs. Eleanor (Copenhaver) ?

Anderson, Maxwell, 1888–1959

Anderson, Sherwood, 1876–1941

Angell, Sir Norman, 1874–1967

Anglin, Margaret, 1876–1958

Anspacher, Mrs. Florence (Sutro), ?

Anspacher, Louis Kaufman, 1878–1947

Appel, Benjamin, 1907–
Archer, William, 1856–1924
Arens, Egmont, 1889–1966
Armour, Richard Willard, 1906–
Arnold, Thurman Wesley, 1891–1969
Arnot, Robert Page, 1890–
Asch, Shalom, 1880–1957
Ashleigh, Charles, ?
Astor, William Vincent, 1891–1959
Atherton, Mrs. Gertrude Franklin (Horn), 1857–1948
Atkinson, Justin Brooks, 1894–
Attlee, Clement Richard Attlee, first earl of, 1883–1967
Austin, Mrs. Mary (Hunter), 1868–1934
Ayres, Clarence Edwin, 1891–
Babson, Roger Ward, 1875–1967
Bacon, Ernst, 1898–
Baer, John Miller, 1886–
Baker, George Pierce, 1866–1935
Baker, Newton Diehl, 1871–1937
Baker, Ray Stannard, 1870–1946
Balabanoff, Angelica, 1878–1965
Baldwin, Mrs. Evelyn (Preston), 1898–1962
Baldwin, Hanson Weightman, 1903–
Baldwin, Roger Nash, 1884–
Barbusse, Henri, 1874–1935
Barker, Mrs. Elsa, 1869?–1954
Barnes, Harry Elmer, 1889–
Barrett, Edward John Boyd, 1883–
Barry, John H., 1874–1955
Barton, Bruce, 1886–1967
Baruch, Bernard Mannes, 1870–1965
Bates, Katharine Lee, 1859–1929
Beach, Rex Ellingwood, 1877–1949

Beard, Charles Austin, 1874–1948
Beard, Mrs. Mary (Ritter), 1876–1958
Beardsley, John, 1876–1946
Beaton, Whelford, ?
Bedford, Hastings William Sackville Russell, twelfth duke of, 1888–1953
Behrman, Samuel Nathaniel, 1893–
Belasco, David, 1853–1931
Belfrage, Cedric, 1904–
Bell, Thelma Harrington, 1896–
Belloc, Hilaire, 1870–1953
Belmont, Mrs. Alva E. (Smith), ?–1933
Belt, Elmer, 1893–
Benchley, Robert Charles, 1889–1945
Benedict, Bertram, ?
Benet, William Rose, 1886–1950
Ben-Gurion, David, 1886–
Bennett, Arnold, 1867–1931
Benson, Allan Louis, 1871–1940
Benson, Robert Hugh, 1871–1914
Bent, Silas, 1882–1945
Bercovici, Konrad, 1882–1961
Berenberg, David Paul, 1890–
Beresford, John Davys, 1873–1947
Berger, Victor Luitpold, 1860–1929
Berkman, Alexander, 1870–1936
Berle, Adolf Augustus, 1895–
Berlin, Irving, 1888–
Bingham, Alfred Mitchell, 1905–
Bird, James Malcolm, 1886–
Birge, Edward Asahel, 1851–1950
Birnbaum, Martin 1878–
Björkman, Edwin August, 1866–1951

Black, Hugo LaFayette, 1886–1971
Blackwell, Alice Stone, 1857–1950
Blaine, John James, 1875–1934
Bland, Richard Howard, 1880–
Blanshard, Paul, 1892–
Blasco-Ibanez, Vicente, 1867–1928
Blatch, Mrs. Harriot (Stanton), 1856–1940
Blatchford, Robert, 1851–1943
Bliven, Bruce Ormsby, 1889–
Bloor, Ella Reeve, 1862–1951
Boardman, Philip, ?
Boddy, Elias Manchester, 1891–1967
Bodwell, Charles S., ?
Bojer, Johan, 1872–1959
Bolton, Frances Payne, 1885–
Bondy, Froncois de, 1875–
Boni, Albert, 1892–
Booth, Henry Kendall, 1876–1942
Borah, William Edgar, 1865–1940
Borglum, John Gutzon de la Mothe, 1871–1941
Borsook, Henry, 1897–
Bottome, Phyllis, 1884–1963
Bowers, Claude Gernade, 1878–1958
Bowman, Isaiah, 1878–1950
Boynton, Henry Walcott, 1869–1947
Boynton, Percy Holmes, 1875–1946
Bradford, Gamaliel, 1863–1932
Bradley, Herbert Dennis, 1878–1934
Brady, Robert Alexander, 1901–1963
Brady, William Aloysius, 1863–1950
Braithwaite, William Stanley Beaumont, 1878–1962
Braley, Berton, 1882–1966
Branch, Anna Hempstead, 1875–1937

Brandeis, Louis Dembitz, 1856–1941
Brandes, Georg Morris Cohen, 1842–1927
Brentano, Bernard von, 1901–
Brett, George Platt, 1858–1936
Brewer, John Marks, 1877–1950
Bridges, Harry, 1901–
Brieux, Eugène, 1858–1932
Brisbane, Arthur, 1864–1936
Brittain, Vera Mary, 1893?–1970
Britton, Lionel, 1887–
Brockway, Archibald Fenner, 1888–
Bromfield, Louis, 1896–1956
Brookhart, Smith Wildman, 1869–1944
Brooks, Charles Wayland, 1897–1957
Brooks, Van Wyck, 1886–1963
Broun, Heywood Campbell, 1888–1939
Browder, Earl Russell, 1891–
Browne, George Forrest, 1833–1930
Browne, Lewis, 1897–1949
Browne, Maurice, ?
Browne, Mrs. Myna Eisner (Lissner), ?
Browne, Porter Emerson, 1879–1934
Bruno, Guido, 1884–
Bryan, William Jennings, 1860–1925
Bryant, Louise, 1890–1936
Buck, Mrs. Pearl (Sydenstricker), 1892–
Budenz, Louis Francis, 1891–
Bullard, Arthur, 1879–1929
Bullitt, William Christian, 1891–1967
Burbank, Luther, 1849–1926
Burke, Edmund, 1871–1947
Burnet, Dana, 1888–1962

Burns, Vincent Godfrey, 1893–
Burroughs, John, 1837–1921
Burt, Maxwell Struthers, 1882–1954
Burton, John, 1894–
Burton, Richard, 1861–1940
Buschlen, John Preston, 1888–
Bush, Vannevar, 1890–
Butler, Ellis Parker, 1869–1937
Bynner, Witter, 1881–
Cahan, Abraham, 1860–1951
Caine, Sir Hall, 1853–1931
Cairns, Huntington, 1904–
Calderwood, Willis Greenleaf, 1866–?
Calverton, Victor Francis, 1900–1940
Camus, Albert, 1913–1960
Canby, Henry Seidel, 1878–1961
Cane, Melville Henry, 1879–
Cantwell, Robert Emmett, 1908–
Carens, Thomas Henry, 1893–1960
Carew, Harold David, 1890–1943
Carman, Bliss, 1861–1929
Carnegie, Dale, 1888–1955
Carpenter, Edward, 1844–1929
Carr, Harry, 1877–1936
Carrel, Alexis, 1873–1944
Carter, James Marshall, 1904–
Castle, Ralph, 1886–
Catlin, George Edward Gordon, 1896–
Catt, Mrs. Carrie (Lane) Chapman, 1859–1947
Cavling, Viggo, 1887–
Cawein, Madison Julius, 1865–1914
Cerf, Bennett Alfred, 1898–1971
Chamberlain, John Rensselaer, 1903–

Chamberlin, William Henry, 1897–
Chambers, Robert William, 1865–1933
Chambless, Edgar, ?
Channing, Edward, 1856–1931
Chanslor, Roy, 1899–
Chaplin, Charles Spencer, 1889–
Chaplin, Ralph, 1887–1961
Chapman, John Jay, 1862–1933
Chapple, Joseph Mitchell, 1867–1950
Chase, Stuart, 1888–
Chiang, Hsi-tseng, ?
Churchill, Winston, 1871–1947
Churchill, Winston Leonard Spencer, 1874–1965
Clark, Barrett Harper, 1890–1953
Cleghorn, Sarah Norcliffe, 1876–1959
Clemens, Cyril, 1902–
Coblenz, Stanton Arthur, 1896–
Cobb, Irvin Shrewsbury, 1876–1944
Cochran, Edward Louis, 1899–
Cochran, William Francis, 1876–1950
Cochrane, R. H., ?
Coe, George Albert, 1862–1951
Coleman, McAlister, 1889–1950
Collins, Seward B., 1899?–1952
Comfort, Will Levington, 1878–1932
Commons, John Rogers, 1862–1944
Conant, James Bryant, 1893–
Cone, Helen Gray, 1859–1934
Conroy, Jack, 1899–
Converse, Florence, 1871–
Cook, George Cram, 1873–1924
Cooke, Edmund Vance, 1866–1932
Cosgrave, Mrs. Jessica (Garretson), 1871–1949

Costigan, Edward Prentiss, 1874–1939
Cové, Emile, 1857–1926
Cové, Mme Lucie (Le Moine), ?
Counts, George Sylvester, 1889–
Cousins, Norman, 1912–
Couzens, James, 1872–1936
Cowley, Malcolm, 1898–
Craig, William Warren, 1883–
Crail, Joe, 1877–1938
Crandon, Le Roi Goddard, 1873–1939
Crane, Frank, 1861–1928
Crane, Walter, 1845–1915
Crawford, Nelson Antrim, 1888–1963
Creel, George, 1876–1953
Crile, George Washington, 1864–1943
Cripps, Sir Richard Stafford, 1889–1952
Crothers, Samuel McChord, 1857–1927
Curley, Michael Joseph, 1879–1947
Curti, Merle Eugene, 1897–
Cutting, Bronson Murray, 1888–1935
Cutting, Henry Colman, ?
Cyril, Victor, ?
Czerny, Josef, 1848–?
Dahlberg, Edward, 1900–
D'Aguila, Vincenzo, ?
Darrow, Clarence Seward, 1857–1938
David, Eduard Heinrich Rudolph, 1863–1930
Davidson, Randall Thomas, 1848–1930
Davies, Albert Emil, 1875–1950
Davies, Joseph Edward, 1876–1958
Davies, William Henry, 1871–1940
Davis, Anna N., ?
Davis, Earl C., ?

Davis, Elmer Holmes, 1890–1958
Davis, Robert Hobart, 1869–1942
Day, Clarence, 1874–1935
Day, Clive, 1871–1951
De Brath, Stanley, ?
Debs, Eugene Victor, 1855–1926
Debs, Theodore, 1864–1945
De Casseres, Benjamin, 1873–1945
Decker, Clarence Raymond, 1904–
Dehmel, Richard, 1863–1920
De La Mare, Walter John, 1873–1956
Dell, Mrs. Berta Marie (Gage), ?
Dell, Floyd, 1887–1969
Dell, Robert Edward, 1865–?
Dellhora, Guillermo, ?
Delmar, Mrs. Vina (Croter), 1905–
De Mille, Mrs. Anna (George)?
De Mille, Cecil Blount, 1881–1959
De Mille, William Churchill, 1878–1955
Deming, Seymour, 1883–
DeMorgan, William Frend, 1839–1917
Dennett, Mrs. Mary (Ware), 1872–1947
Desai, Mahadev Haribhai, 1892–1942
Desmond, Shaw, 1877–1960
DeVoto, Bernard Augustine, 1897–1955
Dewey, John, 1859–1952
De Witt, Samuel Aaron, 1891–
Dickinson, Goldsworthy Lowes, 1862–1932
Diggle, John William, 1847–1920
Dill, Clarence Cleveland, 1884–
Disney, Walter E., 1901–1966
Divine, Major J., 1874?–
Dodd, Lee Wilson, 1879–1933

Dole, Charles Fletcher, 1845–1927
Donovan, William Joseph, 1883–1959
Dos Passos, John, 1896–1970
Douglas, Charles Noel, ?
Douglas, Paul Howard, 1892–
Dowling, Austin, 1868–1930
Downey, Mrs. Helen (Symons), ?
Downey, Sheridan, 1884–1961
Doyle, Sir Arthur Conan, 1859–1930
Dreiser, Mrs. Helen Esther (Patges), 1894 or 1895–1955
Dreiser, Theodore, 1871–1945
Drinkwater, John, 1882–1937
Drohojowski, Jan, ?
Dubois, William Edward Burghardt, 1868–1963
Duffus, Robert Luther, 1888–
Duffy, Philip Gavan, 1873–?
Dulles, Allen Welsh, 1893–
Dunninger, Joseph, 1896–
Durant, William James, 1885–
Dykstra, Clarence Addison, 1883–1950
Dyson, William, 1849–1928
Earley, Robert G., ?
Eastman, Max, 1883–1969
Eaton, Geoffrey Dell, 1894–
Eaton, Walter Prichard, 1878–1957
Eberle, Abastenia St. Leger, 1878–1942
Eddy, George Sherwood, 1871–?
Edstrom, David, 1873–1938
Edward VIII, king of Great Britain, 1894–1972
Eeden, Frederik Willem van, 1860–1932
Ehrenburg, Il'ia Grigorevich, 1891–1967
Ehrmann, Herbert Brutus, 1891–
Ehrmann, Max, 1872–1945

Einstein, Albert, 1879–1955
Einstein, Carl, 1885–
Einstein, Mrs. Elsa (Einstein), ?–1936
Eisenstein, Sergei Mikahailovich, 1898–1948
Eliot, Charles William, 1834–1926
Eliot, George Fielding, 1894–1971
Eliot, Samuel Atkins, 1893–
Ellis, Mrs. Edith Mary Oldham (Lees), 1861–1916
Ellis, Havelock, 1859–1939
Ellis, James Hawes, ?
Elser, Frank Ball, 1885–1935
Epstein, Paul Sophus, 1883–1966
Ernst, Bernard Morris Lee, 1879–1938
Ernst, Morris Leopold, 1888–
Erskine, John, 1879–1951
Estrada, Genaro, 1887–1937
Evans, Bergen, 1904–
Evans, Idrisyn Oliver, 1894–
Ezekiel, Mordecai, 1899–
Fabyan, George, 1867–1936
Fadiman, Clifton, 1904–
Fairbanks, Douglas, 1883–1939
Fairley, James A., ?
Faragoh, Francis Edwards, 1895?–1966
Farley, James Aloysius, 1888–
Farrar, John Chipman, 1896–
Farrell, James Thomas, 1904–
Fast, Howard Melvin, 1914–
Fawcett, James Waldo, ?
Feigenbaum, William Morris, 1886?–1949
Fels, Joseph, 1854–1914
Ferber, Edna, 1887–1968
Ferrero, Guglielmo, 1871–1942

Feuchtwanger, Lion, 1884–1958
Ficke, Arthur Davison, 1883–1945
Field, Sara Bard, 1882–
Fielding, William John, 1886–
Fifield, Arthur C., ?
Filene, Edward Albert, 1860–1937
Finger, Charles Joseph, 1871–1941
Fischer, Louis, 1896–1970
Fisher, Mrs. Dorothea Frances (Canfield), 1879–1958
Fisher, Irving, 1867–1947
Fiske, Mrs. Minnie Maddern (Davey), 1865–1932
Flaccus, Kimball, 1911–
Flavin, Martin, 1883–1967
Fletcher, Horace, 1849–1919
Fletcher, Thomas Brooks, 1879–1945
Flynn, Elizabeth Gurley, 1890–1964
Flynn, Errol Leslie, 1909–1959
Folsom, Franklin, 1907–
Ford, Henry, 1917–
Foster, William Zebulon, 1881–1961
Fox, Mrs. Eva (Leo), ?
Fox, William, 1879–1952
Francke, Kuno, 1855–1930
Frank, Bruno, 1887–1945
Frank, Mrs. Florence (Kiper), 1886–
Frank, Henry, 1854–1933
Frank, Waldo David, 1889–1967
Frankau, Mrs. Julia (Davis), 1864–1916
Frankfurter, Felix, 1882–1965
Freeman, Joseph, 1897–1965
Fuller, Alvan Tufts, 1878–
Furuseth, Andrew, 1854–1938

Fyfe, Henry Hamilton, 1869–1951
Gaer, Joseph, 1897–
Gaige, Crosby, 1882–1949
Gale, Zona, 1874–1938
Gallup, George Horace, 1901–
Galsworthy, John, 1867–1933
Galvez, Manuel, 1882–
Gamow, George, 1904–1968
Gandhi, Mohandas Karamachand, 1869–1948
Gannett, Lewis Stiles, 1891–1966
Garland, Hamlin, 1860–1940
Gartz, Mrs. Kate (Crane), 1865?–1949
Gates, Arnold Francis, ?
Gavit, John Palmer, 1868–1954
Geddes, Norman Bel, 1893–1958
Geist, Rudolf Johann, 1900–
Gellert, Hugo, 1892–
George, Walter Lionel, 1882–1926
Gerber, Julius, ?
Gerhardi, William Alexander, 1895–
Gest, Morris, 1881–1942
Ghent, William James, 1866–1942
Gibson, Edgar Charles Sumner, 1848–1924
Gibson, Lydia, ?
Gibson, Wilfrid Wilson, 1887–1962
Giddings, Franklin Henry, 1855–1931
Gillette, King Camp, 1855–1932
Gilman, Mrs. Charlotte (Perkins), 1860–1935
Gilman, George H., ?
Giovannitti, Arturo, 1884–1959
Glasgow, Ellen Anderson Gholson, 1874–1945
Glaspell, Susan, 1882–1948
Glass, Carter, 1858–1946

Glass, Montague Marsden, 1877–1934
Glassman, Donald, 1903–
Goddard, Paulette, 1911–
Godoy, Alcayaga, Lucila, 1889–1957
Gofman, John William, 1918–
Gold, Michael, 1893–1967
Goldberg, Isaac, 1887–1938
Golden, John, 1874–1955
Goldman, Emma, 1869–1940
Goldring, Douglas, 1887–
Gompers, Mrs. Gertrude Gleaves (Neuscheler), ?
Good, Edward, 1885–
Goudsmit, Samuel Abraham, 1902–
Granville-Barker, Harley Granville, 1877–1946
Greene, Marc Tiffany, 1881–1966
Greenslet, Ferris, 1875–1959
Gregg, Richard Bartlett, 1885–
Gregory, Alyse, 1883–1967
Greiner, Samuel, 1894–
Grew, Joseph Clark, 1880–1965
Grey, Edward Grey, first viscount, 1862–1933
Guiterman, Arthur, 1871–1943
Gumberg, Alexander, 1887–1939
Gunther, John, 1901–1970
Gutkind, Erich, 1877–
Gutkind, Mrs. Lucie, ?
Hacker, Louis Morton, 1899–
Hagedorn, Hermann, 1882–1964
Haggard, Sewell, 1879–1928
Haines, Helen Elizabeth, 1872–1961
Haldeman, Henry, 1919–
Haldeman-Julius, Mrs. Anna Marcet (Haldeman),
    1887–1941

Haldeman-Julius, Emanuel, 1889–1951
Hall, Bolton, 1854–1938
Hall, Granville Stanley, 1846–1924
Hall, Josef Washington, 1894–1960
Hamilton, Albert Edward, 1887–
Hamilton, John Judson, 1854–1947
Hammarskjöld, Dag, 1905–1961
Hammett, Samuel Dashiell, 1894–1961
Hampton, Benjamin Bowles, 1875–1932
Hamsun, *Fru* Marie (Andersen), 1881–
Handy, Lowney Turner, 1904–
Hanford, Benjamin, 1861–1910
Hanna, Paul, ?
Hansen, Harry, 1884–
Hapgood, Charles Hutchins, 1904–
Hapgood, Hutchins, 1869–1944
Hapgood, Norman, 1868–1937
Hapgood, Powers, 1899–1949
Hardy, Mrs. Florence Emily (Dugdale), ? –1937
Harriman, William Averell, 1891–
Harris, Mrs. Corra May (White), 1869–1935
Harris, Frank, 1855?–1931
Harris, Sam H., 1872–1941
Harris, William, 1884–1946
Harrison, Byron Patton, 1881–1941
Harrison, Charles Yale, 1898–1954
Harrison, Henry Sydnor, 1880–1930
Harrow, Benjamin, 1888–
Hart, Joseph Kimmont, 1876–1949
Hart, Moss, 1904–1961
Hartmann, Sadakichi, 1867–1944
Harvey, Alexander, 1868–1949
Hayes, Helen, 1900–

Haynes, John Randolph, 1853–1937
Hays, Arthur Garfield, 1881–1954
Haywood, William Dudley, 1869–1928
Hazlitt, Henry, 1894–
Heard, Gerald, 1889–
Hedges, Marion Hawthorne, 1888–1959
Heijermans, Herman, 1864–1924
Heinemann, William, 1863–1920
Hemingway, Ernest, 1899–1961
Henderson, Archibald, 1877–1963
Henderson, Fred, 1867?–1957
Heney, Francis, Joseph, 1859–1937
Henson, Francis A., ?
Herford, Oliver, 1863–1935
Herrick, Robert, 1868–1938
Herridge, William Duncan, 1888–1961
Herron, George Davis, 1862–1925
Herts, Benjamin Russell, 1888–1954
Hertslet, Edward Lewis Augustine, 1878–1936
Hewlett, Maurice Henry, 1861–1923
Hickens, Robert Smythe, 1864–1950
Hicks, Edward Lee, 1843–1919
Hicks, Granville, 1901–
Hiestand, Edgar Willard, 1888–
Higginson, Thomas Wentworth, 1823–1911
Highet, Gilbert, 1906–
Hill, Creighton, ?
Hillquit, Morris, 1869–1933
Hilton, James, 1900–1954
Hird, Dennis, ?
Hoan, Daniel Webster, 1881–1961
Hoernlé, Reinhold Friedrich Alfred, 1880–1943
Hoffman, Paul Gray, 1891–

Holitscher, Arthur, 1869–1939
Holmes, John Haynes, 1879–1964
Holmström, Axel, ?
Holt, Hamilton, 1872–1951
Hook, Sidney, 1902–
Hoover, John Edgar, 1895–1972
Hopkins, Arthur Melanethon, 1878–1950
Hopkins, Harry Lloyd, 1890–1946
Hopkins, Pryns, 1885–
Horkheimer, Max, 1895–
Hormel, George Albert, 1860–1946
Houdini, Harry, 1874–1926
House, Edward Mandell, 1858–1938
Housman, Laurence, 1865–1959
Howard, George Fitzalan Bronson, 1883–1922
Howard, Sidney Coe, 1891–1939
Howatt, David, 1882–
Howe, Edgar Watson, 1853–1937
Howe, Frederic Clemson, 1867–1940
Howe, Mrs. Julia (Ward), 1819–1910
Howell, Robert Beecher, 1864–1933
Howells, William Dean, 1837–1920
Howland, Hewitt Hanson, 1863–1944
Hubbard, Elbert, 1856–1915
Hudson, Manley Ottmer, 1886–1960
Huebsch, Benjamin W. 1876–1964
Hughes, Joshua Pritchard, 1847–1938
Hughes, Rupert, 1872–1956
Humphries, Rolfe, 1894–1969
Huneker, James Gibbons, 1860–1921
Hunt, George Wylie Paul, 1859–1934
Hunter, Edward, 1902–
Hunter, Robert, 1874–1942

Huxley, Mrs. Marion (Nys), 1899?–1955
Hyndman, Henry Mayers, 1842–1921
Ickes, Harold LeClaire, 1874–1952
Ingersoll, Charles Henry, 1865–1948
Irvine, Alexander Fitzgerald, 1863–1941
Irwin, C. A., ?
Irwin, William Henry, 1873–1948
Jackson, Gardner, 1897–1965
James, Henry, 1843–1916
Jaques-Dalcroze, Emilie, 1865–1950
Jastrow, Joseph, 1863–1944
Jayne, Francis John, 1845–1921
Jerome, Jerome Klapka, 1859–1927
Johns, Orrick, 1887–1946
Johnson, Douglas Valentine, 1900–
Johnson, Hiram Warren, 1866–1945
Johnson, Robert Underwood, 1853–1937
Jones, Bassett, 1877–1960
Jones, Ellis William, 1884–1948
Jordan, David Starr, 1851–1913
Jordan, Frank C., ?
Jourdain, Francis, 1876–1958
Judy, Clinton Kelly, 1879–1955
Jung, Carl Gustav, 1875–1961
Kahn, Otto Hermann, 1867–1934
Kallen, Horace Meyer, 1882–
Kalman, Emerich, 1882–1953
Kaltenborn, Hans von, 1878–1965
Kapadia, Rangildas M., ?
Kauffman, Reginald Wright, 1877–1959
Kaufman, George Simon, 1889–1961
Kautsky, Karl Johann, 1854–1938
Kautsky, Mrs. Louise (Ronsperger), 1870–1919

Kazin, Alfred, 1915–
Keane, James John, 1857–1929
Keating, Edward, 1875–1965
Keith, Joseph Joel, 1901–1967
Keller, Adolf, 1872–
Keller, Helen Adams, 1880–1968
Kelley, Mrs. Edith (Summers), 1883–1956
Kemp, Harry, 1883–1960
Kempner, Walter, 1903–
Kennedy, Charles Rann, 1871–1950
Kennedy, John Fitzgerald, 1917–1963
Kennerley, Mitchell, 1878–1950
Kennion, George Wyndham, 1845–1922
Kent, William, 1864–1928
Kerr, Robert Samuel, 1896–1963
Kettner, William, 1864–1930
Key, Ellen Karolina Sofia, 1849–1926
Kilmer, Joyce, 1886–1918
Kimball, Mrs. Henrietta D., ?
Kimbrough, Hunter Southworth, 1900–
Kissin, Rita, ?
Klein, Charles, 1867–1915
Klyce, Scudder, 1879–1933
Koestler, Arthur, 1905–
Konti, Isidore, 1862–1938
Korzybski, Alfred, count, 1879–1950
Koul, Braj Kishan, ?
Krekeler, Heinz L., 1906–
Krishnamurti, Jiddu, 1895–
Kropotkin, Petr Aleksieevich, knlaz, 1842–1921
Kropotkin, Princess Sophie, ?
Kruse, William F., ?
Krutch, Joseph Wood, 1893–1970

Krymov, Vladimir Pimenovich, 1878–
Kus-Nikolajev, Mirko, 1896–
LaFollette, Fola, 1882?–1970
LaFollette, Philip Fox, 1897–1965
LaFollette, Robert Marion, 1855–1925
LaFollette, Robert Marion, 1895–1953
Lagerlof, Selma Ottiliana Lovisa, 1858–1940
LaGuardia, Fiorello Henry, 1882–1947
Laidler, Harry Wellington, 1884–1970
Lamont, Corliss, 1902–
LaMotte, Ellen Newbold, 1873–1961
Land, Rene, ?
Lane, Alfred Church, 1863–1948
Lane, Mrs. Rose (Wilder), 1887–
Lang, Cosmo Gordon, 1864–1945
Lang, Harry, 1895?–1953
Lang, Mrs. Lucy (Fox) Robins, ?–1962
Lansbury, George, 1859–1940
Lardner, Hubert , ?
Laski, Harold Joseph, 1893–1950
Lasky, Victor, 1918–
Latimer, Margery, 1899–1932
Latzko, Adolph Andreas, 1876–
Laurie, T. Werner, c. 1857–1944
Lawrence, David Herbert, 1885–1930
Lawson, John Howard, 1895–
Laxness, Halldór Kiljan, 1902–
Leach, Henry Goddard, 1880–
Leacock, Stephen Butler, 1869–1944
Lee, Algernon, 1873–1954
Lee, Gerald Stanley, 1862–1944
LeGallienne, Eva, 1899–
LeGallienne, Gwendolyn, ?

LeGallienne, Richard, 1866–1947
Leonard, William Ellery, 1876–1944
Lerbs, Karl, 1893–
Lescarboura, Austin Celestin, 1891–1962
Lesser, Sol, 1890–
Levine, Isaac Don, 1892–
Lewis, Harve Spencer, 1883–1939
Lewis, John Llewellyen, 1880–1969
Lewis, Lena Morrow, ?
Lewis, Sinclair, 1885–1951
Lewisohn, Ludwig, 1882–1955
Lie, Trygve Halvdan, 1896–1968
Lilienthal, David Eli, 1899–
Lindsay, Mrs. Elizabeth (Couner), 1901–1954
Lindsay, Nicholas Vachel, 1879–1931
Lindsey, Benjamin Barr, 1869–1943
Lindsey, Mrs. Henrietta (Brevoort), ?
Linville, Henry Richardson, 1866–1941
Lippmann, Walter, 1889–
Litvinov, Maksim Maksimovich, 1876–1951
Liveright, Horace Brisbin, 1886–1933
Llewis, Franklin, ?
Lloyd, Mrs. Lola (Maverick) 1875–1944
Lloyd, William Bross, 1875–1946
Lockhart, Eugene, 1891–1957
Lodge, Sir Oliver Joseph, 1851–1940
Loeb, Mrs. Anna (Leonard), (Mrs. Jacques Loeb),
1862?–1951
Loeb, Jacques, 1859–1924
London, Mrs. Charmian (Kittredge), 1870?–1955
London, Jack, 1876–1916
Lonquet, Jean, ?

Loos, Anita, 1894–
Lorant, Stefan, 1901–
Lovestone, Jay, ?
Lovett, Robert Morss, 1870–1956
Low, Sir David, 1891–1963
Lowrie, Donald, ?
Ludwig, Emil, 1881–1948
Lunacharskii, Anatolii Vassil'evich, 1875–1933
Lunn, Sir Henry Simpson, 1859–1939
Lush, Samuel Beryl, 1893?–
Lydenberg, Harry Miller, 1874–
Lyons, Eugene, 1898–
McAdoo, William Gibbs, 1863–1941
MacArthur, Douglas, 1880–1964
McCabe, Joseph, 1867–?
McCloy, John Jay, 1895–
McClure, Samuel Sidney, 1857–1949
McConnell, Francis John, 1871–1953
McCoy, Samuel Duff, 1882–1964
McDaniel, Walton Brooks, 1871–
McDevitt, William, ?
McDougall, William, 1871–1938
MacDowell, Mrs. Marian Griswold (Nevins), 1857–1956
Macfadden, Bernarr Adolphus, 1868–1955
MacGill, Patrick, 1890–
MacGowan, Alice, 1858–
Macgowan, Kenneth, 1888–1963
McIntyre, Marvin Hunter, 1878–1943
McKay, Claude, 1890–1948
Mackaye, Percy, 1875–1956
MacLeish, Archibald, 1892–
Macleod, Norman H. F., 1875–1948
Macy, John Albert, 1877–1932

Melish, John Howard, 1875–
Mellinkoff, Mrs. Helen, ?
Mencken, Henry Louis, 1880–1956
Merwin, Samuel, 1874–1936
Metcalf, Keyes DeWitt, 1889–
Miller, Marvin Alwin, 1903–
Miller, Ogden D., ?
Millikan, Clark Blanchard, 1903–1966
Millikan, Robert Andrews, 1868–1953
Minor, Robert, 1884–1952
Moffett, Cleveland, 1863–1926
Moley, Raymond, 1886–
Monro, Harold, 1879–1932
Monroe, Harriet, 1860–1936
Montross, Lynn, 1895–1961
Mooney, Thomas J., 1882–1942
Moore, Charles, 1855–1942
Moore, Fred H., ?
Mora, Constancia de la, 1906–1950
Mordell, Albert, 1885–
Morgan, Angela, 1873?–1957
Morgenthau, Henry, 1891–1967
Morison, Samuel Eliot, 1887–
Morley, Christopher Darlington, 1890–1957
Morris, Mrs. Anna (Wharton), 1868–?
Morrison of Lambeth, baron Herbert Stanley, 1888–1965
Mosely, Philip Edward, 1905–
Mowbray-Clarke, John Frederick, 1869–1953
Muldoon, Sylvan Joseph, ?
Mumford, Lewis, 1895–
Munger, Mrs. Dell H., 1862–?
Munzenberg, Willi, 1889–1940
Murphy, Frank, 1890–1949

Murray, Gilbert, 1866–1957
Murray, Philip, 1886–1952
Murrow, Edward Roscoe, 1908–1965
Musmanno, Michael Angelo, 1897–1968
Mussey, Henry Raymond, 1875–1940
Muzzey, David Saville, 1870–1965
Nash, Ogden, 1902–1971
Nasser, Gamal Abdel, 1918–1970
Nathan, George Jean, 1882–1958
Nathan, Robert, 1894–
Nathan, Robert Roy, 1908–
Nearing, Scott, 1883–
Nehru, Jawaharlal, 1889–1964
Neihardt, John Gneisenau, 1881–
Neil, Henry, 1863– ?
Nesbit, Wilbur Dick, 1871–1927
Nethersole, Olga, 1870–1951
Neuberger, Richard Lewis, 1912–1960
Nevins, Allan, 1890–1971
Nicotri, Gaspare, ?
Nobili, Riccardo, ?
Norris, Charles Gilman, 1881–1945
Norris, George William, 1861–1944
Norris, Mrs. Kathleen (Thompson), 1880–1966
Noyes, Alfred, 1880–1958
O'Brien, Edward Joseph Harrington, 1890–1941
O'Brien, Frederick, 1869–1932
O'Connell, Jerry J., 1909–
Odets, Clifford, 1906–1963
O'Higgins, Harvey Jerrold, 1876–1929
Older, Mrs. Cora Miranda (Baggerly), ?
Older, Fremont, 1856–1935
Oliver, John Rathbone, 1872–1943

Perigord, Paul, 1882–1959
Perry, Bliss, 1860–1954
Pettigrew, Richard Franklin, 1848–1926
Phelps, William Lyon, 1865–1943
Phillips, John Sanburn, 1861–1949
Phillpotts, Eden, 1862–1960
Pickford, Mary, 1893–
Pinchot, Amos Richard Eno, 1873–1944
Pinchot, Gifford, 1865–1946
Piscator, Erwin, 1893–1966
Plumb, Glenn Edward, 1866–1922
Podwysocki, Anthony, ?
Pollock, Bertram, 1863–1943
Poole, Ernest, 1880–1950
Poole, Mrs. Margaret (Winterbotham), ?
Post, Louis Freeland, 1849–1928
Postif, Louis, ?
Poulaille, Henri
Pound, Mrs. Dorothy (Shakespear), ?
Pound, Ezra Loomis, 1885–
Powys, Llewelyn, 1884–1939
Preminger, Otto L., 1906–
Priestley, John Boynton, 1894–
Prince, Morton, 1854–1929
Prince, Walter Franklin, 1863–1934
Pulitzer, Ralph, 1879–1939
Purnell, Idella, 1901–
Putnam, Mrs. Nina (Wilcox), 1888–1962
Quick, Herbert, 1861–1925
Quinn, Arthur Hobson, 1875–1960
Radhakrishnan, Sir Sarvepalli, 1888–
Raffé, Walter George, 1888–
Rainer, Luise, 1912?–

Randall, David Anton, 1905–
Ratcliffe, Samuel Kerkham, 1868–?
Rauschenbusch, Walter, 1861–1918
Reass, Benjamin, ?
Redfield, Casper Lavater, 1853–1943
Reed, John, 1887–1920
Reedy, William Marion, 1862–1920
Regier, Cornelius C., 1884–
Remarque, Erich Maria, 1898–1970
Reuther, Victor G., 1912–
Reuther, Walter Philip, 1907–1970
Reynolds, Quentin James, 1902–1965
Rhine, Joseph Banks, 1895–
Rhys, Mrs. Grace (Little), 1865–1929
Rice, Cale Young, 1872-1943
Rice, Elmer L., 1892–1967
Richardson, Friend William, 1864 or 5–1943
Ridgeway, Charles John, 1841–1927
Riesel, Victor, 1917–
Rinehart, Mrs. Mary (Roberts), 1876–1958
Rios y Urrute, Fernando de los, 1879–1949
Rittenhouse, Jessie Belle, 1869–1948
Rivera, Diego, 1886–1957
Roberts, Kate Louise, ?–1941
Robinson, Boardman, 1876–1952
Robinson, Edward G., 1893–
Robinson, James Harvey, 1863–1936
Robinson, Joseph Taylor, 1872–1937
Robinson, William Josephius, 1867–1936
Roche, Josephine Aspinwall, 1886–
Rockefeller, Nelson Aldrich, 1908–
Rogers, Robert Emmons, 1888–1941
Rogers, Will, 1879–1935

Rohrbach, Paul, 1869–?
Rolland, Madeleine, ?
Rolland, Romain, 1866–1944
Romaine, Mrs. Rose Harriet (Pastor), 1879–1933
Roosevelt, Mrs. Anna Eleanor (Roosevelt), 1884–1962
Roosevelt, Franklin Delano, 1882–1945
Roosevelt, James, 1907–
Roosevelt, Theodore, 1858–1919
Ross, Edward Alsworth, 1866–1951
Ross, John Elliot, 1884–1946
Rostovtsev, Mikhail Ivanovich, 1870–1952
Royall, Kenneth Claiborne, 1894–
Russell, Bertrand Russell, third earl, 1872–1970
Russell, Charles Edward, 1860–1941
Russell, George William, 1867–1935
Russell, Isaac, ?
Russell, John Francis Stanley Russell, second earl, 1865–1931
Russell, Lady Mollie (Cooke), ?
Russell, Lady Patricia (Blackwood), 1902–
Rutzebeck, Hjalmar, ?
Ryskind, Morrie, 1895–
Sacco, Nicola, 1891–1927
Salten, Felix, 1869–1945
Samson, Leon, ?
Sandburg, Carl, 1878–1967
Sanger, Mrs. Margaret (Higgins), 1883–1966
Sansum, William David, 1880–1948
Santayana, George, 1863–1952
Sargent, Porter Edward, 1872–1951
Saroyan, William, 1908–
Sayer, Ettie, ?–1923
Schauffler, Robert Haven, 1879–1964
Scheffauer, Herman George, 1878–1927

Scherer, James Augustin Brown, 1870–1944
Schiller, Ferdinand Canning Scott, 1864–1937
Schlesinger, Arthur Meier, 1888–1965
Schlesinger, Arthur Meier, 1917–
Schoenberner, Franz, 1892–1970
Schoonmaker, Edwin Davies, 1873–1940
Scollard, Clinton, 1860–1932
Scott, Mrs. Evelyn (Dunn), 1893–
Scott, Howard, 1890–
Scott, James Brown, 1866–1943
Scott, Leroy, 1875–1929
Scripps, Edward Wyllis, 1854–1926
Scripps, Robert Paine, 1895–1938
Scudder, Vida Dutton, 1861–1954
Scully, Frank, 1892–
Seabrook, William Buehler, 1887–1945
Seldes, George, 1890–
Selwyn, Edgar, 1875–1944
Selwyn, Mrs. Margaret (May), ?
Senior, Clarence, 1903–
Seton, Ernest Thompson, 1860–1946
Sevareid, Arnold Eric, 1912–
Seymour, Charles, 1885–1963
Shaw, Anna Howard, 1847–1919
Shaw, Mrs. Charlotte Frances (Payne-Townshend),
    1857–1943
Shaw, George Bernard, 1856–1950
Shaw, John William, 1863–1934
Sheean, Vincent, 1899–
Shay, Felix, ?
Sheppard, Morris, 1875–1941
Shepperley, William, ?
Sherman, Harold Morrow, 1898–

Sherman, Stuart Pratt, 1881–1926
Sherwood, Robert Emmet, 1896–1955
Shipley, Mrs. Miriam Allen (DeFord), 1888–
Shippey, Henry Lee, 1884–1969
Shipstead, Henrik, 1881–1960
Shirer, William Laurence, 1904–
Shirley, Wayne, 1900–
Shotwell, James Thomson, 1874–1965
Shuler, Robert P., ?
Shumlin, Herman, 1898–
Shuster, George Nauman, 1894–
Silvay, Challiss, ?
Simons, Algie Martin, 1870–1950
Sinclair, Harry Ford, 1876–1956
Sinclair, May, 1865?–1946
Sinclair, Mrs. Meta (Fuller); see Stone, Mrs. Meta
Singer, Isador, 1857–1927
Skinner, Clarence Russell, 1881–1949
Slaten, Arthur Wakefield, 1880–1944
Sleeswijk, Jan Gerard, 1879–
Slosson, Edwin Emery, 1865–1929
Smertenko, Johan Jacob, 1895–
Smith, Marjorie E., 1900–
Smith, Paul Jordan, 1885–
Smith, Sarah Bixby, 1871–1935
Sokolsky, George Ephraim, 1893–1962
Soule, George Henry, 1887–1970
Spargo, John, 1876–1966
Speight, Harold Edwin Balme, 1887–
Sperber, Manes, 1905–
Spingarn, Joel Elias, 1875–1939
Springer, Francis Edwin, 1872–1940
Stalin, Iosif, 1879–1953

Starrett, Vincent, 1886–
Stearns, Myron Morris, 1884–
Steffens, Joseph Lincoln, 1866–1936
Steinbeck, John Ernst, 1902–1968
Sterling, George, 1869–1926
Stern, Benjamin H., 1873?–1950
Stern, Simon, 1878?–
Stevens, Leslie Clark, 1895–1956
Stevenson, Adlai Ewing, 1900–1965
Stillman, Clara Gruening, ?
Stokes, James Graham Phelps, 1872–1960
Stolberg, Benjamin, 1891–1951
Stone, Irving, 1903–
Stone, Mrs. Meta (Fuller), 1880–1964
Stong, Philip Duffield, 1899–
Stout, Rex, 1886–
Strachey, John, 1901–1963
Straton, Norman Dumenil John, 1840–1918
Strauss, George Russell, ?
Street, Julian Leonard, 1879–1947
Streibert, Theodore Cuyler, 1899–
Streit, Clarence Krishman, 1896–
Stringer, Arthur John Arbuthnott, 1874–1950
Strong, Anna Louise, 1885–1970
Strong, Philip Duffield, 1899–1957
Stout, Rex Todhunter, 1886–
Stuart, Jesse, 1907–
Suggett, Mrs. Laura Steffens, ?
Sullivan, Mark, 1874–1952
Sunday, William Ashley, 1863–1935
Swing, Raymond Gram, 1887–1968
Swinnerton, Frank Arthur, 1884–
Symons, Arthur, 1865–1945

Tabor, Paul, 1908–
Tagore, Sir Rabindranath, 1861–1941
Tarbell, Ida Minerva, 1857–1944
Taylor, Harry Grant, 1899–1936
Thacker, Mrs. Addie May (Dixon), ?
Thalberg, Irving Grant, 1899–1936
Thomas, Augustus, 1857–1934
Thomas, Edith Matilda, 1854–1925
Thomas, Lowell Jackson, 1892–
Thomas, Norman Mattoon, 1884–1968
Thompson, Carl Dean, 1870–1949
Thompson, Clarence Bertrand, 1882–1969
Thompson, Dorothy, 1894–1961
Thompson, Emmett, ?
Thompson, William Goodrich, 1864–1935
Thompson, William Hale, 1869–1944
Tietjens, Mrs. Eunice (Hammond), 1884–1944
Toller, Ernst, 1893–1939
Tolman, Richard Chace, 1881–1948
Tolstoi, Ilia Lo'vovich, graf, 1866–1933
Torrence, Frederic Ridgely, 1875–1950
Toscanini, Arturo, 1867–1957
Towne, Charles Hanson, 1877–1949
Traubel, Horace, 1858–1919
Trent, Lucia, 1897–
Tresca, Carlo, 1879–1943
Trevelyan, Sir Charles Philips, 1870–1958
Trotskii, Lev, 1879–1940
Trotskii, Mrs. Natalia Ivanova (Sedova), 1882–1962
Truman, Harry S., 1884–
Tugwell, Rexford Guy, 1891–
Tully, Mrs. Florence (Bushnell), (Mrs. Jim Tully), ?
Tully, Jim, 1888–1947

Tumulty, Joseph Patrick, 1879–1954
Turner, George Kibbe, 1869–1952
Turner, John Kenneth, ?
Underwood, John Curtis, 1874–1949
Undset, Sigrid, 1882–1949
Untermann, Ernest, 1864?–1956
Untermeyer, Louis, 1885–
Untermyer, Mrs. Minnie (Carl), ?–1924
Untermyer, Samuel, 1858–1940
Updegraff, Allan Eugene, 1883–1965
Upward, Allen, 1863–1926
U'Ren, William Simon, 1859–1949
Vanderbilt, Cornelius, 1898–
Vanderlip, Frank Arthur, 1864–1937
Van Doren, Carl Clinton, 1885–1950
Van Doren, Mrs. Irita (Brooks), 1891–1966
Van Doren, Mark, 1894–
Van Loon, Hendrik Willem, 1882–1944
Van Paassen, Pierre, 1895–1968
Van Vechten, Carl, 1880–1964
Vanzetti, Bartolomeo, 1888–1927
Vardaman, James Kimble, 1861–1930
Vasudevan, Thayyil K., ?
Veblen, Thorstein, 1857–1929
Venkataramani, Kaneripatha Sidhanatha, 1891–
Verlinsky, Vladimir I., ?
Vesey-Fitzgerald, Brian Seymour, 1900–
Viereck, George Sylvester, 1884–1962
Viertel, Berthold, 1885–1953
Vijaya-Tunga, Jinadasa, 1902–
Villard, Oswald Garrison, 1872–1949
Vogan, Boris Andreevich, 1894–
Voorhis, Mrs. Alice Louise (Livingston), ?

Voorhis, Horace Jeremiah, 1901–
Waddell, Elizabeth, ?
Wagner, Robert Ferdinand, 1877–1953
Wagner, Robert Leicester, 1872–1942
Wagstaff, Mrs. Blanche (Shoemaker), 1888–
Walker, Charles Rumford, 1893–
Walker, Irma M., 1881–
Walker, Mrs. Maude Helena (Davis), ?–1925
Walker, Ryan, 1870–1932
Wallace, Sir Alfred Russel, 1823–1913
Wallace, Henry Agard, 1888–1965
Walling, William English, 1877–1936
Walsh, Francis Patrick, 1864–1939
Walsh, Thomas James, 1859–1933
Walter, Eugene, 1874–1941
Wangenheim, Julius, 1866–1942
Warbasse, James Peter, 1866–1957
Ward, Charles Henshaw, 1872–1935
Ward, Harry Frederick, 1873–1966
Waring, Julius Waties, 1880–1968
Warren, Fred D., 1872–1959
Warwick, Frances Evelyn (Maynard) Greville, countess of,
    1861–1938
Washburn, Abbott McConnell, 1915–
Wassermann, Jakob, 1873–1934
Watson, Thomas Edward, 1856–1922
Watson, Sir William, 1858–1935
Weeks, Edward Augustus, 1898–
Welles, Sumner, 1892–1961
Wells, Geoffrey Harry, 1900–
Wells, Herbert George, 1866–1946
Wentworth, Mrs. Marion Jean (Craig), 1872–?
Werfel, Mrs. Alma (Schindler), 1879–1964

Werfel, Franz V., 1890–1945
Westermann, William Linn, 1873–1954
Wharton, Mrs. Edith Newbold (Jones), 1862–1937
Wharton, James B., ?
Wheeler, Burton Kendall, 1882–
Wheelock, John Hall, 1886–
Whitaker, Robert, 1863–1944
White, Bouck, 1874–1951
White, Hervey, 1866–1944
White, Stewart Edward, 1873–1946
White, Walter Francis, 1893–1955
White, William Allen, 1868–1944
White, William Lindsay, 1900–
Whitehead, Carle, ?
Whiteing, Richard, 1840–1928
Whitlock, Brand, 1869–1934
Whitney, Charlotte Anita, 1866–1955
Widdemer, Margaret, 1897–
Wilberforce, Albert Basil Orme, 1841–1916
Wilcox, Mrs. Ella (Wheeler), 1855–1919
Wiley, Harvey Washington, 1844–1930
Wilkinson, Mrs. Marguerite Ogden (Bigelow), 1883–1928
Williams, Albert Rhys, 1883–1962
Williams, Jesse Lynch, 1871–1929
Williams, John Sharp, 1854–1932
Williams, Mrs. Lucita (Squier), ?
Williams, Michael, 1877–1950
Wilshire, Henry Gaylord, 1861–1927
Wilshire, Mrs. Mary (McReynolds), ?
Wilson, Edmund, 1895–1972
Wilson, William Bauchop, 1862–1934
Winchell, Walter, 1897–1972
Winter, Ella, 1898–

Winnington-Ingram, Arthur Foley, bishop of London, 1858–1946
Wirin, A. L., ?
Wise, Stephen Samuel, 1874–1949
Wister, Owen, 1860–1938
Wittels, Fritz, 1880–1950
Wittfogel, Karl August, 1896–
Wolf, Robert L., ?
Wood, Charles Erskine Scott, 1852–1944
Wood, Clement, 1888–1950
Wood, Eugene, 1860–1923
Woodberry, George Edward, 1855–1930
Woodcock, Amos Walter Wright, 1883–1964
Woodman, Hannah Rea, 1870–1951
Woods, Ralph Louis, 1904–
Woodward, Mrs. Helen (Rosen), 1882–
Woodward, William Edward, 1874–1950
Woollcott, Alexander, 1887–1943
Wotherspoon, Mrs. Marion (Foster), 1863–1944
Wright, Harold Bell, 1872–1944
Wuppermann, Carlos, ?
Yard, Robert Sterling, 1861–1945
Yashima, Taro, 1908–
Young, Arthur Henry, 1866–1943
Young, Mahonri Mackintosh, 1877–1957
Young, Stark, 1881–1963
Zangwill, Israel, 1864–1926
Zilahy, Lajos, 1891–
Zolotow, Maurice, 1913–
Zueblin, Charles, 1866–1924
Zur Muhlen, Herminia, 1883–
Zwicky, Fritz, 1898–

Institution	Number of Letters	Inclusive Dates	Correspondent
Allegheny College	2	8 Mar 1911– 13 Sept 1919	Ida M. Tarbell (1)
American Academy of Arts and Letters	17	27 Feb [1908 or 1909]– 14 Mar 1928	Bolton Hall (2)
		2 Nov 1948– 28 Feb 1952	Van Wyck Brooks (2)
		21 Dec 1943	Henry Seidel Canby (1)
		1 Oct 1914	Circular (1)
		6 Mar 1963	Marchette Chute (1)
		6 Feb 1966	Leon Edel (1)
		5 Apr 1944– 4 Jan 1966	Felicia Geffen (3)
		28 Apr 1950	Mrs. Josephson (1)
		5 Dec 1907	Moffat Yard (1)
		22 Jan 1945	Pres. Nat. Inst. of Arts (1)
		23 Feb 1950	Chauncey B. Tinker (1)
		24 Jan 1953– 23 Jan 1961	The Academy (2)
Brooklyn Public Library	3	6 Aug 1931– 19 Oct 1931	Benjamin de Casseres (3)
Colby College Library	3	27 Dec 1929 28 Jan 1965	R. H. Burnside (1) John Eastman, Jr. (1)

INSTITUTION	NUMBER OF LETTERS	INCLUSIVE DATES	CORRESPONDENT
		n.d.	Nathan N. Wallack (1)
Columbia University	7	30 Nov 1909– 21 May 1928	Lincoln Steffens (4)
		7 Oct 1936– 14 Jan 1937	Ella Winter (3)
Cornell University	8	2 Oct–25 Oct	George Lincoln Burr (3)
		1922	Circular (1)
		11 Oct 1932	Theodore Dreiser (1)
		28 July, 8, 25 Aug 1939	Prof. Robert Elias (3)
Duke University (Perkins Library)	55	25 May 1933	All Opponents of War (1)
		29 Dec 1939	Gerry Allard (1)
		2 Nov 1933	Siegfried Ameninger (1)
		6 June 1929	W. H. Barnes (1)
		24 Oct 1939	*The Call* (1)
		Feb-Oct 1933	Circular Letters (3)
		10 Feb 1–Mar 1958	Clarence C. F. Gohdes (2)
		26 Dec 1924– 5 Jul 45	[?] Holmes (7)
		7 Oct 1937– 7 May 1947	Holmes Book Store (2)
		6 Feb–17 June 1940	Leo W. Johnson (6)

Institution	Number of Letters	Inclusive Dates	Correspondent
		8 Feb–25 Dec 1933	Harold Kelso (2)
		14 Sept 1923	Isabel King (1)
		19 Feb 1933	Hilda Kruggel (1)
		1909	John Long (1)
		16 Aug 1939	J. G. Moore (1)
		30 Aug 1929– 6 June 1935	Clarence O. Senior (12)
		7 Dec 1933	Socialist Party of Amer. (1)
		28 Dec 1931– 1 Dec 1937	Nathan N. Wallack (9)
		22 Oct 1917	Thomas Woodrow Wilson (1)
Harvard University	110	14 Mar–16 Apr 1901	Thomas Bailey Aldrich (2)
		1918	John Basil Barnhill (1)
		1 June 1927– 4 Sept 1931	Gamaliel Bradford (5)
		21 Sept 1914	William S. Braithwaite (1)
		14 Apr 1919	Louise Bryant (1)
		1927–1928	Creighton J. Hill (45)
		1921–1939	Joseph Ishill (4)
		21 Mar 1925	Henry Whsyam Lanier (1)
		1936–1941	John Phillips Marquand (3)
		4, 31 Dec 1951	Perry Miller (2)

INSTITUTION	NUMBER OF LETTERS	INCLUSIVE DATES	CORRESPONDENT
		n.d.	Arthur Ernest Morgan (1)
		1914–1919	John Reed (8)
		1919–1930	Oswald G. Villard (28)
		[ca. 1900]–1914	George E. Woodberry (8)
Haverford College	2	26 Oct 1934	Clarence G. Hoag (1)
		28 July 1921	Christopher Morley (1)
Henry E. Hunt- ington Library	74	29 Mar 1911– 28 Mar 1933	Mary Austin (3)
		n.d.	Ina Coolbrith (1)
		1905–1930	Jack London (63)
		15 July 1915– 12 July 1925	Alice Park (5)
		31 Aug 1914– 29 Apr 1929	Albert B. Payne (2)
Historical Society of Penn- sylvania	6	2 Apr [?]	Dreer Collection Prose (2)
		25 Oct [?]	
		25 June 1918	Mr. Fawcett (1)
		1921	G. H. Lorimer (2)
		28 Sept [?]	Simms (1)
Los Angeles Public Library	8	16 Jan 1957– 27 Jan 1959	To Library (8)
Middlebury College	4	26 Apr 1934	Viola C. White (1)
		17 Sept 1914	"Miss Wilkinson" (1)
		1 Oct 1914	Mrs. Wilkinson (1)
		n.d.	M.W. (1)

INSTITUTION	NUMBER OF LETTERS	INCLUSIVE DATES	CORRESPONDENT
New York Public Library	344	13 June 1922– 23 Oct 1936	V. F. Calverton (25)
		19 July 1926– 30 Jan 1929	Floyd Dell (10)
		1903–1921	Macmillan Company (233)
		25 Sept 1914– 29 Apr 1929	Joel Spingarn (10)
		1901–1948	Miscellaneous (66) (Includes letters to Robert H. Davis, R. W. Gilder, Isaac Goldberg, Bolton Hall, and H. L. Mencken)
Newberry Library	52	1911–1960 9 Aug 1928	Floyd Dell (51) Creighton J. Hill (1)
Occidental College Library	30	28 Apr 1941– 27 Mar 1946	Elmer Belt (11)
		25 Jan 1909	Paul Gerson (1)
		1 Nov 1920– 5 Apr 1941	William McDevitt (16)
		30 Nov 1927– 8 Jan 1929	Willard S. Morse (2)
Pack Memorial Public Library	2	3 Sept 1949– 21 Feb 1951	Myra Champion (2)
Plainfield Public Library	1	25 Feb 1940	Alexander Woollcott

INSTITUTION	NUMBER OF LETTERS	INCLUSIVE DATES	CORRESPONDENT
Princeton University	23	11 Sept 1940 26 Feb 1901–	Julian P. Boyd (1)
		1 Sept 1902	W. C. Brownell (13)
		17 Aug 1901	E. L. Burlingame (1)
		9 Jan 1967 21 Aug 1914–	Alfred L. Bush (1)
		20 Aug 1931	Editor, *Scribner's Magazine* (3)
		1 June 1942– [ca. 8 Dec 1947]	Whit Burnett (4)
San Francisco Public Library	1	16 July 1930	Charmian London
Southern Illinois University	7	1 Aug 1930– 5 Feb 1940	Robert Carleton Brown (6)
		1907	Ward Edwards (1)
Stanford University Libraries	257	8 Mar 1911 17, 19 June 1935	Ambrose Bierce (1) Manchester Boddy (2)
		(unsigned carbons) 2 June 1936	Cyril Clemens (1)
		23 Oct, 2 Nov 1922	George E. Crothers (2)
		22 May 1934	Mimeo. Circular Letter (1)
		17 Nov 1930– 1 Feb 1965	Mrs. Lorna D. Smith (41)

Institution	Number of Letters	Inclusive Dates	Correspondent
		10 Sept 1908–7 Feb 1915	George Sterling (2)
		20 Sept 1907–12 Feb 1914	To various persons (207)
State Historical Soc. of Wisconsin	17	1905–1913 1905–1919 1919–1920	Morris Hillquit (9) Edward A. Ross (7) Algie M. Simon (1)
St. John's Seminary		6 Apr 1905	"My dear Col. Higginson"
Swathmore College	1	14 Jan 1909	Dear Sirs
University of California, Berkeley	86	1943–1947 1933–1952 1921–1938 1909–1935 1909	Gertrude Atherton (6) Peter Gulbrandsen (35) Tom Mooney (28) Fremont Older (8) Blanche Partington (9)
University of California, Los Angeles	46	1915–1934 1929–1941	Theodore Gerson (16) Rob Wagner (30)
University of Chicago	4	5 Dec 1949 5 July 1911–5 Sept 1924	Editor of Poetry (1) Harriet Monroe (3)
University of Missouri	7	26 Mar 1923	Clarence W. Alvord (1)

Institution	Number of Letters	Inclusive Dates	Correspondent
		10 Aug 1914–21 Sept 1923	John G. Neihardt (6)
University of Pennsylvania	30	1 Oct 1914–6 Sept 1940	Theodore Dreiser (30)
University of Rochester	3	1 Nov 1949	Wilmer H. Baatz (1)
		15 Dec 1949	John R. Russell (1)
		7 Mar 1921	Louis Wiley (1)
University of Southern California	7	20 Nov 1940–23 Feb 1948	W. Arthur Boggs (2)
		23 Feb 1948	Dept. of Classical Languages (1)
		21 Sept 1932	R. W. Francis (1)
		8 Mar 1911–5 Apr 1939	Hamlin Garland (2)
		9 Jan 1942	Harry Lichtig (1)
University of Texas	8	2 Aug 1923	Witter Bynner (1)
		30 July 1912–22 Sept 1922	Frank Harris (2)
		1 July 1924	H. L. Mencken (1)
		20 Feb, 5 June 1924	Miss Purnell (2)
		21 May 1912	Dan Rider (1)
		1 July 1929	White (1)
University of Virginia	67	16 Jul 1902	To _____ (1)
		ca. 1914–1917	Curtis Brown (2)
		24 Jul 1924	Mr. Earley (1)
		22 Mar 1918	Mr. Gaines (1)

INSTITUTION	NUMBER OF LETTERS	INCLUSIVE DATES	CORRESPONDENT
		19 Sept 1935	Irvin Haas (1)
		8 May 1945	E. J. Halter (1)
		23 Feb 1907	Latouche Hancock (1)
		ca. 1916–1917	Frank Harris (22)
		1937–1938	James L. Harte (5)
		8 Apr 1910	Mrs. Howe (1)
		8 Oct 1937	A. Y. King (1)
		ca. 1900–1934	Edwin Markham (5)
		15 June 1920	Mary E. McAuley (1)
		29 Mar 1937	Helene Mullins (1)
		Sept 1908	Louis E. Shattuck (1)
		16 Oct 1931	Nathan Wallack (1)
		8 Mar 1922	J. Ellis Wells (1)
		23 Apr 1906	Stewart White (1)
		2 Nov 1939	W. W. Woodson (1)
		1914–	To miscellaneous persons (20)
Wagner College	8	1904–1957	Edwin Markham (8)
Wellesley College Library	3	15 Feb 1918	Dear Comrade (1)
		12 Oct [?]	My dear Sir (1)
		12 Feb 1933	The Librarian (1)
Yale University	25	14 Feb 1918	Estelle Dyke (1)
		8 Aug 1939	John Fall (1)
		11 Jan 1914– 13 Dec 1928	Arthur D. Ficke (3)
		14 Oct 1915– 4 Jan 1921	Sinclair Lewis (2)
		24 Mar 1937	F. B. Millett (1)

INSTITUTION	NUMBER OF LETTERS	INCLUSIVE DATES	CORRESPONDENT
		26 Feb 1909	Ellen Montague Stedman (1)
		2 June 1927– 21 Feb 1931	W. L. Phelps (3)
		1897–1907	Laura Stedman (12)
		11 Apr 1911	Dr. Watkins (1)
Yivo Institute for Jewish Research	5	20 Apr 1918	William Edlin (1)
		29 Apr 1929	Horace Kallen (1)
		20 June 1922– 17 Apr 1925	Ezekiel Leavitt (2)
		18 Jan 1915	Morris Rosenfeld (1)

C.

RELATED MANUSCRIPTS

The manuscripts below are filed with Sinclair's, but appear not to be written by him. The user is reminded that many of Mary Craig Sinclair's manuscripts, also in the Lilly Library, bear her husband's corrections or are otherwise pertinent to the study of his career.

Citation: THE CHOSEN PEOPLE; t. ms.; ribbon; InU.

Title: THE CHICKEN PEOPLE | (Upton Sinclair)

Key Words: It is some time since . . . made effective—as unusual comedy.

Collation: 5; white laid; 26.7 x 19; 1–5; none; good.

Contents: Complete; unrevised; not by Sinclair; it is a critique of one of his plays; ms. has been initialed in ink at bottom of page 5: A.H.?

Dates: Comp. ca. 15 November 1910.

Citation: CONDITIONS IN 1947 WERE ENTIRELY DIFFERENT FROM NOW; t. ms.; carbon; InU.

Title: CONDITIONS IN 1947 WERE ENTIRELY DIFFERENT FROM NOW.

Key Words: What must be clarified in . . . space to store our things.

Collation: 12; white watermarked; 28.1 x 21.8; 1–12; none; good.

Contents: Complete; unrevised; apparently by MCS.

Dates: Comp. ca. 1951–52.

Citation: THE CRITICAL SPIRIT; t. ms.; carbon; InU.

Title: THE CRITICAL SPIRIT

Key Words: The literature of satire and . . . than any other American novelist.

Collation: 6; white watermarked; 28 x 21.6; [1] 2–6; none; good.

Contents: Complete; unrevised; chap. 10 from *Creating the Modern American Novelist,* by Harlan Hatcher.

Dates: Pub. 1935.

Citation: I FULLY AGREE . . . ; t. ms.; carbon; InU.

Title: [none]

Key Words: I fully agree with Professor . . . agony of a dying man."

Collation: 4; white; 28 x 21.7; 1–4; none; good.

Contents: Complete; infrequently revised in pencil, not in Sinclair's hand.

Dates: Comp. ? Pub. ?

Citation: JEROME ALEXANDER, M. Sc.; t. ms.; ribbon, carbon; InU.

Title: JEROME ALEXANDER, M. Sc.

Key Words: Last night I took time . . . a long and useful life.

Collation: 6; white watermarked; 28 x 21.6; unnumbered; none; good.

Contents: Complete; infrequently revised in blue ink, un-identified hand; page one is a letter (13 January 1951) from Jerome Alexander, Consulting Chemist and Chemical Engineer, 50 East 41st Street, New York, to Sinclair indicating that he encloses duplicate copies of the poems Sinclair contributed to *The College Mercury* while Alexander was editor; six poems follow: "My Belated Valentine," signed S.U.B., [Untitled], signed S.U.B., "Ye Olds Tyme Tale of Ye Wolff And Ye (Soph) Kid," signed Upton B. Sinclair, *College Mercury*, 14 June 1895, "He Knew," signed U.B.S., "Love Will Find a Way," signed U.B.S., [Untitled], signed S.U.B., *College Mercury* 21 May 1896; page six is a letter from Edwin G. Conklin, Biology Department, Princeton University, to Jerome Alexander, complimenting Alexander's new book that Alexander, in turn, in his letter commends to Sinclair's attention.

Dates: Pub. 1895–96.

Citation: MENTAL THERAPEUTICS; t. ms.; carbon; InU.

Title: MENTAL THERAPEUTICS

Key Words: Whatever may be the ultimate . . . with much more successful results.

Collation: 8; white; 28 x 21.6; [1] 2–8; none; good.

Contents: Complete; unrevised.

Dates: Comp. ca. 1910–15?

Citation: NOTES ON UPTON SINCLAIR'S JESUS LIVES [A PERSONAL JESUS]; t. ms.; carbon; InU.

Title: NOTES ON UPTON SINCLAIR'S | *JESUS LIVES*

Key Words: "Yesse" for "Jesse." What is . . . of Abraham, Moses, or Isaiah.

Collation: 19; white watermarked; 27.9 x 21.6; [1] 2–19; none; good.

Contents: Complete; infrequently revised in blue ink, pencil; not all in Sinclair's hand; apparently not written by Sinclair.

Dates: Comp. ca. 1951.

Citation: PROSPERITY: THE OLD VS. THE NEW;
t. ms.; carbon; InU.

Title: PROSPERITY: THE OLD VS. THE NEW

Key Words: The age of scarcity is . . . better government
of our affairs?

Collation: 10; white watermarked; 27.8 x 21.5; [1] 2–10;
none; good.

Contents: Complete; unrevised.

Dates: Comp. ca. 1933.

Citation: REPORT ON ENEMY IN THE MOUTH;
t. ms.; ribbon; InU.

Title: REPORT ON: ENEMY IN THE MOUTH

Key Words: A book which the author . . . we can use the
book.

Collation: 1; white watermarked; 28 x 21.7; [1]; none; good.

Contents: Complete; unrevised.

Dates: Comp. ca. 1955.

Citation: SARPEDON; t. ms.; ribbon, carbon; InU.

Title: [none]

Key Words: How can I call you . . . lines 10–11, and add
(insert 666a)

Collation: 1; white; 28 x 21.6; 666a; none; good.

Contents: Complete; moderately revised in pencil; poem by
Edwin Markham intended as insert in some other ms.

Dates: Comp. ? Pub. ?

Citation: THE TALE OF THE RELUCTANT PRINCE;
t. ms.; ribbon; InU.

Title: The Tale of THE RELUCTANT PRINCE

Key Words: I was not born a . . . of the brotherhood of man.

Collation: 10; white, white watermarked; 28 x 21.7, 28 x 21.6; 124a, 125–133; none; good.

Contents: Complete; infrequently revised in blue ink, pencil.

Dates: Comp. ca. 1940s?

Citation: THE TALE OF THE RELUCTANT PRINCE; t. ms.; carbon; InU.

Title: THE TALE OF THE RELUCTANT PRINCE

Key Words: My father was an old-fashioned . . . of the World listened to—

Collation: 10; white watermarked; 27.9 x 21.6; 125–134; none; good.

Contents: Incomplete; infrequently revised in blue ink, pencil.

Dates: Comp. ca. 1940s?

Citation: THIS TIME, A TRUCE!; t. ms., a. ms.; carbon, blue ink; InU.

Title: This Time, A Truce!

Key Words: The people everywhere are standing . . . truth whenever an occasion arises.

Collation: 10; white watermarked, white; 24 x 12.2, 27.8 x 21.5; 1, 2, [1] 2–4, [1] 2–4; none; good.

Contents: Complete; infrequently revised in pencil; apparently by MCS.

Dates: Comp. ? Pub. ?

Citation: THUNDER OVER MEXICO; t. ms.; ribbon; InU.

Title: IDOLS BEFORE ALTARS [Title of book on Mexico by Anita Brenner; known to have influenced Eisenstein]

Key Words: Idols went out of style . . . be again kindled into fire.

Collation: 40; yellow lined notebook; 4.8 x 20.4 to 33 x 20.4; unnumbered; 1, 4, 9, 11, 12, 18, 22, 25, 33, 35, 36, 37; fair.

Contents: Incomplete; moderately revised in black, orange, regular pencil, ink, none of it apparently bv Sinclair; folder is labeled: Scenario Plans.

Dates: Comp. ca. July 1931.

Citation: TO; t. ms.; ribbon; InU.

Title: TO

Key Words: The man who knows; wher-e'er . . . take the reins and manage!

Collation: 2; white lined; 18.7 x 11.7; unnumbered; none; good.

Contents: Complete; unrevised; poem addresses Sinclair to come forth and take over; paper has embossed M in blue in upper left corner of page one.

Dates: Comp. ca. 1930s?

Citation: [UNTITLED]; t. ms.; ribbon; InU.

Title: [none]

Key Words: Dear Dave: | Just came on . . . of happiness on her face.)

Collation: 82; white; 26.6 x 20.3; [2], 1–58, [80]–101; 1, 4; good.

Contents: Incomplete; infrequently revised in pencil; ms. not by Sinclair; he explains in cover note that it is a play with revisions by MCS: "It may have been written by her—or by Ellen Barrows, my secty at the time (1912), who was in close touch with us at Arden"; play without title based on Sinclair's "split with . . . (his) first wife.

Dates: Comp. ca. 1912.

INDEXES

The indexes that follow are two. The first records proper names of real persons—authors, editors, critics, and the like—referred to in the body of the text. (It does not, however, include those names listed in the letters appendix material because those are for the most part already arranged alphabetically, and thus can be easily consulted separately.) The second provides an alphabetical listing according to the "Citation" element of the format for all items in the body of the text in four categories: published, publication uncertain, unpublished, and, finally, related manuscripts. The lists of unpublished works and of those whose publication was uncertain at the time this calendar was completed will, of course, change as research on Upton Sinclair goes forward. In this connection, *Upton Sinclair: An Annotated Checklist* (Kent State University Press, 1973) should be consulted.

Index to Works

PUBLISHED

PUBLICATION UNCERTAIN

RELATED MANUSCRIPTS